PERGAMON INTERNATIONAL LIBRARY
of Science, Technology, Engineering and Social Studies

The 1000-volume original paperback library in aid of education,
industrial training and the enjoyment of leisure
Publisher: Robert Maxwell, M.C.

Introduct

Prog

An inspectior
gladly be ser
adoption or
receipt and re
for adoption
the inspectio
pleased to re
important In

International Series in

MODERN APPLIED MATHEMATICS AND COMPUTER SCIENCE

Volume 1–*General Editor* E. Y. RODIN

Other titles of interest

Other Pergamon titles of interest

Books

CHIRGWIN & PLUMPTON
A Course of Mathematics for Engineers and Scientists

GARTENBERG & SHAW
Mathematics for Financial Analysis

GEORGE
Machine Takeover

KANTOROVICH & AKILOV
Functional Analysis, 2nd Edition

LEMARECHAL & MIFFLIN
Nonsmooth Optimization

POLLARD
An Introduction to the Mathematics of Finance, Revised edition

*Journals**

Annual Review in Automatic Programming
Computer Languages
Computers and Graphics
Computers and Mathematics with Applications
Computers and Operations Research

*Free specimen copy available on request

NOTICE TO READERS

Dear Reader

If your library is not already a standing order customer or subscriber to this series, may we recommend that you place a standing or subscription order to receive immediately upon publication all new issues and volumes published in this valuable series. Should you find that these volumes no longer serve your needs your order can be cancelled at any time without notice.
The Editors and the Publisher will be glad to receive suggestions or outlines of suitable titles, reviews or symposia for consideration for rapid publication in this series.

ROBERT MAXWELL
Publisher at Pergamon Press

Introduction to Dynamic Programming

by

LEON COOPER

and

MARY W. COOPER

Southern Methodist University, Dallas, Texas, USA

PERGAMON PRESS

OXFORD · NEW YORK · TORONTO · SYDNEY · PARIS · FRANKFURT

U.K.	Pergamon Press Ltd., Headington Hill Hall, Oxford OX3 0BW, England
U.S.A.	Pergamon Press Inc., Maxwell House, Fairview Park, Elmsford, New York 10523, U.S.A.
CANADA	Pergamon of Canada, Suite 104, 150 Consumers Road, Willowdale, Ontario M2J 1P9, Canada
AUSTRALIA	Pergamon Press (Aust.) Pty. Ltd., P.O. Box 544, Potts Point, N.S.W. 2011, Australia
FRANCE	Pergamon Press SARL, 24 rue des Ecoles, 75240 Paris, Cedex 05, France
FEDERAL REPUBLIC OF GERMANY	Pergamon Press GmbH, 6242 Kronberg-Taunus, Hammerweg 6, Federal Republic of Germany

Copyright © 1981 Pergamon Press Ltd.

First edition 1981

British Library Cataloguing in Publication Data

Cooper, Leon
Introduction to dynamic programming. — (Pergamon international library: international series in modern applied mathematics and computer science; vol. 1).
1. Dynamic programming
I. Title
519.7'03   T57.83   79-42640
ISBN 0-08-025065-3 Hardcover
ISBN 0-08-025064-5 Flexicover

Printed in Hungary by Franklin Printing House

Preface

THE purpose of this book is to present a clear and reasonably self-contained introduction to dynamic programming. We have tried to steer a middle ground between presentation of the underlying mathematical ideas and results, and the application of these ideas to various problem areas. Consequently, there is a large number of solved practical problems as well as a large number of computational examples to clarify the way dynamic programming is used to solve problems.

This book is definitely introductory and makes no claim to cover the whole subject; if an attempt had been made to approach completeness the book would be many times larger than it is. However, We hope that it will give a good insight into the fundamental ideas of the subject, a good working knowledge of the relevant techniques and an adequate starting-point for further study into those regions of the subject not dealt with here.

A consistent notation has been applied throughout for the expression of such quantities as state variables, decision variables, etc. It is felt that this should be helpful to the reader in a field where the notational conventions are far from uniform. In Section 6.9 a new application is presented and in Section 7.7 a new method for state dimensionality is presented.

The book should be suitable for self-study or for use as a text in a one-semester course on dynamic programming at the senior or first-year, graduate level for students of mathematics, statistics, operations research, economics, business, industrial engineering, or other engineering fields.

We are indebted to the many comments of students in a course on dynamic programming who used this book in the form of preliminary lecture notes.

Southern Methodist University
Dallas

LEON COOPER
MARY W. COOPER

Contents

Chapter 1

Introduction

1.1. Optimization

Dynamic programming is a particular approach to optimization. By optimization what we usually mean is finding the best solution to some problem from a set of alternatives. In this book we shall consider "problems" which can be quantitatively formulated. Hence we shall deal with *mathematical models* of situations or phenomena which exist in the real world. By a mathematical model, we mean that we have abstracted or isolated from an incomparably richer background, certain salient features which can be described in the language of mathematics. If we have a valid isolate, i.e., the characteristics that we have ignored have negligible effects, then we can expect that the solution to our model will provide a deeper understanding and a reasonably accurate description of the phenomenon under study. The generation of suitable models in the sense just described is more of an art than an exact science. Nevertheless, it is a widely practiced art and one which is increasingly successful. The development of powerful computational tools, i.e., digital computers, has had a very strong impact on the impetus to develop increasingly complex and sophisticated mathematical models.

Let us now consider the basic components of any mathematical optimization model. These are:

1. *Variables* (or decision variables or policy variables or independent variables). These are the quantities or factors that can be manipulated to achieve some desired outcome or objective. Most often variables will be represented as $x_1, x_2, \ldots, x_n$ or the vector of variables $\mathbf{x} = (x_1, x_2, \ldots, x_n)$. We will often speak of $\mathbf{x} = (x_1, x_2, \ldots, x_n)$ as a point in an n-dimensional Euclidean space (see Appendix).

2. *Objective function* (or return function or profit function). This is a measure of the effectiveness or the value or utility which is associated with some particular combination of the variables. In many instances it is some single-valued function of the variables, i.e., $z = f(x_1, x_2, \ldots, x_n)$. This is the function that is to be optimized (maximized or minimized). In most instances, the function $z = f(\mathbf{x})$ is a known function. However, there are optimization problems in which this is not the case. In these problems, usually considered in the calculus of variations (and also in a different way in dynamic programming), the function itself is not known and is the solution to the optimization problem. As an example of such problems, we might minimize some integral I, where

$$I = \int_a^b F(x, y, y') \, dx \tag{1.1.1}$$

1

In (1.1.1) $y = f(x)$ is the particular function (and is to be determined) that will minimize I and $F(x, y, y')$ is some known function of x, y, and $y' \equiv dy/dx$. Hence there are two distinct kinds of objective functions. In the first kind we seek values of $\mathbf{x} = (x_1 \ldots x_n)$ that maximizes or minimizes $f(\mathbf{x})$. In the second kind, we seek, as our unknown, a function $y = f(x)$ that maximizes or minimizes a *functional, $I = \int_a^b F(x, y, y') \, dx$*. There are more complex examples of this type which will be dealt with later.

3. *Constraints* (or feasibility conditions). These are algebraic equations or inequalities or in some cases differential equations, that the variables must satisfy, in addition to providing a maximum or minimum value of the objective function. Usually constraints can be represented as

$$\left. \begin{array}{l} h_i(x_1, x_2, \ldots, x_n) \leqslant 0 \\ h_i(x_1, x_2, \ldots, x_n) = 0 \\ h_i(x_1, x_2, \ldots, x_n) \geqslant 0 \end{array} \right\} \quad (i = 1, 2, \ldots, m) \tag{1.1.2}$$

where for a given i, only one of the three may hold. In some instances, notably in variational problems, differential equation constraints may also be present. For example, we might wish to minimize

$$I(y) = \int_a^b F(x, y, y') \, dx$$

subject to

$$\frac{dy}{dx} = h(x, y) \tag{1.1.3}$$

$$y(a) = C$$

In summary, the general variable optimization problem is to

maximize[†]

$$z = f(\mathbf{x})$$

subject to

$$h_i(\mathbf{x}) \{\leqslant, =, \geqslant\} 0 \quad (i = 1, 2, \ldots, m) \tag{1.1.4}$$

We shall not consider general variational problems at this point. Details of the application of dynamic programming to variational problems will be presented in a later chapter.

1.2. Separable Functions

An important criterion which is often used to characterize functions appearing in either the objective function or the constraints of a mathematical optimization (or *mathematical programming*, as it is usually called) problem is whether or not the functions are *separable*. A separable function is one in which the function consists of a sum of functions of a single variable, i.e.,

$$f(\mathbf{x}) = f_1(x_1) + f_2(x_2) + \ldots + f_n(x_n) \tag{1.2.1}$$

---

† It should be apparent that $\min[f(\mathbf{x})] = -\max[-f(\mathbf{x})]$. Hence we can restrict our concerns to either maximization or minimization problems.

There are other forms of "separability" which will be dealt with in subsequent chapters. The form shown in (1.2.1) is probably the most often used in dynamic programming problem formulations.

At first glance, it would seem that the form shown in (1.2.1) restricts one unduly, since many important functions are not separable. For example,

$$f(x_1, x_2) = 3x_1x_2 + 2x_1 \sin x_2$$

is clearly *not* in separable form. However, it is not difficult to see that most (but not all) functions can be transformed into separable form by introducing auxiliary variables and additional constraints. In [2] it is shown that the method for separating any "factorable" function (defined below) consists of two basic steps which are repeatedly used until one obtains a separable function. These two steps are:

(1) Replace any product term of the form

$$h_1(x_1) h_2(x_2) \quad \text{by} \quad y_1^2 - y_2^2$$

and add the constraints

$$h_1(x_1) = y_1 - y_2, \quad h_2(x_2) = y_1 + y_2$$

(2) Replace any term of the form

$$H(h(\underline{x})) \quad \text{by} \quad H(y)$$

and add the constraint

$$h(\underline{x}) = y$$

The class of nonlinear functions which can be separated by repeated use of the above steps comprises what have been called *factorable* functions. A *factorable function* is a function of n variables which is generated by first composing (adding or multiplying) functions of a single variable, transforming those functions, composing those, ..., etc., a finite number of times.

As an example of how this process operates, suppose we wished to put the following problem in separable form:

$$\underset{\{x_1, x_2\}}{\text{maximize}} \quad x_1 e^{(x_1 + x_2)^2} \tag{1.2.2}$$

Applying step (1) we have

$$\underset{\{x_1, x_2, y_1, y_2\}}{\max} \quad y_1^2 - y_2^2$$

subject to

$$y_1 - y_2 = x_1$$
$$y_1 + y_2 = e^{(x_1 + x_2)^2} \tag{1.2.3}$$

The second constraint in (1.2.3) is still not in separable form so we now apply step (2) to obtain

$$\underset{\{x_1, x_2, y_1, y_2, y_3\}}{\max} \quad y_1^2 - y_2^2$$

subject to

$$y_1 - y_2 = x_1 \tag{1.2.4}$$
$$y_1 + y_2 = e^{y_3}$$
$$(x_1 + x_2)^2 = y_3$$

The last constraint in (1.2.4) is nonseparable so we reapply step (2) to obtain

$$\max_{\{x_1,\, x_2,\, y_1,\, y_2,\, y_3,\, y_4\}} y_1^2 - y_2^2$$

subject to

$$y_1 - y_2 = x_1$$
$$y_1 + y_2 = e^{y_3} \qquad\qquad (1.2.5)$$
$$y_4^2 = y_3$$
$$x_1 + x_2 = y_4$$

Equation (1.2.5) is now a mathematical programming problem in completely separable form and is completely equivalent to (1.2.2).

1.3. Convex and Concave Functions

There is an important property of certain functions which is related to the existence of minima and maxima. This property is known as *convexity* and its opposite as *concavity*. In Fig. 1.3.1(a) we have shown a convex function of a single variable. Intuitively,

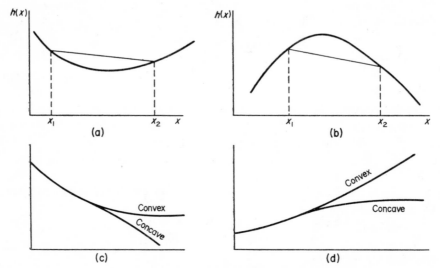

FIG. 1.3.1. Convex and concave functions of a single variable.

as Fig. 1.3.1(a) shows, a function of a single variable is *convex* if a line segment drawn between any two points on its graph falls entirely on or above the graph. Similarly, a function is *concave* if a line segment drawn between any two points on its graph falls entirely on or below the graph. Such a function is shown in Fig. 1.3.1(b). If the line segment falls entirely above (below) the graph the function is said to be *strictly convex* (*strictly concave*).

Formally, a function $f(x)$ of a single variable x is said to be convex over some interval in x, if for any two points x_1, x_2 in the interval and for all λ, $0 \leq \lambda \leq 1$,

$$f[\lambda x_1 + (1-\lambda)x_2] \leq \lambda f(x_1) + (1-\lambda) f(x_2) \qquad\qquad (1.3.1)$$

Similarly, a function $f(x)$ is said to be concave over some interval in x, if for any two points x_1, x_2 in the interval and for all λ, $0 \leqslant \lambda \leqslant 1$,

$$f[\lambda x_1 + (1-\lambda)x_2] \geqslant \lambda f(x_1) + (1-\lambda)f(x_2) \tag{1.3.2}$$

It should be clear from these definitions that if $f(x)$ is convex, $-f(x)$ is concave and vice versa. It will be seen that (1.3.1) and (1.3.2) correspond to the definition given in terms of the graph of a function.

We can generalize the definitions of convexity and concavity just given to the case of functions of several variables. A function $f(\underline{x})$ is *convex* over some convex set[†] X in E^n if for any two points $\mathbf{x}_1$ and $\mathbf{x}_2$ in X and for all λ, $0 \leqslant \lambda \leqslant 1$,

$$f[\lambda \mathbf{x}_1 + (1-\lambda)\mathbf{x}_2] \leqslant \lambda f(\mathbf{x}_1) + (1-\lambda)f(\mathbf{x}_2) \tag{1.3.3}$$

Similarly, a function $f(\underline{x})$ is *concave* over some convex set X in E^n if for any two points $\mathbf{x}_1$ and $\mathbf{x}_2$ in X and for all λ, $0 \leqslant \lambda \leqslant 1$,

$$f[\lambda \mathbf{x}_1 + (1-\lambda)\mathbf{x}_2] \geqslant \lambda f(\mathbf{x}_1) + (1-\lambda)f(\mathbf{x}_2) \tag{1.3.4}$$

For a function of a single variable, a function was convex if the line segment joining any two points on its curve fell entirely on or above the curve. A similar interpretation can be given to (1.3.3). A function $z = f(\mathbf{x})$ is a hypersurface in $(n+1)$-dimensional space. It is convex if the line segment which connects any two points $(\mathbf{x}_1, z_1)$ and $(\mathbf{x}_2, z_2)$ on the surface of this hypersurface lies entirely on or above the hypersurface.

Some properties relating to convex and concave functions that we shall have occasion to refer to in subsequent chapters are as follows. Proofs of these assertions can be found in Cooper and Steinberg [1].

PROPOSITION 1.3.1. *If the functions* $h_k(\mathbf{x})$, $k = 1, 2, \ldots, s$ *are convex functions over some convex set* X *in* E^n, *then the function* $h(\mathbf{x}) = \sum_{k=1}^{s} h_k(\mathbf{x})$ *is also a convex function over* X.

What Proposition 1.3.1 asserts is that the sum of convex functions is also a convex function over some convex set. For a function of a single variable, it is clearly true. The convex set is the x axis (or some portion of it) and, as an example, we show in Fig. 1.3.2 the sum of two convex functions $h_1(x) = x^2$ and $h_2(x) = 2x$ over $0 \leqslant x \leqslant 4$.

Just as the sum of convex functions is a convex function, it is also true that the sum of concave functions over a convex set is a concave function. Hence, this leads us to:

PROPOSITION 1.3.2. *If the functions* $h_k(\mathbf{x})$, $k = 1, 2, \ldots, s$ *are concave functions over some convex set* X *in* E^n, *then the function* $h(\mathbf{x}) = \sum_{k=1}^{s} h_x(\underline{x})$ *is also a concave function.*

A result of some importance is the following:

PROPOSITION 1.3.3. *If* $h(\underline{x})$ *is a convex function over the nonnegative orthant of* E^n, *then if* $W = \{\mathbf{x} \mid h(\mathbf{x}) \leqslant b, \mathbf{x} \geqslant 0\}$ *is not empty, W is a convex set.*

---

† See the Appendix.

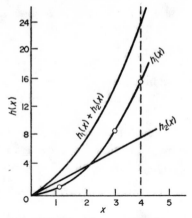

FIG. 1.3.2. Sum of convex functions.

A simple example of Proportion 1.3.3 is shown in Fig. 1.3.3. We have chosen $h(\mathbf{x}) = 2x_1^2 + 3x_2^2$. It is easily verified that this is a convex function. If we examine the set $W = \{\mathbf{x} \mid h(\mathbf{x}) \leqslant 12, \mathbf{x} \geqslant 0\}$, we see that it is a convex set.

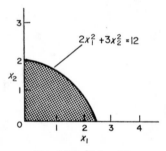

FIG. 1.3.3. $h(x) \leqslant 12$.

In a similar fashion, we can show the following:

PROPOSITION 1.3.4. *If $h(\underline{x})$ is a concave function over the nonnegative orthant of E^n, then if $W = \{\mathbf{x} \mid h(\mathbf{x}) \leqslant b, \mathbf{x} \geqslant 0\}$ is not empty, W is a convex set.*

1.4. Optima of Convex and Concave Functions

Generally, if we are seeking the maximum or minimum of some arbitrary function $z = f(\mathbf{x})$ and we have no particular characterization of the function, we can only hope to find a local maximum or minimum with any existing methods. This is true even if we know as much about the function as that it is both continuous and differentiable in the region of interest. However, if the function to be maximized or minimized over some convex region is either convex or concave, then there is considerably more information available to us. In addition, great simplifications in computational procedures can often be made. To this end we shall state two results of great importance. Proofs of these propositions can be found in [1].

PROPOSITION 1.4.1. *Let* $h(\mathbf{x})$ *be a convex function over a closed convex set X in E^n. Then any local minimum of $h(\mathbf{x})$ in X is also the global minimum of $h(\mathbf{x})$ in X.*

The importance of Proposition 1.4.1 is very great. It gives us a condition under which we do not need to be concerned about the presence of many local maxima or minima.

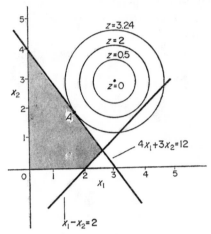

FIG. 1.4.1. Optimal solution on constraint boundary.

An example illustrating this result is shown graphically in Fig. 1.4.1. The function $z = (x_1-3)^2+(x_2-3)^2$ is a convex function. The constraints

$$4x_1+3x_2 \leqslant 12$$
$$x_1-x_2 \leqslant 2 \tag{1.4.1}$$
$$x_1 \geqslant 0$$
$$x_2 \geqslant 0$$

generate a convex set as is seen in Fig. 1.41. Hence, we know immediately that the solution we have obtained, i.e., $(x_1, x_2) = (1.56, 1.92)$ and $z = 3.24$, is a globally minimum solution. In this case it is also unique.

In a similar fashion one can show a corresponding result for concave functions.

PROPOSITION 1.4.2. *Let* $h(\mathbf{x})$ *be a concave function over a closed convex set X in E^n. Then any local maximum of $h(\mathbf{x})$ in X is also the global maximum of $h(\mathbf{x})$ in X.*

Propositions 1.4.1 and 1.4.2 deal with the case of minimizing a convex function or maximizing a concave function over a convex set. Let us now consider the reverse case, i.e., maximizing a convex function or minimizing a concave function over a convex set. This gives rise to the following results.

PROPOSITION 1.4.3. *Let X be a closed convex set bounded from below and let $h(\mathbf{x})$ be a convex function over X in E^n. If $h(\mathbf{x})$ has global maxima at points $\mathbf{x}^0$ with $|\mathbf{x}^0|$ finite, then one or more of the $\mathbf{x}^0$ are extreme points of X.*

PROPOSITION 1.4.4. *Let X be a closed convex set bounded from below and let $h(\mathbf{x})$ be a concave function over X in E^n. If $h(\mathbf{x})$ has global minima at points $\mathbf{x}^0$ with $|\mathbf{x}^0|$ finite, then one or more of the $\mathbf{x}^0$ are extreme points of X.*

What these results tell us is that we can be sure that the global maximum or minimum will be at an extreme point of the convex set of feasible solutions. Since the number of extreme points is often finite, this often results in computationally feasible methods for examining some subset of this finite set.

An example of Proposition 1.4.3 is the following problem:

$$\text{max} \quad z = x_1^2 + x_2^2$$
$$-x_1 + x_2 \leqslant 4$$
$$x_1 + x_2 \leqslant 12 \tag{1.4.2}$$
$$x_1, x_2 \geqslant 0$$

The problem of (1.4.2) is shown in Fig. 1.4.2. We can see that the global maximum occurs at an extreme point, designated A, of the convex set generated by the constraints of (1.4.2). At this point the maximum value $z = 144$ is obtained. There is also a local maximum at the point of intersection of the two lines in Fig 1.4.2. where $z = 80$

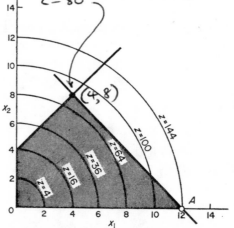

FIG. 1.4.2. Extreme point solution.

1.5. Dynamic Programming

Dynamic programming is a particular "approach" to optimization. We use the word "approach" advisedly because dynamic programming is not a particular algorithm in the sense that Euclid's algorithm is a well-defined procedure for finding the greatest common divisor of two integers or in the sense that Dantzig's simplex algorithm is a well-defined set of rules for solving a linear programming problem. Dynamic programming is an approach to solving certain kinds of optimization problems, some of which can, in principle, be solved by other procedures. Dynamic programming is a way of looking at a problem which may contain a large number of interrelated decision variables so that the problem is regarded as if it consisted of a sequence of problems, each of which required the determination of only one (or a few) variables. Ideally, what we seek to do is, in effect, substitute solving n single variable problems for solving one n variable problem. Whenever this is possible, it usually requires very much less computational effort. Solving n smaller problems requires a computational effort which is proportional to n, the number of single variable problems if each problem contains one variable. On the other hand, solving one larger problem with n variables usually requires a computational effort which is very roughly proportional to a^n, where a is some constant. Hence the desirability of transforming or considering an n-dimensional problem as n one-dimensional problems.

The principle or point of view that enables us to carry out the transformation we have just discussed is known as the *principle of optimality*. It was first enunciated by Bellman [3]. It has an intuitively obvious basis (Bellman's justification consists of the single statement, "A proof by contradiction is immediate"). We shall have more to say about this later. The principle of optimality is:

An optimal policy has the property that whatever the initial state and the initial decision are, the remaining decisions must constitute an optimal policy with respect to the state which results from the initial decision.

A simpler rendition of this principle, which shows its intuitive character more transparently, consists of the statement: *Every optimal policy consists only of optimal subpolicies.*

It is important, even if only vaguely and intuitively at this point, to understand what the above statements of the principle of optimality mean. Consider the following optimization problem. An investor has a fixed sum of money, D dollars, which can be invested in five different investment opportunities (stocks, bonds, land, etc.). In actual fact he wishes to invest this money *at the same time* (the present), assuming that he has a prediction of what kind of return he can expect from each investment. Since each investment has certain stipulations that must be met (minimum or maximum amounts required, deferred earnings, different tax rates, etc.), he wants to know how much of his total D should he invest in each of the five investments so as to maximize the total return from all the investments.

One approach to solving such a problem is to generate all possible combinations of the five investments and see which one provides the largest return. This approach is called *total enumeration* and is generally not practical, even with computers, for problems with a realistic number of variables. If we assume that the amount to be invested in any of the investment opportunities is fixed, the decision that must be made is to invest or not invest. Even for this simplified case we have one way to invest in all of the investment opportunities, five ways to invest in four of them, ten ways to invest in three of them, ten ways to invest in two of them, and five ways to invest in one, i.e., the total number of ways to invest in five investment opportunities (for a fixed investment amount in each one) is

$$\binom{5}{5} + \binom{5}{4} + \binom{5}{3} + \binom{5}{2} + \binom{5}{1} = 31$$

For 20 investments we would have to evaluate 1,048,575 combinations. The number increases very rapidly with the number of investments, and hence total enumeration rapidly becomes impractical, even on a computer.

What we shall do in dynamic programming is examine only a very small subset of the total number of combinations. However, the subset is guaranteed, under the right conditions, to contain the optimal solution. Hence we shall find this optimal solution. Let us now return to our five-investment problem and consider the dynamic programming approach. Even though all investments are to be made at one time, we shall pretend that the investment decisions are made in some order. What this means is that we invest some amount I_1 in investment 1, amount I_2 in investment 2, etc. The only restriction that we have is that the sum of $I_1 + I_2 + I_3 + I_4 + I_5 = D$ and that the investments are nonnegative amounts. Now let us apply the principle of optimality. What it says is that no matter how much of the total amount D has been spent on the first k investments, the remaining money must be optimally distributed among the remaining 5-k investments. Let us now apply this principle.

Suppose we had numbered the investments 1 through 5 as indicated above. If we have already spent a certain amount of the money on the first four investments, then whatever remains will be invested in the fifth investment opportunity. Hence no decision is made here. Let us now consider how much should be invested in I_4. Here we make a decision but it is a very simple decision. It involves deciding how much to invest in I_4 and how much to save for I_5. This involves a decision involving only *one variable*, i.e., how much to invest in I_4. Let us now consider how much to invest in I_3. Again we are involved in a single variable decision process, i.e., how much to invest in I_3 and how much to save for the combined investments in I_4 and I_5. This analysis continues for I_2 and I_1. In brief, the decision maker has to make five simple one-variable decisions instead of one complex five-variable decision. What we are saying when we make a decision is, e.g., that when we decide how much to invest in I_3, no matter how much we invest in I_1 and I_2, the amount we invest in I_3 must be optimal with respect to the remaining capital. Since we do not yet know what we shall invest in I_4 and I_5, the optimal investment and return from I_3 must be determined for *all* feasible amounts remaining to be invested. The details of how this is done will be discussed in the next chapter.

1.6. Dynamic Programming: Advantages and Limitations

We have already alluded to one of the main advantages of dynamic programming. That is, that when we use dynamic programming, we transform a single n-dimensional optimization problem into n one-dimensional optimization problems which can be solved one at a time. The classical extremum methods of analysis cannot do this.

A second extremely important advantage of dynamic programming over almost all other extant computational methods, and especially classical optimization methods, is that dynamic programming determines absolute (global) maxima or minima rather than relative (local) optima. Hence we need not concern ourselves with the vexing problem of local maxima and minima.

In virtually all other optimization techniques, certain kinds of constraints can cause significant problems. For example, the imposition of integrality on the variables of a problem cannot be handled by classical methods. However, in dynamic programming the requirement that some or all of the variables be integers greatly simplifies the computational process. Similar considerations apply to such restrictions as nonnegativity of the decision variables. In short, certain kinds of constraints on the variables help in dynamic programming whereas they destroy the utility of other computational methods.

A further characteristic of dynamic programming is the "embedding" characteristic of the functional equations that we shall derive and discuss in subsequent chapters. What this means is that, e.g., in the problem of the five investments discussed in Section 1.5, if we solved the five-investment problem by dynamic programming, we would automatically find the optimal solution to the problems of four investments, three investments, etc. This characteristic of solving a class of problems whenever one solves one problem is extremely useful in certain kinds of analyses of contingencies or changes in problem structure with time.

There are, however, certain limitations to the use of dynamic programming. The principal one is that of the dimensionality of the state space. What this means in simple language is that if there are more than two or three "state" variables (as distinct from decision variables), then we have computational problems relating to the storage of information as well as the time it takes to perform the computation. For example, the total amount of money D that was available to invest in the investment problem of Section 1.5 was the only state variable we had. For such a problem it is a simple matter to compute the solution, as we shall see. In other problems there may be several state variables. The higher the dimensionality of the state space, i.e., the more components there are of a vector which describes the state space, the greater the computational difficulties we shall encounter. As we shall see there are some methods for dealing with this problem but none of them are completely satisfactory.

1.7. The Development of Dynamic Programming

Dynamic programming was founded by Richard Bellman. The first systematic treatment of the subject was given in [3] in 1957 although much work appeared earlier in numerous Rand Corporation reports as well as other publications by Bellman. Other books by Bellman and his collaborators have subsequently appeared on applied dynamic programming [4] and on the application of dynamic programming to control theory [5, 6]. The application of dynamic programming to Markov processes is discussed in [7]. There are numerous books and papers giving applications to chemical engineering, inventory theory, calculus of variations, optimal control theory, and economics. Some of these applications will be discussed in subsequent chapters.

Exercises—Chapter 1

1.1. Convert the following problem to one which is in separable form:

$$\min \quad z = x_1 \ln x_2 + 10x_2^2 x_3$$

subject to

$$x_1 x_2 x_3 \geqslant 100$$
$$x_1, x_2, x_3 \geqslant 0$$

1.2. Convert the following problem to one which is in separable form:

$$\min \quad z = x_1 \sin x_2 + x_2^2 \ln x_1 x_2^2 + x_3^3 \cos (x_1 + x_2)$$

subject to

$$4e^{x_1}x_2 + 3e^{x_2}x_3^2 + 2e^{x_3}x_1^3 \geqslant 20$$

1.3. Convert the following problem to separable form:

$$\max \quad z = \prod_{j=1}^{n} \left[x_j x_{j+1}^2 x_{j+2}^3 + x_j \ln (x_{j+1}x_{j+2}) + x_j e^{x_j+1} \right]$$

subject to

$$\sum_{j=1}^{n} (x_j^2 + 4x_j x_{j+1} + x_{j+1}^2) \leqslant 100$$

$$x_j \geqslant 0, \qquad (j = 1, 2, \ldots, n)$$

1.4. Prove that e^x is a convex function.

1.5. Is $|x|$ a convex function of x?

1.6. Prove Proposition 1.3.1.

1.7. Prove that if $f(\mathbf{x})$ is a convex function of $\mathbf{x}$ in E^n, then $f(\mathbf{x}+\mathbf{a})$ is a convex function of $\mathbf{x}$ for any $\mathbf{a}$.

1.8. Suppose $f(x)$ is continuous and that $f(x) \geqslant 0$, $-\infty \leqslant x \leqslant \infty$. Prove that the function

$$\psi(x) = \int_{x}^{\infty} (u-x) f(u) \, du$$

is a convex function, providing that the integral converges.

1.9. Prove that the function $1/x$ is strictly convex for $x > 0$ and strictly concave for $x < 0$.

1.10. Find the solution to the following problem by using a graphical analysis:

$$\min \quad z = 4x_1^2 + x_2^2 + 2x_1 x_2 + 2x_1 + 3x_2$$

subject to

$$x_1 - x_2 \geqslant 0$$
$$x_1 + x_2 \leqslant 4$$
$$x_1 \leqslant 3$$

1.11. Find the solution to the following problem by graphical means:

$$\max \quad z = 5x_1 + 3x_2$$
$$2x_1 - x_2 \geqslant 0$$

subject to

$$x_1 - 2x_2 \leqslant 0$$
$$x_1, x_2 \geqslant 0, \qquad x_1, \text{integer}$$
$$x_2, \text{continuous}$$

Chapter 2

Some Simple Examples

2.1. Introduction

In this chapter we shall develop, by means of examples, the approach to problem solving that is typical of dynamic programming. No attempt will be made to provide detailed theoretical justification of the methodology. We shall develop that in Chapter 3. However, the approach we use in these examples will be correct and this will be quite apparent in the working out of the solutions to the problems.

2.2. The Wandering Applied Mathematician

An applied mathematician with more brains than money finds that he has a great desire to travel. Suppose, with reference to Fig. 2.2.1, that he is in city 1 and wishes to go to city 10. This is a long journey and he must make three intermediate stops. However, he has a choice of two or three different cities at which to stop for each of the three inter-

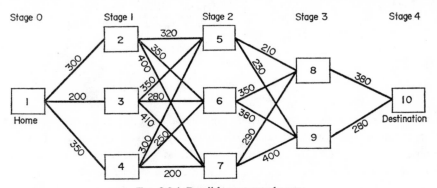

FIG. 2.2.1. Possible routes and costs.

mediate stages of his journey. The costs of the trip are different depending upon how he chooses his intermediate stops. The costs between cities as well as the connections are shown in Fig. 2.2.1. Since he wishes to minimize his total cost for the journey, he wishes to determine what his intermediate stops should be. It is easily seen that he could solve this problem by total enumeration, i.e., enumerating all 18 possible routes. However, he wonders if there is not a better way to find the solution he seeks. It is not difficult to see that there *must* be a better way. For example, suppose we were at city 5. We would reach our destination, city 10, via city 8 or 9. It is clear, however, that we do not wish to ever use city 8 in this case, since the route 5–9–10 is much less costly. Since we can reach city 5 by three different routes, we can see that in complete enumeration we are doing a lot of unnecessary work. This seemingly innocent and quite obvious observation will be the key to solving this problem.

Let us now proceed to solve our problem. We shall analyze the problem by proceeding *backwards* from the destination. If we are at stage 3 we can reach 10 by city 8 or 9. Hence we have a table which says:

	City	Minimum cost	Path
Stage 3	8	380	8–10
	9	280	9–10

Now suppose we are at stage 2 and ask which is the minimum path to 10. If we are at 5 the path of least cost is the minimum of (210+380, 230+280) which is 510 and uses the path 5–9–10. Similarly, if we are at 6 the path of least cost is the minimum of (350+380, 380+280), which is 660 with a path of 6–9–10. We can analyze city 7 in a similar fashion. The least cost path from city 7 is the minimum of (290+380, 400+280) which is 670 with a path of 7–8–10. The results are summarized in the following table:

	City	Minimum cost	Path
Stage 2	5	510	5–9–10
	6	660	6–9–10
	7	670	7–8–10

Now we suppose we are at stage 1. By making an analysis similar to that of stage 2 we can see, for example, that the least cost path from city 2 is the minimum of (320+510, 350+660, 400+670) =830, and the least cost path is 2–5–9–10. The first term in the sums is the distance from city 2 to 5, 6, 7, and the second term is the *least cost* distance from each of cities 5, 6, 7 to 10, which were obtained from the stage 2 table. A complete calculation for stage 1 is given by:

	City	Minimum cost	Path
Stage 1	2	830	2–5–9–10
	3	860	3–5–9–10
	4	810	4–5–9–10

Finally, we suppose we are at city 1, which is where we wish to start. Now we know that we must go from city 1 to either of cities 2, 3, 4. Which is the least cost? Using the stage 1 table and the known distances from city 1 to each of those cities, we have that the minimum cost of the entire trip is

$$\text{minimum}(300+830,\ 200+860,\ 350+810)$$
$$= \min(1130,\ 1060,\ 1160) = 1060$$

and that the minimum cost path is 1–3–5–9–10.

What we have done is deceptively simple and illustrates the principle of optimality, which says that the optimal policy must have only optimal policies as subpolicies. In the context of our brilliant but penurious applied mathematician, he argued as follows. No matter what city I find myself in, *starting at the last city*, I will always choose the best (least cost) path. If I am in city 10 (stage 4), I stay there. If I am in stage 3, I go to city 10 from either 8 or 9. I continue this argument until I find myself in city 1 (stage 0) and I have sequentially found the least cost solution and the path that results in that least cost. Note that not until we got to stage 0 was it clear what the optimal solution would be. At that stage we noted that adding 200 to the minimum cost of going from city 3 to 10 would give the least overall cost. This is characteristic of the dynamic programming approach. Note further, that if we changed our mind and decided to start at *any other* city, we know the optimal solution. For example, suppose we wished to start at city 3. The stage 1 table tells us that the optimal path is 3–5–9–10 and the cost is 860. That is another characteristic of dynamic programming. In the course of solving the problem we are interested in, we also solve all the subproblems that are embedded in the larger problem. In the case of the traveling applied mathematician, we solve all problems of the form: Starting at city j where $j = 1, 2, \ldots, 10$, what is the least cost solution from city j to city 10? This is almost a defining characteristic of the approach of dynamic programming.

2.3. The Wandering Applied Mathematician (continued)

Having reached his destination, our applied mathematician desires to purchase some local "goods" which he intends to smuggle back home and resell to his colleagues at what he hopes will be a truly shameless profit. He deduces that he can only secrete a maximum of 20 lb in his baggage without being caught. He can purchase four different types of goods with the following characteristics:

Item	Weight (lb)	Estimated profit
1	2	110
2	3	160
3	5	260
4	4	210

Since it is not possible to pack a fraction of one of these items, we must restrict our concern to integer multiples of the four items.

Let x_1, x_2, x_3, x_4 be the number of items of each type to be taken home. Since he wishes to maximize his expected profit and choose values of x_1, x_2, x_3, x_4 that do not exceed a total of 20 lb, the problem he wishes to solve is

$$\max \quad P = 110x_1 + 160x_2 + 260x_3 + 210x_4 \tag{2.3.1}$$

subject to
$$2x_1 + 3x_2 + 5x_3 + 4x_4 \leqslant 20 \tag{2.3.2}$$

$$x_1, x_2, x_3, x_4 \geqslant 0, \quad \text{integer} \tag{2.3.3}$$

In other words, we wish to find values of x_1, x_2, x_3, and x_4 that make P as large as possible and still satisfy constraints (2.3.2) and (2.3.3).

In order to develop the dynamic programming rationale for solving this problem, let us suppose that we know the optimal values of x_2, x_3, and x_4. We shall designate them x_2^*, x_3^*, x_4^*. If this was the case, we would only have to solve a one-variable problem, since if we substitute x_2^*, x_3^*, and x_4^* into (2.3.1)–(2.3.3) we obtain

$$\max[110x_1 + (160x_2^* + 260x_3^* + 210x_4^*)] \tag{2.3.4}$$

subject to
$$2x_1 \leqslant 20 - 3x_2^* - 5x_3^* - 4x_4^* \tag{2.3.5}$$

$$x_1 \geqslant 0, \quad \text{integer} \tag{2.3.6}$$

Since $160x_2^* + 260x_3^* + 210x_4^*$ is a constant (if we knew the values of x_2^*, x_3^*, x_4^*), the objective function (2.3.4) is merely

$$\max_{x_1 \geqslant 0} \quad 110x_1 \tag{2.3.7}$$

Of course we do not know x_2^*, x_3^*, x_4^*. However, we do know that x_2^*, x_3^*, x_4^* must satisfy

$$20 - 3x_2^* - 5x_3^* - 4x_4^* \geqslant 0 \tag{2.3.8}$$

Otherwise the problem (2.3.4)–(2.3.6) would have no solution. If we now define a new variable λ, usually called a *state variable*, then we may rewrite (2.3.5) as

$$2x_1 \leqslant \lambda \tag{2.3.9}$$

where we shall allow λ to assume any of the values $0, 1, \ldots, 20$, since we really do not know what x_2^*, x_3^*, x_4^* are at this point.

Now suppose we solve the one-dimensional problem given by (2.3.7) and (2.3.9), i.e.,

$$\max_{x_1 \geqslant 0} \quad 110x_1 \tag{2.3.10}$$

subject to
$$2x_1 \leqslant \lambda, \quad (\lambda = 0, 1, \ldots, 20) \tag{2.3.11}$$

This problem is easily solved for each value of λ. For example:

$$\max \quad 110x_1, 2x_1 \leqslant 0 \quad \text{yields} \quad x_1^*(0) = 0$$
$$\max \quad 110x_1, 2x_1 \leqslant 4 \quad \text{yields} \quad x_1^*(4) = 2$$

If we define

$$g_1(\lambda) \equiv \max_{x_1 \geqslant 0} \quad 110x_1 \tag{2.3.12}$$

then $g_1(\lambda)$ gives us the maximum value of $110x_1$ and $x_1^*(\lambda)$ is the value of x_1 that yielded the maximum value. They are both functions of λ since the maximization is restricted by some particular value of λ. If we solve (2.3.10) and (2.3.11) for all values of λ we can obtain Table 2.3.1.

TABLE 2.3.1

λ	$g_1(\lambda)$	$x_1^*(\lambda)$	λ	$g_1(\lambda)$	$x_1^*(\lambda)$
0	0	0	11	550	5
1	0	0	12	660	6
2	110	1	13	660	6
3	110	1	14	770	7
4	220	2	15	770	7
5	220	2	16	880	8
6	330	3	17	880	8
7	330	3	18	990	9
8	440	4	19	990	9
9	440	4	20	1100	10
10	550	5			

Bear in mind that we now *know* how the optimal value $x_1^*(\lambda)$, which satisfies the constraints of the original problem (2.3.1)–(2.3.3), depends upon λ and hence *any* possible restriction of the original problem. Now let us consider the following problem:

$$g_2(\lambda) \equiv \max_{x_2 \geq 0} \left\{ \left[\max_{x_1 \geq 0} 110x_1 \right] + 160x_2 \right\} \qquad (2.3.13)$$

subject to
$$2x_1 \leq \lambda - 3x_2 \qquad (2.3.14)$$

where the max $110x_1$ is taken over nonnegative x_1 satisfying (2.3.14). Why should we consider a problem of the form (2.3.13) and (2.3.14)? First of all, we note that any feasible solution to this problem is also a feasible solution to the original problem. Secondly, if λ is fixed at some value, then the problem is a one-variable problem. This can be seen as follows. Using definition (2.3.12), we see that max $110x_1$ over x_1 in (2.3.13) is $g_1(\lambda - 3x_2)$. Therefore, we may write (2.3.13) as

$$g_2(\lambda) = \max_{x_2 \geq 0} [g_1(\lambda - 3x_2) + 160x_2] \qquad (2.3.15)$$

Note that for fixed λ, (2.3.15) is a one-variable optimization problem. However, (2.3.15) is not complete. From (2.3.14) and the nonnegativity of x_1, x_2, x_3, x_4, we see that

$$\lambda - 3x_2 \geq 0$$

Therefore we have that

$$0 \leq x_2 \leq \left[\frac{\lambda}{3} \right] \qquad (2.3.16)$$

where $[a] \equiv$ the greatest integer $\leqslant a$. Hence we can write (2.3.15) as

$$g_2(\lambda) = \max_{0 \leqslant x_2 \leqslant [\lambda/3]} [g_1(\lambda - 3x_2) + 160x_2] \qquad (2.3.17)$$

where $\lambda = 0, 1, \ldots, 20$.

Equation (2.3.17) is quite important. First, as mentioned, it is a single-variable optimization problem and hence easily solved, since we have already calculated in Table 2.3.1 all possible values of $g_1(\lambda)$. Hence it is a simple matter to evaluate $g_1(\lambda - 3x_2)$, since for any given value of x_2, $g_1(\lambda - 3x_2)$ is an entry in Table 2.3.1. For example, if $\lambda = 12$ and $x_2 = 3$, then $g_1(\lambda - 3x_2) = g_1(12 - 9) = g_1(3) = 110$. Therefore, by a straightforward calculation, we can generate a table of values for $g_2(\lambda)$, using (2.3.17) and Table 2.3.1. For example:

$$g_2(0) = \max_{0 \leqslant x_2 \leqslant 0} [g_1(0-0) + 160(0)] = 0$$

and $x_2^*(0) = 0$

$$g_2(10) = \max_{0 \leqslant x_2 \leqslant [\frac{10}{3}]} [g_1(10 - 3x_2) + 160x_2]$$

$$= \max[g_1(10) + 160(0), \; g_1(7) + 160(1), \; g_1(4) + 160(2), \; g_1(1) + 160(3)]$$

$$= \max[550, 490, 540, 480] = 550$$

and $x_2^*(10) = 0$

In a similar fashion we obtain all the entries in Table 2.3.2.

TABLE 2.3.2

λ	$g_2(\lambda)$	$x_2^*(\lambda)$	λ	$g_2(\lambda)$	$x_2^*(\lambda)$
0	0	0	11	600	1
1	0	0	12	660	0
2	110	0	13	710	1
3	160	1	14	770	0
4	220	0	15	820	1
5	270	1	16	880	0
6	330	0	17	930	1
7	380	1	18	990	0
8	440	0	19	1040	1
9	490	1	20	1100	0
10	550	0			

We shall now repeat the same argument which led from (2.3.13) and (2.3.14) to (2.3.17) except that now we shall examine

$$g_3(\lambda) \equiv \max_{x_3 \geqslant 0} \left\{ \max_{x_2 \geqslant 0} \left[\left(\max_{x_1 \geqslant 0} 110x_1 \right) + 160x_2 \right] + 260x_3 \right\} \qquad (2.3.18)$$

subject to $2x_1 + 3x_2 \leqslant \lambda - 5x_3 \qquad (2.3.19)$

The similarity of (2.3.18) and (2.3.19) to (2.3.13) and (2.3.14) is fairly clear. Moreover, if we use the fact that $g_2(\lambda)$ is given by (2.3.13) we can write (2.3.18) as

$$g_3(\lambda) = \max_{x_3 \geq 0} [g_2(\lambda - 5x_3) + 260x_3] \qquad (2.3.20)$$

and since $\lambda - 5x_3 \geq 0$ we obtain the form similar to (2.3.17), viz.,

$$g_3(\lambda) = \max_{0 \leq x_3 \leq [\lambda/5]} [g_2(\lambda - 5x_3) + 260x_3] \qquad (2.3.21)$$

where $\lambda = 0, 1, \ldots, 20$.

We may now use (2.3.21) and the known values of $g_2(\lambda)$ given in Table 2.3.2 to construct a table of values of $g_3(\lambda)$. For example:

$$g_3(1) = \max_{0 \leq x_3 \leq 0} [g_2(1 - 5x_3) + 260x_3]$$
$$= g_2(1) = 0 \quad \text{and} \quad x_3^*(1) = 0$$
$$g_3(5) = \max_{0 \leq x_3 \leq 1} [g_2(5 - 5x_3) + 260x_3]$$
$$= \max[g_2(5), \, g_2(0) + 260]$$
$$= \max(270, 0 + 260) = 270 \quad \text{and} \quad x_3^*(5) = 0$$

A complete calculation of $g_3(\lambda)$ is given in Table 2.3.3.

TABLE 2.3.3

λ	$g_3(\lambda)$	$x_3^*(\lambda)$	λ	$g_3(\lambda)$	$x_3^*(\lambda)$
0	0	0	11	600	0
1	0	0	12	660	0
2	110	0	13	710	0
3	160	0	14	770	0
4	220	0	15	820	0
5	270	0	16	880	0
6	330	0	17	930	0
7	380	0	18	990	0
8	440	0	19	1040	0
9	490	0	20	1100	0
10	550	0			

Let us now consider how the one-variable optimization problems given by (2.3.10) and (2.3.11), (2.3.13) and (2.3.14), (2.3.18) and (2.3.19) are related to the original problem we wished to solve, which was given by (2.3.1), (2.3.2), and (2.3.3). In order to do so we consider one last one-variable problem:

$$g_4(\lambda) \equiv \max_{x_4 \geq 0} [g_3(\lambda - 4x_4) + 210x_4] \qquad (2.3.22)$$

where the maximization is taken over integers x_4 between 0 and $\lambda/4$.

If we combine (2.3.12), (2.3.15), (2.3.21), and (2.3.22) we obtain

$$g_4(\lambda) = \max_{x_4}[g_3(\lambda-4x_4)+210x_4]$$

$$= \max_{x_4}\left\{\max_{x_3}[g_2(\lambda-4x_4-5x_3)+260x_3]+210x_4\right\}$$

$$= \max_{x_4}\left\langle\max_{x_3}\left\{\max_{x_2}[g_1(\lambda-4x_4-5x_3-3x_2)+160x_2]+260x_3\right\}+210x_4\right\rangle$$

$$= \max_{x_4}\left\langle\max_{x_3}\left\{\max_{x_2}\left[\max_{x_1}(110x_1)+160x_2\right]+260x_3\right\}+210x_4\right\rangle \quad (2.3.23)$$

The ranges over which the maximizations are taken in (2.3.23) are, respectively,

$$0 \leqslant x_4 \leqslant \left(\frac{\lambda}{4}\right) \quad (2.3.24)$$

$$0 \leqslant x_3 \leqslant \left(\frac{\lambda-4x_4}{5}\right) \quad (2.3.25)$$

$$0 \leqslant x_2 \leqslant \left(\frac{\lambda-4x_4-5x_3}{3}\right) \quad (2.3.26)$$

$$0 \leqslant x_1 \leqslant \left(\frac{\lambda-4x_4-5x_3-3x_2}{2}\right) \quad (2.3.27)$$

If we multiply (2.3.27) by 2 and recalling that x_1, x_2, x_3, x_4 are nonnegative integers, we have that

$$0 \leqslant 2x_1+3x_2+5x_3+4x_4 \leqslant \lambda \quad (2.3.28)$$

If we now compare our original constraint (2.3.2) with (2.3.28) we see that if $\lambda = 20$, a solution to our original problem is also a solution to (2.3.24)–(2.3.27) and vice versa. Hence, it is true that if P^* is the optimal solution to (2.3.1)–(2.3.3) we then have from (2.3.23) that

$$P^* = \max_{x_1, x_2, x_3, x_4} (110x_1+160x_2+260x_3+210x_4)$$

or, in other words,

$$g_4(20) = P^* \quad (2.3.29)$$

What (2.3.29) tells us is that in order to solve our original four-variable problem, we need only calculate $g_4(20)$. This is now a simple matter to do. From (2.3.22) we have that

$$g_4(20) = \max_{0 \leqslant x_4 \leqslant 5} [g_3(20-4x_4)+210x_4]$$

$$= \max[g_3(20), \; g_3(16)+210, \; g_3(12)+420, \; g_3(8)+630, \; g_3(4)+840, \; g_3(0)+1050]$$

$$= \max(1100, 1090, 1080, 1070, 1060, 1050)$$

$$= 1100$$

and the value that gave us $P^* = 1100$ was $x_4^* = 0$. Now it is necessary to find x_3^*, x_2^*, and x_1^*. From (2.3.23) we know that

$$P^* = g_4(20) = g_3(20-4x_4^*)+210x_4^*$$
$$= g_3(20)+210(0) = g_3(20)$$

We now examine the entry for $g_3(20)$ in Table 2.3.3 and find that $x_3^* = 0$. Continuing in this fashion, using (2.3.23) we have that

$$P^* = g_4(20) = g_2(20-4x_4^*-5x_3^*)+260x_3^*$$
$$= g_2(20)+260(0) = g_2(20)$$

Going to Table 2.3.2 we find that for $g_2(20)$, $x_2^* = 0$. Repeating the argument, we now have

$$P^* = g_4(20) = g_1(20-4x_4^*-5x_3^*-3x_2^*)+160x_2^*$$
$$= g_1(20)+160(0) = g_1(20)$$

Corresponding to $g_1(20)$ in Table 2.3.1 we find that $x_1^* = 10$.

The optimal solution to the original problem is

$$P^* = 1100, \quad x_1^* = 10, \quad x_2^* = 0, \quad x_3^* = 0, \quad x_4^* = 0$$

In other words, in order to maximize his profit, our wandering applied mathematician should purchase only item 1 and not purchase any of the others.

We again note in this example all of the characteristics of dynamic programming we have previously described.

(1) We solved four one-variable optimization problems instead of one four-variable optimization problem.

(2) We treated the problem as though he first wished to purchase any amount of item 1, then any amount of item 2, etc., as a four-stage problem. Only at the end did we find the optimal profit.

(3) Although we were only interested in the case of $\lambda = 20$, we had to solve the problem for all integer values of λ, $0 < \lambda < 20$, except for the last stage, where we only solved for $\lambda = 20$.

The procedure we followed to solve this problem is summarized as follows:

(1) A parameter λ was introduced which could assume values $\lambda = 0, 1, \ldots, 20$.

(2) For each value of λ, a one-variable optimization problem was solved for each of the variables x_1, x_2, x_3.

(3) For $\lambda = 20$, a one-variable optimization problem was solved which yielded P^* and x_4^*.

(4) The optimal values of x_3, x_2, and x_1 were obtained from the tables which were generated in step (2).

It is of interest to contrast the relatively small amount of calculation with what would be required if we enumerated all possible combinations of x_1, x_2, x_3, and x_4. We would have to evaluate the objective function $(21)^4 = 194, 481$ times. Hence, the computational savings is quite large. ✳

✳ From 2.3.2 ($2x_1 + 3x_2 + 5x_3 + 4x_4 \leq 20$) we have
$0 \leq x_1 \leq 10$, $0 \leq x_2 \leq 6$, $0 \leq x_3 \leq 4$, $0 \leq x_4 \leq 5$
∴ no. of evaluation is $< 11 \times 7 \times 5 \times 6 = 2310$
In fact a more realistic interpretation of 2.3.2
(eg if $x_1 = 10$, $x_2 = x_3 = x_4 = 0$) leads to < 192

2.4. A Problem in "Division"

We shall now consider a problem much different in several ways from those discussed in Sections 2.2 and 2.3. We shall point out these differences as we solve the problem by dynamic programming.

We are given a known and positive quantity b which is to be divided into n parts in such a way that the product of the n parts is to be a maximum. We shall solve this problem using a dynamic programming approach.

First we note that n is unspecified. Let us consider the simplest problem. That is surely the case of $n = 1$. For this problem, the maximum value of the product is b. Hence we define

$$g_1(b) = b \tag{2.4.1}$$

Let us now consider $n = 2$. First we define   *the product on*

$g_n(b) \equiv$ maximum value of subdividing b into n parts when one part is y and the remaining quantity is optimally divided   (2.4.2)

Let us then consider $g_2(b)$. If one part is y, then we wish to divide the remaining part optimally. Note carefully this explicit use of the principle of optimality. Therefore we may write

$$g_2(b) = \max_{0 \leqslant y \leqslant b} [yg_1(b-y)] \tag{2.4.3}$$

What (2.4.3) says is that the maximum value of dividing b into two parts is given by maximizing over all products of y and the *maximal* solution to dividing $b-y$ into one part. However, by (2.4.1) we know that $g_1(b-y) = b-y$. Hence we may write (2.4.3) as

$$g_2(b) = \max_{0 \leqslant y \leqslant b} [y(b-y)] \tag{2.4.4}$$

Note that in the previous examples, the $g_k(\cdot)$ were all represented as tables of values. In the present example, (2.4.1) is given by an analytic representation and we shall see that we can do the same for $g_2(b)$. In (2.4.4) we are asked to maximize the function $f = y(b-y)$. By simple calculus, we have that

$$\frac{df}{dy} = b - 2y = 0 \tag{2.4.5}$$

Therefore, $y = b/2$. We see that this is a maximum since $(d^2f)/(dy^2) = -2 < 0$. Hence, combining (2.4.4) and (2.4.5) we have that

$$g_2(b) = \frac{b}{2}\left(b - \frac{b}{2}\right) = \frac{b^2}{4} \tag{2.4.6}$$

and $y = b/2$ and $b-y = b/2$. Therefore, the optimal policy is to subdivide b into two equal parts.

Now suppose we have solved the problem for $n = 1, 2, 3, \ldots, k$ and we wish to consider the solution for $n = k+1$. If we take the first of the $k+1$ parts as y, we have an amount $b-y$ left to be divided into k parts. Using the principle of optimality is no more than saying that the best we can do is to subdivide this amount $b-y$ *optimally* into k parts. Using the definition (2.4.2) we see that

$$g_{k+1}(b) = \max_{0 \le y \le b} [y\, g_k(b-y)] \tag{2.4.7}$$

Since we assumed that we knew the form of the function $g_k(\cdot)$, the process of solving for $g_{k+1}(\cdot)$ is a one-variable optimization problem involving the variable y. For example, since we know from (2.4.6) that

$$g_2(\lambda) = \frac{\lambda^2}{4} \tag{2.4.8}$$

we can find $g_3(b)$ by solving

$$g_3(b) = \max_{0 \le y \le b} [y\, g_2(b-y)]$$

$$g_3(b) = \max_{0 \le y \le b} \left[y\, \frac{(b-y)^2}{4} \right] \tag{2.4.9}$$

If $f = [y(b-y)^2]/4$ then

$$\frac{df}{dy} = \frac{1}{4}[(b-y)^2 - 2y(b-y)] = 0 \tag{2.4.10}$$

The solution y^* to (2.4.10) is $y^* = b/3$. Since $(d^2f)/dy^2 = -b/2 < 0$, it follows that $y^* = b/3$ is a maximum. Therefore

Another Solution is $y = 0$ but this does not lead to Maxima

$$g_3(b) = \frac{b}{3} \left[\left(b - \frac{b}{3} \right)^2 \middle/ 4 \right] = \frac{b^3}{27} \tag{2.4.11}$$

and each part should be $b/3$. We see that this is so since if $y = b/3$ and $2b/3$ is subdivided into two parts, each part will be $b/3$.

Since $g_2(b) = b^2/4$ and the optimal policy is $(b/2, b/2)$ and $g_3(b) = b^3/27$ with an optimal policy of $(b/3, b/3, b/3)$ we might conjecture that the solution for $k = n$ is

$$g_n(b) = \left(\frac{b}{n} \right)^n \tag{2.4.12}$$

with an optimal policy $(b/n, b/n, \ldots, b/n)$.

We shall prove by induction that (2.4.12) is the solution to the original problem. We proceed by assuming that (2.4.12) holds for $n = k$. Hence, we may write

$$g_k(b) = \left(\frac{b}{k} \right)^k \tag{2.4.13}$$

We know that for $k = 2$, (2.4.13) yields

$$g_2(b) = \left(\frac{b}{2} \right)^2 = \frac{b^2}{4}$$

3

which we have already verified. We now wish to show that

$$g_{k+1}(b) = \left(\frac{b}{(k+1)}\right)^{k+1} \tag{2.4.14}$$

From (2.4.7) we have

$$g_{k+1}(b) = \max_{0 \leqslant y \leqslant b} [y \, g_k(b-y)] \tag{2.4.15}$$

From (2.4.13) and (2.4.15) we have

$$g_{k+1}(b) = \max_{0 \leqslant y \leqslant b} \left[y\left(\frac{b-y}{k}\right)^k \right] \tag{2.4.16}$$

Consider $f = y\left(\dfrac{b-y}{k}\right)^k$. To find the value of y^* which maximizes f, we note that

$$\frac{df}{dy} = \left(\frac{b-y}{k}\right)^k - y\left(\frac{b-y}{k}\right)^{k-1} = 0 \tag{2.4.17}$$

Solving (2.4.17) for y^* yields   *Also $y=0$*

$$y^* = \frac{b}{k+1} \tag{2.4.18}$$

Therefore we have established that

$$g_{k+1}(b) = \left(\frac{b}{k+1}\right)\left[\frac{b-(b/k+1)}{k}\right]^k$$

$$= \left(\frac{b}{k+1}\right)^{k+1} \tag{2.4.19}$$

which completes the proof.

The above example has several features worth noting. It was possible using simple classical optimization theory, *assuming* that $y\left(\dfrac{b-y}{n}\right)^n$ is a continuous function, to find the optimal value of $g_n(b)$. In the two previous examples, because the variables were integers, we could not use classical optimization techniques. Furthermore, we were able, without use of tabular functions, to solve a problem using continuous functions and variables. This will not always be possible, as we shall see in later chapters.

It is worth noting that if b can take on only integral values, and y is similarly constrained to be an integer, our analysis and solution would be much like that of the two previous examples. We would not be able to arrive at a simple result like (2.4.12). For this case we would have that

$$g_1(b) = b, \quad b \text{ integer} \tag{2.4.20}$$

and $g_2(b)$ would be computed from

$$g_2(b) = \max_{\substack{y \leqslant b \\ y \text{ integer}}} [y(b-y)] \tag{2.4.21}$$

The maximization required in (2.4.21) cannot be performed by classical methods. However, it can be shown that the solution is

$$g_2(b) = \left\lfloor \frac{b^2}{4} \right\rfloor \tag{2.4.22}$$

$$y^* = \left\lfloor \frac{b}{2} \right\rfloor, \quad \left\lceil \frac{b}{2} \right\rceil \tag{2.4.23}$$

where $\lfloor a \rfloor \equiv$ greatest integer $\leqslant a$ and $\lceil a \rceil \equiv$ least integer $\geqslant a$. For example:

$$g_2(3) = \max[0(3), 1(2), 2(1), 3(0)] = 2$$

and

$$y^* = (1, 2)$$
$$g_2(4) = \max[0(4), 1(3), 2(2), 3(1), 4(0)] = 4$$
$$y^* = (2, 2)$$

A partial tabulation of $g_2(b)$ is given in Table 2.4.1. Using the insight of Table 2.4.1, a proof by induction may be constructed, that $g_2(b)$ is given by (2.4.22).

TABLE 2.4.1

b	$g_2(b)$	y
0	0	0
1	0	0, 1
2	1	1
3	2	1, 2
4	4	2
5	6	2, 3
6	9	3
7	12	3, 4
8	16	4
.	.	.
.	.	.
.	.	.

2.5. A Simple Equipment Replacement Problem

A chemical process uses a piece of equipment which is particularly subject to deterioration by corrosion which affects its productivity. Let us suppose the net revenue (after operating costs have been subtracted) from its operations, when it is t years old, is given by

$$I = \begin{cases} 26 - 2t - \frac{1}{2}t^2 & (0 \leqslant t \leqslant 4) \\ 0 & (t > 4) \end{cases} \tag{2.5.1}$$

It can be seen from (2.5.1) that this piece of equipment has no salvage value. The cost of replacement is 22 and when it is replaced it again has a productive life of five years.

3*

We currently have a unit in operation which is one year old. If a decision is made annually to keep the current unit or to replace it, what is the policy that maximizes the total profit for the next five years?

Since (2.5.1) gives the net income we see that the annual profit will be the difference between income and costs other than operating costs. Hence the profit $P(t)$ will be

$$P(t) = \begin{cases} 26-2t-\frac{1}{2}t^2 & (0 \leqslant t \leqslant 4) \\ 0 & (t > 4) \end{cases} \qquad (2.5.2)$$

if we keep the unit. However, if we replace the unit, then the profit is ~for that year~

$$P(t) = 26-22 = 4 \qquad (2.5.3)$$
~at the start of the year~

Since this piece of equipment has no salvage value, the net profit from a new unit does not depend upon the age of the unit being replaced. Hence $P(0) = 4$ is the first-year profit for a new unit. Let us now formulate our problem.

We wish to find a sequence of five annual decisions, i.e., to keep (K) or to replace (R) which will maximize the total profit from five years of operation. Therefore we wish to

$$\max_{\{K_j, R_j\}} \sum_{j=1}^{5} P_j(t) \qquad (2.5.4)$$

where $P_j(t)$ is given by (2.5.2) or (2.5.3) depending on which decision is made. Let us now approach this problem as a multistage optimization problem.

It will facilitate the analysis if we number the stages *backwards*, i.e., stage 1 means we have one year left. Hence we start with stage 5. Figure 2.5.1 indicates the notation we shall use, for time (t_j) and the decisions (d_j) which are keep (K) or replace (R).

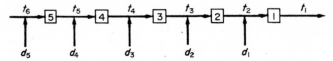

FIG. 2.5.1. Stages of decision problem.

It can be seen that t_j is given by

$$t_j = t_{j+1}+1 \qquad (2.5.5)$$

if the decision is to keep the unit and $t_j = 1$ if the unit is replaced. Figure 2.5.2 explains the above notation and conventions in further detail.

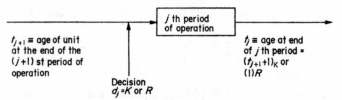

FIG. 2.5.2. Decision problem notation.

Now suppose we have one year of operation left (the last stage). Let us define

$$g_1(t_2) = \text{maximum profit obtained by } K \text{ or } R \text{ upon entering the last year of operation with a unit of age } t_2$$

Then it is clear that

$$g_1(t_2) = \max_{d_1=\{K, R\}} [P(t_2)] \qquad (2.5.6)$$

Sample calculations using (2.5.6) are as follows:

$$g_1(1) = \max[26-2(1)-\tfrac{1}{2}(1)^2, \ 4] = 23.5(K)$$
$$g_1(3) = \max[26-2(3)-\tfrac{1}{2}(9), \ 4] = 15.5(K)$$

The first column of Table 2.5.1 contains all the calculations for units of varying ages when there is one year of operation left.

$g_1(t_2) \qquad \downarrow g_2(t_3)$

TABLE 2.5.1. Maximum profit

Age of unit t_{j+1}	Years of operation left				
	1	2	3	4	5
1	23.5(K)	43.5(K)	59(K)	71(K)	91(K)
2	20(K)	35.5(K)	47.5 (K or R)	67.5(K)	83(K)
3	15.5(K)	27.5(R)	47.5(R)	63(K or R)	78.5(K)
4	10(K)	27.5(R)	47.5(R)	63(R)	75(R)
5	4(R)	27.5(R)	47.5(R)	63(R)	75(R)
6	4(R)	27.5(R)	47.5(R)	63(R)	75(R)

We now need to develop the general approach to calculation of the maximum profit for units which have two or more years of operation left. We define

$$g_j(t_{j+1}) \equiv \text{maximum profit obtained by } K \text{ or } R \text{ upon entering the } j\text{th year of operation with a unit of age } t_{j+1}$$

It is clear from the definition of $g_j(t_{j+1})$ that

$$g_j(t_{j+1}) = \max_{\text{all } K, R} \left[\sum_{k=1}^{j} P_k(t_{k+1}) \right] \qquad (2.5.7)$$

Using the principle of optimality, the definition of $g_j(t_{j+1})$ and (2.5.7), we have that

$$g_j(t_{j+1}) = \max_{d_j=\{K, R\}} [P_j(t_{j+1})+g_{j-1}(t_j)] \qquad (j = 2, 3, 4, 5) \qquad (2.5.8)$$

Now let us use (2.5.8) to calculate $g_2(t_3)$. Recall from (2.5.5) that $t_j = t_{j+1}+1$. Some sample calculations are

$$g_2(1) = \max\begin{cases} P(1)+g_1(2) & \text{if we keep} \\ P(0)+g_1(1) & \text{if we replace} \end{cases}$$

We have already calculated $g_1(t_2)$. Hence we have

$$g_2(1) = \max \begin{cases} 26 - 2(1) - \frac{1}{2}(1)^2 + 20 = 43.5(K) \\ 4 + 23.5 = 27.5(R) \end{cases}$$

$$= 43.5(K)$$

Similarly,

$$g_2(3) = \max \begin{cases} P(3) + g_1(4) \\ P(0) + g_1(1) \end{cases}$$

$$= \max \begin{cases} 26 - 2(3) - \frac{1}{2}(3)^2 + 10 = 25.5(K) \\ 4 + 23.5 = 27.5(R) \end{cases}$$

$$= 27.5(R)$$

The results of the remaining calculations are shown in the columns of Table 2.5.1.

Now we can return to answering our original question. If we currently have a unit which is one year old, we enter Table 2.5.1 at $t_{j+1} = 1$ and in column 5, since we wish to calculate the optimal five-year policy. We see then that the maximum profit is 91 and we keep the unit one more year. We now move over to column 4 and row 2, since the unit is now two years old. We see that the optimal policy is to keep the unit. We now move to column 3 and row 3 and we must replace the unit. If we do so, we now move to column 2 and row 1. We now keep that unit and move to column 1 and row 2. This path is traced in Table 2.5.1. We see that the optimal policy is $(KKRKK)$. What this says is that for the first two years of operation we keep the unit, replace it in the third year, and keep it for the next two years. This will maximize our profit, which will be 91.

We can, of course, use the table we have calculated to answer other questions which might be posed. For example, suppose we wished to maximize the profit over the next five years, starting with a unit that was two years old. For this case there are two optimal policies which yield the same profit of 83. These optimal policies are

$$(KKRKK) \quad \text{and} \quad (KRKKK)$$

The reader should follow these paths through Table 2.5.1. While these two policies yield the same overall profit of 83, they are not completely equivalent if one considers that $(KKRKK)$ gets a profit of 43.5 in the first two years of the five-year period, whereas $(KRKKK)$ gets only 35.5 in the first two years. If it is desirable to get as much profit as early as possible (and it often is), then the first policy is preferable to the second.

2.6. Summary

We have presented several examples in a relatively informal and discursive way in this chapter in order to convey the flavor of the application of dynamic programming as a problem-solving technique. We now need to attend to developing the mathematical theory that provides the justification for what we have been doing and allows us to deal with more complex problems. The next chapter will be devoted to an examination of this theory.

Exercises—Chapter 2

2.1. Dividends on four different investments are known to be:

Investment	Return on investment
1	0.07
2	0.08
3	0.02
4	0.04

An investor has $150,000 to invest and wants to know how much of the total amount to invest in each of the four investment opportunities. He decides that he does not want to invest more than 35% of the total in investment 1 or 2 and wants at least 40% to be invested in 1 and 3. Formulate the optimization problem to find the optimal allocation of the $150,000.

2.2. A chemical company markets a fertilizer for which it receives an order of 10,000 lb. The fertilizer is a mixture of three chemical components which will be called raw materials 1, 2, and 3. The cost of these raw materials is:

Raw material	Cost/lb ($)
1	1.50
2	2.15
3	3.10

It is required that the fertilizer mixture must meet the following specifications:

(a) It must not contain more than 3400 lb of raw material 1.
(b) It must contain at least 2000 lb of raw material 2.
(c) It must contain at least 1200 lb of raw material 3.

Formulate the optimization problem whose solution gives the mixture of minimum cost that satisfies the requirements.

2.3. A manufacturer of electrical motors has three manufacturing plants and five regional warehouses to which he ships the motors for subsequent distribution to customers. The three plants produce the following number of units each week:

Plant	1	2	3
Units available	700	500	600

The five warehouses have the following weekly requirements:

Warehouse	1	2	3	4	5
Units required	250	290	350	600	310

The shipping costs (per motor) from each plant to each warehouse are given by the following table:

From \ To	Warehouses				
	1	2	3	4	5
Plants					
1	2	1	3	1	2
2	4	2	1	3	1
3	2	1	1	3	4

Formulate the optimization problem which will minimize the total shipping costs subject to the constraints on availability and requirements of the motors.

2.4. Suppose that three products are to be manufactured by being sequenced for various operations on n machines. Each item must be processed first on machine 1, then on machine 2, ..., and, finally, on machine n. The sequence of jobs may be different for each machine. Let t_{ij} be the time required to process item i on machine j. Formulate an optimization model in which the total time is minimized for completing the processing of all the items. You must be sure that no two items occupy the same machine at the same time and that an item does not begin processing on machine $j+1$ until it finishes processing on machine j.

2.5. A truck dispatcher for a freight-hauling company must pick up x_1 different shipments that require a_1 units of space each and x_2 different shipments that require a_2 units of space each. He has n trucks available for dispatching. Truck j has a capacity of b_j units of space and costs c_j to operate. Formulate an optimization problem for finding a minimum cost selection of trucks for picking up all the shipments.

Chapter 3

Functional Equations: Basic Theory

3.1. Introduction

It was indicated in Chapter 1 that dynamic programming has been applied to a large, diverse variety of problem areas and types. What is more noteworthy, however, is that dynamic programming can be applied to problems whose initial mathematical representations are quite different. The reader will realize how different this is from, say, linear programming, where the form of the mathematical representation is always the same. We have previously mentioned that this was so, when it was pointed out that dynamic programming was not an "algorithm" in the sense that the simplex method for linear programming is one. Rather, dynamic programming is a way of structuring certain problems so that a certain methodology can be used. This being the case, one would like to be able to know in advance, if possible, what properties an optimization problem must possess so that its initial mathematical formulation can be converted into an equivalent formulation which is amenable to dynamic programming methodology.

It is not possible, despite a number of partially useful attempts, to give a completely satisfactory and "exact" description of the characteristics that the mathematical structure of a problem must *always* possess in order that dynamic programming can be applied. Bellman [3] approaches this matter by exhibiting a large number of specific kinds of problems and problem structures. Mitten [8] gives a sufficient condition for multistage processes to be capable of solution by dynamic programming, i.e., to have the principle of optimality apply. In addition, Denardo and Mitten [9, 13], Karp and Held [10], and Elmaghraby [11] give similar conditions on the monotonicity of the return (objective) functions in order that a sequential decision process be amenable to treatment by dynamic programming. However, this condition is not *necessary* but only sufficient, and it has some other shortcomings which will be discussed in Section 3.4. The general framework we shall use to develop the basic theory will hopefully clarify some of these matters. It will also emphasize that so-called necessary and sufficient conditions for allowing a given mathematical formulation to be treated by dynamic programming are of little help in applying dynamic programming methodology. This will be discussed in greater detail in Section 3.4.

The following discussion of sequential decision processes is indebted in general outline to the discussion of this subject in refs. [9] and [13].

3.2. Sequential Decision Processes

Problems to which dynamic programming has been applied are usually stated in the following terms. A physical, operational, or conceptual system is considered to progress through a series of consecutive *stages*. At each stage the system can be described or characterized by a relatively small set of parameters called the *state variables* or *state vector* (state for short). At each stage, and no matter what state the system is in, one or more *decisions* must be made. These decisions may depend on either stage or state or both. It is also true that the past history of the system, i.e., how it got to the current stage and state, are of no importance. In ohter words, the decisions depend only upon the current stage and state. When a decision is made a *return*† or reward is obtained and the system undergoes a *transformation* or *transition* to the next stage. The return is determined by a known single-valued function of the input state. Similarly, the transformed state results from a known single-valued function of the decision acting upon the current state. The overall purpose of the staged process is to maximize or minimize some function of the state and decision variables.

The key elements that one associates with a dynamic programming problem are stages, states, decisions, transformations, and returns. We shall now define these terms more precisely. We shall illustrate their definitions as we proceed by referring to the interpretation of the wandering applied mathematician problem (Section 2.2) and occasionally to the other problems discussed in Chapter 2.

Stages

The concept of a stage is required so that decisions can be ordered. This is accomplished by means of an index variable associated with each stage. Most often, the stage variable is discrete. Hence the stages are sequentially numbered by the natural integers, 1, 2, ..., . In this connection it should be noted that a *discrete* dynamic programming problem is considered to be discrete with respect to the structure of the stage process, not with respect to the structure of the state variables. There are situations in which the stage variable is considered to be continuous. This is the case when the stage variable is time and a decision can be made at any arbitrary time. Certain Markov decision processes [7] have this characteristic and these will be discussed in Chapter 8. This continuous stage structure also occurs in problems which have been hitherto considered by the classical methods of the calculus of variations [3, 12] and which we shall consider in Chapter 9.

The sole purpose of the stage variable is to sequentially number successive subdivisions of the process being studied. In many problem areas there is a long history of thinking in terms of staged processes. For example, chemical engineers habitually model a distillation column as a series of stages, with each tray of the column considered as a stage. There is an input associated with each tray or stage consisting of various streams of

---

† In a minimization problem "cost" might be a more appropriate term.

chemicals, a set of decision variables (various operating conditions), and an output that leaves the stage with the concentrations of the various streams transformed by the stage operation.

Many other problems, which do not have a natural description in terms of stages, can be so regarded. For example, in the case of the wandering applied mathematician, we grouped together certain cities as the first stage of the journey, another group as the second stage, etc. The essential property of a multivariable optimization problem that enables it to be regarded as a multistage decision process is that it can be regarded in terms of decisions made in some arbitrary sequence, where each step of the sequence is represented as a stage. The important characteristic of each stage is what states are necessary to define or characterize a stage. We consider this now.

States

A state space is a nonempty set Λ. An element $\lambda \in \Lambda$ is called a *state* and is a description of one of the variables (or sets of variables) that describe the condition of the system or process under study. The state space Λ consists of the set of all possible states in which the system might be allowed to exist. For example, in the case of the wandering applied mathematician's first problem, the state variable describing the system (him) was the number of the city he was currently in. The state space Λ consisted of all possible cities. In the second problem, the state variable $\lambda \in \Lambda$ described the weight in lb available to accommodate any number of each of the four items. The state space Λ consisted of all integral weights from 0 to 20. Therefore $\Lambda = \{0, 1, 2, \ldots, 20\}$ and $\lambda = 6$ would mean that the total weight of one or more of the items could not exceed 6 lb.

State variables may be discrete or continuous. In the physical world there really are no continuous variables, either because we deal with discrete entities or because of the inherent accuracy limitations of all physical measurements. However, mathematical continuity is often an advantageous fiction in dealing with certain problems.

States may be single variables or states may be vectors, i.e., they may have several components which describe the system at any stage.

An important property of states that we shall introduce subsequently as an assumption relates to the fact that current and future returns (or costs) will depend only on the current state and not on the particular history of previous states and decisions, i.e., which decisions were made in which states at prior stages of the process under consideration. This property has been given various names by various authors including the Markovian property, state separation property, regeneration point property, and contraction assumption. While these are not all completely equivalent, their function is to produce the same result, viz., that returns or costs associated with current and subsequent decisions depend only on the current state but not on prior states.

Decisions

The state of the system must contain all the information that is required to identify the set of allowable decisions at some given stage. Therefore, associated with each state $\lambda \in \Lambda$ there is a nonempty set X_λ which is called the *decision set* for λ. An element $x_s(\lambda) \in X_\lambda$ is called a *decision* or *decision variable* and represents one of the choices that is available when the system or process is in state λ at stage s. The decision set X_λ consists of the set of all possible choices that might be made when the system is in state λ. In the wandering applied mathematician first example, suppose he is in state 2 at stage 1, i.e., in city 2, and that a decision or choice has to be made whether to go to city 5, 6, or 7. Then the decision set for $\lambda = 2$ may be described as $X_2 = \{2\text{-}5, 2\text{-}6, 2\text{-}7\}$, which is a shorthand way of saying that he can choose the route from city 2 to city 5, city 2 to city 6, or city 2 to city 7. Similarly, if $\lambda = 3$, i.e., he was in city 3, $X_3 = \{3\text{-}5, 3\text{-}6, 3\text{-}7\}$.

Transformations

The process under study in a dynamic programming problem passes from stage to stage. As it does so it moves through one of the states $\lambda \in \Lambda$ to another state in Λ, as a result of the decision $x_s(\lambda)$ which is made in state λ at stage s. What this means is that if the process is in state λ, choosing decision $x_s(\lambda)$ determines a set of states $T(\lambda, x_s(\lambda))$ to which the process can move from state λ. The set function $T(\lambda, x_s(\lambda))$ is called a *transformation function* or transformation operator and it determines the way in which the process evolves from state to state.

The transformation function may be of two basically different kinds, which we might call "deterministic" and "nondeterministic", although this is not quite precise and the nondeterministic case covers several quite different situations, which we shall mention. The simplest case is the deterministic case. This is illustrated by the wandering applied mathematician routing problem (first example). If he is in a given city he will move to another city with complete certainty, i.e., he will *not* sometimes go to one city and sometimes another if he is in a given city. In such a case the set of states given by $T(\lambda, x_s(\lambda))$ would consist of a single element. For example, if our applied mathematician was in city 3, we see that the optimal route was to go next to city 5. Therefore, we see that $T(3, 3 \rightarrow 5) = 5$. In the second applied mathematician problem, suppose at stage 2 he was in state $\lambda = 13$, then $T(13, 1) = 10$, assuming the progression is *backwards* with $\lambda = 20$ corresponding to the four-stage problem. We see this is so since if

$$2x_1 + 3x_2 \leqslant 13$$

and if $x_2 = 1$, then $2x_1 \leqslant 10$.

It is possible for the set function $T(\lambda, x_s(\lambda))$ to consist of more than one element, even in a deterministic case. This would be so if two or more different decisions $x_s(\lambda)$ would yield the same return, then alternate optimal values $x_s^*(\lambda)$ would be possible for the same value of λ. We shall see examples of this phenomenon in the next chapter.

In the case where we do *not* know the outcome of a decision with certainty but the state and decision at each stage is determined as a result of some known probability distribution governing the transformations that occur, the set function $T(\lambda, x_s(\lambda))$ will contain more than one element. Bellman [3] refers to such processes as *level 1* systems. We might call such systems *stochastic* systems. There are many examples of such systems in inventory theory and applications, as well as elsewhere. Howard [7] considers Markov processes that fall in this category.

Bellman [3] also considers stochastic systems of greater complexity than those cited above. We shall not discuss these in great detail at this point. They generally consist of systems which are stochastic but for which we either do not have a definite probability distribution governing the transformations at each stage or systems for which the transformations do depend on past observations.

One last characteristic of transformations is whether or not the selection of a particular decision $x_s(\lambda)$ will cause the process to terminate. If $x_s(\lambda)$ is a *terminating decision* at state λ, $T(\lambda, x_s(\lambda)) = \emptyset$, the null set and no further transformations are possible. There are processes, as we shall see later, in which $T(\lambda, x_s(\lambda)) = \emptyset$ for every $x_s(\lambda) \in X_\lambda$. Such a state λ is called a *terminal state* for the process. The reader who is familiar with Markov processes will see immediately that absorbing states are an illustration of a terminal state.

Policies

Before discussing returns, we need to define the concept of *policy*. The return of a process or system depends upon the decisions that are made at each stage. Hence we need to consider the combination of decisions that are made. A policy is an ordered set of decisions, there being one decision for each state, $\lambda \in \Lambda$. If we designate each possible policy as γ, then the set of all possible policies is the *policy space* Γ. For example, the policy space for the first applied mathematician problem consists of the following possible policies: (1, 2, 5, 8, 10), (1, 2, 5, 9, 10), (1, 2, 6, 8, 10), (1, 2, 6, 9, 10), (1, 2, 7, 8, 10), (1, 2, 7, 9, 10), (1, 3, 5, 8, 10), (1, 3, 5, 9, 10), (1, 3, 6, 8, 10), (1, 3, 6, 9, 10), (1, 3, 7, 8, 10), (1, 3, 7, 9, 10), (1, 4, 5, 8, 10), (1, 4, 5, 9, 10), (1, 4, 6, 8, 10), (1, 4, 6, 9, 10), (1, 4, 7, 8, 10), (1, 4, 7, 9, 10).

Each policy is a conceivable sequence of cities that could actually be visited according to the constraints of the problem. As this example indicates, the policy space is the set of all possible policies and is defined mathematically as the Cartesian product of the decision sets. In mathematical terms we have the $\Gamma = \underset{\lambda \in \Lambda}{\huge\times} X_\lambda$. In our example, the Cartesian product of $\{1\} \times \{2, 3, 4\} \times \{5, 6, 7\} \times \{8, 9\} \times \{10\}$ gives rise to the set of policies and hence the policy space that is listed above.

We will sometimes wish to associate the particular decision in the policy γ that applies to state λ. We will indicate this by γ_λ. For example, in the policy $\gamma = (1, 2, 6, 9, 10)$, the decision in γ corresponding to state 2 is to proceed to 6. Therefore we can write $\gamma_2 = 2\text{-}6$. In the second of our applied mathematician problems, if he had a policy of $\gamma \equiv (x_1, x_2, x_3, x_4) = (1, 1, 2, 1)$, the decision in γ corresponding to $\lambda = 20$ (at stage 4) is to set $x_4 = 1$. Therefore we write $\gamma_{20} = 1$.

Returns

Since a dynamic programming problem is an optimization problem, there is an objective function which can be evaluated for some given policy. We may wish to evaluate the objective function in states which are different from the final state because of the embedding property of dynamic programming. Therefore we shall define a *return function* $r_y(\lambda)$ which is associated with the state λ and policy y. $r_y(\lambda)$ is the return (value of the relevant part of the objective function) that would be obtained if the process started in state λ and decisions associated with the policy λ were used at each of the states through which the process progressed. The total return $r_y(\lambda)$ is some combination of the stage returns (e.g., a sum or product) which are accumulated as the process moves from state to state (and stage to stage). We denote the stage returns as $s(\lambda, y_\lambda)$. It should also be pointed out that it is possible for the return functions to vary from stage to stage. All that is necessary is a well-defined stage return for each stage.

The simplest and most common kind of return or objective function that one encounters in dynamic programming problems is an additive return function in which the total return is the sum of the returns associated with each of the states through which the process has passed. For example, if our wandering applied mathematician adopted policy (1, 2, 6, 8, 10) the cost (return) associated with this policy and each of the states listed is

$$300 + 350 + 350 + 380 = 1380 \qquad (3.2.1)$$

In (3.2.1) the total return $r_y(\lambda)$, corresponding to the policy $y = (1, 2, 6, 8, 10)$ and $\lambda = 1$ is 1380. The various stage returns $s(\lambda, y_\lambda)$ are as follows:

$$s(8, y_8) = 380, \qquad s(2, y_2) = 350$$
$$s(6, y_6) = 350, \qquad s(1, y_1) = 300$$

Note that a return is clearly associated with a state and a policy. In the case of (1, 2, 6, 8, 10) we started in stage 1 and used the policy stated. If we wanted to start in state 3 and use the policy (3, 5, 9, 10) we would have a return of

$$350 + 230 + 280 = 860$$

We shall not restrict ourselves to additive return functions. However, as we shall see, assumptions will be adopted concerning the return function which enable a recursive property to hold. These assumptions may take a variety of forms but what they all seek to assure is that the return function has the following characteristic. If $\otimes$ is some operator (such as addition or multiplication but not necessarily restricted to them),

$$r_y(\lambda_1) = \begin{cases} s(\lambda_1, y_{\lambda_1}) & \text{if} \quad T(\lambda_1, y_{\lambda_1}) = \emptyset \\ s(\lambda_1, y_{\lambda_1}) \otimes r_y(\lambda_2) & \text{if} \quad T(\lambda_1, y_{\lambda_1}) = \lambda_2 \end{cases} \qquad (3.2.2)$$

Equation (3.2.2) states that the total return from state λ_1 using policy y is the result of the operation $\otimes$, between the stage return for the current state λ_1 using decision y_{λ_1}, $s(\lambda_1, y_{\lambda_1})$ and the total return $r_y(\lambda_2)$ using the policy y in the state λ_2. The state λ_2 results from choosing y_{λ_1} while in state λ_1. It will be seen that the recursion equations for the example of Section 2.3 are an example of the equations (3.2.2) when $\otimes$ is interpreted as addition.

The purpose of solving a dynamic programming problem is to find the optimal return for any state and in particular the value of the state variable that corresponds to the statement of the original problem. This *optimal return* is given by

$$g_s(\lambda) = \max_{\gamma \in \Gamma} r_\gamma(\lambda) \tag{3.2.3}$$

We assume for the present in (3.2.3) that the maxima are attained over values of γ in the set Γ.

3.3. Functional Equations and the Principle of Optimality

In the examples of Chapter 2 we made use of functional equations in an informal way. Some typical examples of these functional equations were:

$$g_3(\lambda) = \max_{0 \le x_3 \le [\lambda/5]} [g_2(\lambda - 5x_3) + 260x_3] \tag{2.3.21}$$

$$g_{k+1}(b) = \max_{0 \le y \le b} [y\, g_k(b-y)] \tag{2.4.7}$$

$$g_j(t_{j+1}) = \max_{d_j = \{K, R\}} [P_j(t_{j+1}) + g_{j-1}(t_j)] \tag{2.5.8}$$

It can be seen that the above functional equations are special cases of (3.2.2) and (3.2.3). Before proceeding we shall adopt a slightly modified notation which we shall use henceforth.

Suppose we have an *n*-stage problem. Let the stages be designated $s = 1, 2, \ldots, n$. Let λ_s denote a vector containing the state variables which describe the system at stage s. The objective function that is being maximized will be *assumed* for our purposes here to be $\sum_{j=1}^{n} f_j(x_j)$. Others are possible. This one is only illustrative at this point. $g_s(\lambda_s)$ is defined as the optimal value of the objective function (or return function) when there are s stages and the state variables are given by λ_s. We shall sometimes call $g_s(\lambda_s)$ *state functions*. $x_s(\lambda_s)$ will denote a vector containing the decision variables to be selected at stage s. It will be noted that the decision variables depend upon the values of state variables.

We now continue the discussion of functional equations. We assume that once λ_s and $x_s(\lambda_s)$ are selected, the vector of the state variables for the remaining $s-1$ stages is given by $T(\lambda_s, x_s(\lambda_s))$. The underlying similarity of all dynamic programming processes is the creation of a set of functional equations of a particular type, called *recurrence relations*. These recurrence relations enable one to calculate $g_s(\lambda_s)$ in a particularly simple fashion from $g_{s-1}(\lambda_s)$. A typical set of such recurrence relations or functional equations involving maximization is as follows:

$$g_s(\lambda_s) = \max_{x_s} \{f_s[\lambda_s, x_s(\lambda_s)] + g_{s-1}\langle T[\lambda_s, x_s(\lambda_s)]\rangle\} \quad (s = 2, \ldots, n) \tag{3.3.1}$$

$$g_1(\lambda_1) = \max_{x_1} \{f_1[\lambda_1, x_1(\lambda_1)]\} \tag{3.3.2}$$

The particular form given by (3.3.1) and (3.3.2) is not the only one that functional equations can take in dynamic programming. Others will be illustrated in the following chapters. We use (3.3.1) and (3.3.2) to calculate the $g_s(\lambda_s)$ in a sequential fashion. At the same time that we perform the one-dimensional maximization indicated, we also note the particular value of x_s that led to the optimal value of $g_s(\lambda_s)$. It should now be readily apparent that (2.3.21), (2.4.7), and (2.5.8) are special cases of (3.3.1) and (3.3.2).

The underlying principle that enables one to derive functional equations for sequential decision processes is Bellman's principle of optimality which we now state as:

An optimal policy $(x_1, x_2, \ldots, x_n)$ *has the property that whatever the initial state* λ_0 *and the initial decision* x_1 *are, the remaining decisions* $(x_2, x_3, \ldots, x_n)$ *must constitute an optimal policy for the* $(n-1)$-*stage process starting in the state* λ_1, *which results from the first decision* x_1.

There are two conditions that must be met in order for the principle of optimality to be invoked and lead to recurrence relations and hence the valid application of dynamic programming. These are:

(1) separability of the objective function;
(2) the state separation property.

We shall discuss each of these in turn.

Separability of the Objective Function

By separability of the objective function we mean that the objective function must be separable in the sense that, for all k, the effect of the final k stages on the objective function of an n-stage process depends only on state λ_{n-k} and upon the final k decisions $x_{n-k+1}, x_{n-k+2}, \ldots, x_n$. The "additive" type of separability was discussed in Chapter 1 and illustrated by (3.3.1). We see that (3.3.1) satisfies our definition of separability since the recurrence relation at any stage s depends only on λ_{s-1} and on decision x_s. Equation (2.4.7) illustrates a different kind of separability, viz., multiplicative separability. In terms of our present notation, we would write the general recurrence relation as follows.

Given that the objective function is $\prod_{j=1}^{n} f_j(x_j)$, then the appropriate recurrence relations are:

$$g_1(\lambda_1) = \max_{x_1} \{f_1[\lambda_1, x_1(\lambda_1)]\}, \tag{3.3.3}$$

$$g_s(\lambda_s) = \max_{x_s} \{f_s[\lambda_s, x_s(\lambda_s)] \, g_{s-1}\langle T[\lambda_s, x_s(\lambda_s)]\rangle\} \tag{3.3.4}$$

We shall discuss some other types of "separability" in subsequent examples.

State Separation Property

By state separation we mean that after decision x_{s+1} is made in stage $s+1$, the state λ_{s+1} that results from that decision depends only on λ_s and x_{s+1} and does *not* depend upon the previous states $\lambda_0, \lambda_1, \ldots, \lambda_{s-1}$. Another way of representing this is one we have already employed in (3.3.1) and (3.3.4), i.e., that λ_{s+1} is related only to x_{s+1} and $g_s(\lambda_s)$. This property, sometimes called the Markovian state property, emphasizes that the *only* information available to use about past states is contained in λ_s when we are about to make decision x_{s+1}. We do not use any direct information about the previous states of the process under study. Another way of stating the state separation property is to describe the system being considered as "memoryless", i.e., that the next state at any stage depends only on the current state and the current decision and that we can completely ignore all past states and decisions that led to the current state.

Having described the two essential conditions that must hold in order to use the principle of optimality, let us examine this principle more closely. What it clearly says is that no matter how we got to state λ_1, for the remaining $n-1$ decisions left to us, starting in λ_1 we should make the best possible decisions $x_2, x_3, \ldots, x_n$. If we do so, this set of decisions, together with x_1, will be optimal with respect to the complete n-stage process.

To see how we use the principle of optimality to derive recurrence equations in a fairly general framework, we shall consider the problem

$$\max \ \sum_{j=1}^{n} f_j(x_j)$$

subject to $\qquad\qquad x_j \in S_j \quad (j = 1, 2, \ldots, n)$ $\qquad\qquad$ (3.3.5)

The constraints $x_j \in S_j$ limit the range of x_j to be members of certain sets S_j. One additional fact that must be available is either the initial or final state we wish to reach. Let us consider that in the final stage we have a boundary or terminal state which we shall designate $\lambda_n \equiv b$. For example, $\lambda_n \equiv b$, the final state value might be the largest value of $x_n \in S_n$, i.e., $b = \max(x_n \mid x_n \in S_n)$. Since a final value b is being given, this implies that we shall use a backwards solution from the final state, to find the values of $x_{n-1}, x_{n-2}, \ldots, x_1$. Hence we shall need to vary the values of $\lambda_1, \lambda_2, \ldots, \lambda_{n-1}$ over all possible values, when we apply the principle of optimality. It should be noted that in this example the state variables λ_s and decision variables $x_s(\lambda_s)$ are scalars, i.e., the vectors λ_s, x_s each have only one component.

We shall now apply the principle of optimality at each stage to solve (3.3.5). First we consider the one-stage problem which is

$$\max \ f_1(x_1)$$

subject to $\qquad\qquad x_1 \in S_1$ $\qquad\qquad$ (3.3.6)

Since we do not know what the value of λ_1 should be as we work backwards, we must allow λ_1 to vary over its full allowable range. Since x_1 will usually depend upon λ_1, we are then led to finding $g_1(\lambda_1)$, the optimal value of $f_1(x_1)$ from

$$g_1(\lambda_1) = \max_{x_1 \in \delta_1(\lambda_1)} f_1(x_1) \qquad\qquad (3.3.7)$$

where $\delta_1(\lambda_1)$ depends upon $x_1 \in S_1$ and the specific value of λ_1. This dependence will be different for different problems. The particular way the state variable λ_1 is defined will influence the dependence of $\delta_1(\lambda_1)$ upon λ_1. Again it should be noted that since we do *not* know what specific value λ_1 will have in stage 1, $g_1(\lambda_1)$ is to be determined for all permissible values of λ_1.

Next we define $g_2(\lambda_2)$ as the maximum value of $f_1(x_1)+f_2(x_2)$ for some value of λ_2. From the principle of optimality we know that the state variable λ_2 resulting from the decision x_2 depends only on λ_1 and x_1. A mathematical transliteration of this statement is

$$\lambda_1 = T(\lambda_2, x_2) \tag{3.3.8}$$

where we have given the inverse relationship, for convenience, in (3.3.8). Therefore, for the two-stage process we have, from the definition of $g_2(\lambda_2)$, that

$$g_2(\lambda_2) = \max_{x_2 \in \delta_2(\lambda_2)} \{g_1[T(\lambda_2, x_2)]+f_2(x_2)\} \tag{3.3.9}$$

when $\delta_2(\lambda_2)$ is defined similarly to $\delta_1(\lambda_1)$. Repeated application of the principle of optimality will yield $g_3(\lambda_3)$ from $g_2(\lambda_2)$, and so on. Therefore we may write for an n-stage process, the following functional equations:

$$g_1(\lambda_1) = \max_{x_1 \in \delta_1(\lambda_1)} f_1(x_1) \tag{3.3.10}$$

$$g_s(\lambda_s) = \max_{x_s \in \delta_s(\lambda_s)} \{g_{s-1}[T(\lambda_s, x_s)]+f_s(x_s)\} \qquad (s = 2, 3, \ldots, n) \tag{3.3.11}$$

where $\delta_s(\lambda_s)$ depends upon $x_s \in S_s$ and the particular value of λ_s. Hence we see that the functional equations of dynamic programming follow from the application of the principle of optimality.

We have shown how the principle of optimality and the properties that make it valid underly the functional equations of dynamic programming. Having done this, it is only fair to say that, in general, we shall not obtain the recurrence equations in this fashion. We shall instead derive them from the definition of the state functions. Dynamic programming was developed in this fashion by Bellman and his collaborators and followers. It is still the only practical method for utilizing dynamic programming methodology. Why this is so is discussed in the following section. This situation again points up the rather loose methodological base of applying dynamic programming. It is usually clear how the n-stage separability can be achieved (although not always). It is also true that once the state functions are defined, the recurrence relations are easily derived. However, the most elusive part of this enterprise is the proper definition of state functions. The success or failure of a dynamic programming formulation usually hangs on this rather subtle step of defining the state functions suitably.

3.4. The Principle of Optimality—Necessary and Sufficient Conditions

In the previous section we described and discussed two conditions that must hold so that the principle of optimality could be validly applied. These two properties were "separability" of the objective function and the Markovian property. The difficulty that one faces, as we have already mentioned, is to take a given mathematical representation of a problem and determine whether or not a valid separability can be induced and the even more difficult task of finding the appropriate definition of states for the problem.

This may be easy to do, may be difficult in some cases, and may be "impossible" in others. When we say "impossible", what we really mean is that it is not possible to define the states and stages in such a way as to have a computationally useful representation. In principle, one can *always* find a representation of an optimization problem in a dynamic programming format. We can illustrate this important point as follows.

Suppose we wish to solve

$$\max \quad z = f(x_1, x_2, \ldots, x_n) \tag{3.4.1}$$

subject to $\quad h_i(x_1, x_2, \ldots, x_n) \leqslant 0 \quad (i = 1, 2, \ldots, m)$

We define state variables y_s by

$$y_s = (x_1, x_2, \ldots, x_s) \quad (s = 1, 2, \ldots, n) \tag{3.4.2}$$

The constraints $h_i(x_1, x_2, \ldots, x_n) \leqslant 0$ can be replaced by a sequence of relationships of the following form:

$$x_1 \in R_1, \ x_2 \in R_2(x_1), \ldots, x_s \in R_s(x_1, x_2, \ldots, x_{s-1}), \ldots, x_n \in R_n(x_1, x_2, \ldots, x_{n-1}) \tag{3.4.3}$$

where $R_s(x_1, x_2, \ldots, x_{s-1})$ is some region in which x_s is constrained to lie when $x_1, x_2, \ldots, x_{s-1}$ are specified.

For example, suppose $n = 2$ and

$$h_1(x_1, x_2) \equiv a_{11}x_1 + a_{21}x_1^2 + a_{31}x_2 - b_1$$
$$h_2(x_1, x_2) \equiv a_{21}x_1 + a_{22}x_2 + a_{32}x_2^2 - b_2$$

then

$$R_1 \equiv \{x_1 \mid a_{11}x_1 + a_{21}x_1^2 + a_{31}x_2 \leqslant b_1,$$
$$a_{21}x_1 + a_{22}x_1^2 + a_{32}x_2 \leqslant b_2, \ x_2 \text{ specified}\}$$
$$R_2(x_1) = \{x_2 \mid x_2 \leqslant \min[(b_1 - a_{11}x_1 - a_{21}x_1^2)/a_{31},$$
$$(b_2 - a_{21}x_1^2 - a_{22}x_1^2)/a_{32}]\}$$

and (3.4.3) can be rewritten in terms of the state variables y_s as

$$y_1 \in Y_1, \quad y_2 \in Y_2(y_1), \ldots, y_s \in Y_s(y_{s-1}), \ldots, y_n \in Y_n(y_{n-1}) \tag{3.4.4}$$

We can now put our original problem in a dynamic programming format as

$$g_{n-1}(y_{n-1}) = \max_{y_n \in Y_n(y_{n-1})} [f(y_n)]$$

$$g_{n-2}(y_{n-2}) = \max_{y_{n-1} \in Y_{n-1}(y_{n-2})} [g_{n-1}(y_{n-1})]$$

$$\vdots$$

$$\tag{3.4.5}$$

$$g_s(y_s) = \max_{y_{s+1} \in Y_{s+1}(y_s)} [g_{s+1}(y_{s+1})]$$

$$\vdots$$

$$g_1(y_1) = \max_{y_2 \in Y_2(y_1)} [g_2(y_2)]$$

4*

Finally,

$$\max \quad z = \max_{y_1 \in Y_1} [g_1(y_1)]$$

It should be noted that the numbering of the stages is *backwards* in (3.4.2)–(3.4.5), as shown in the following diagram:

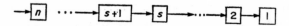

The difficulty with this general solution, which is due to White [14], resides in whether or not the characterization of the state variables and the sets R_s (or Y_s) can be carried out, i.e., it depends on the precise form of the functions and constraints. In all cases known to the authors, if the approach just outlined will succeed, it is a far simpler matter to examine the particular problem at hand and derive the recurrence relations by an intuitive satisfaction of the principle of optimality. Hence this formulation is only of theoretical value.

Since the difficult part of using dynamic programming is defining the state variables and the "stages" of the separable calculation, it is not surprising that a number of people have tried to state sufficient, and in some cases necessary and sufficient, conditions for a sequential decision process to be formulated as a dynamic programming problem. If one examines these attempts, one finds that while they provide some increased insight into the required mathematical properties that return functions must have, etc., they do not provide much more guidance than the above general formulation, to the all important question of how to represent a given problem in terms of states and transformations. We shall briefly examine the history of some of these efforts.

The earliest and most important work in dynamic programming was that of Bellman [3–6]. Bellman's approach is generally heuristic. With great insight, he adapted dynamic programming to a bewildering variety of different problems. He states and makes reference to the principle of optimality, which does in fact paraphrase necessary and sufficient conditions of a kind. However, no clear mathematical transliteration of these conditions was given. The determination of how to represent a given problem in terms of stages, states, and transitions was presented by numerous examples, as a guide to the reader. In general, these examples required mathematical dexterity of a high order to decide when it was permissible to change the order of operators, etc. As long as one did this correctly and possessed the requisite insight, the functional equations of dynamic programming were obtainable. This is not to say that there are not examples where errors have been made. However, dynamic programming is not the only applied mathematical discipline where this situation exists and is far from being the worst offender.

Mitten [8] appears to have been the first to propose some sufficient conditions for determining whether or not a given dynamic programming return function satisfies one of a number of different recursively exploitable properties that enable its use in solving a sequential decision (multistage) process. While Mitten's monotonicity condition on the return function can sometimes be used to test whether a return composition function meets the requisite condition, it fails to provide any guidance at the outset as to how to structure the sequential decision process. Furthermore, the monotonicity condition is sufficient and not necessary. Nemhauser [15] states Mitten's sufficiency condition and gives a simple example of its use. It is clear that cases of return functions that violate the sufficiency condition can be constructed and solved by dynamic programming.

Denardo and Mitten [9, 13] have also stated a form of the monotonicity condition on return functions, and they have given a number of examples of recursion forms that satisfy this sufficient condition. However, as is always the case, these recursion forms can be derived without any knowledge of the monotonicity assumption and, indeed, all or most of them were so derived. That is not to say that Mitten and Denardo's explorations are not valuable. They do provide insight into some of the ways that permissible return functions can be constructed.

Karp and Held [10] have also developed a mathematical formalism for treating what they call discrete decision processes and sequential decision processes. Monotone sequential decision processes (which turn out to be finite automata with a particular cost structure) correspond to what we have called dynamic programming algorithms. Not surprisingly, a monotonicity condition is utilized. Karp and Held do give necessary and sufficient conditions for the constructing of dynamic programming algorithms once the original problem has been formalized as a discrete decision process. However, this procedure requires the finding of a certain equivalence relation satisfying the conditions of a theorem. No general procedure is known for accomplishing this task. Future work may extend the insights of this approach.

Elmaghraby [11] has also stated necessary and sufficient conditions for deducing from the statement of the original problem, which usually is not stated in terms of states and transformations, a solution method in terms of dynamic programming. However, it is not entirely clear whether or not this analysis aids the problem formulator any more than the previous efforts. Elmaghraby does provide an example to show how the choice of a state variable will be invalid if the conditions he enunciates are violated. However, the choice of the correct state variable is, as usual, a rather subtle matter and it is not clear how a knowledge of the necessary and sufficient conditions would have helped *ab initio*.

Bonzon [16] has given a set of necessary and sufficient conditions for "deriving" the dynamic programming algorithm for any discrete optimization problem. However, upon close examination it appears that the constraints have to satisfy a condition called being a "chained graph" which turns out to be equivalent to the Markovian property on states which is stated in Section 3.3. It is also the case that the objective function has to be what the authors call a "chained function" which is exactly the separability property which we defined earlier in Section 3.3. Hence, in actual fact the utilization of Bonzon's necessary and sufficient conditions do not provide any real insight into how to rearrange the original statement of the mathematical problem into what he calls "chained graphs" and "chained functions."

As of this date it does not seem that one can do much better than to gain as much experience as possible in previous uses of dynamic programming. This will provide the best basis for assessing the most convenient and tractable ways of defining stages, states, decision variables, and transformations. We shall endeavor, in the remaining chapters of this book, to provide as much insight into this process as possible.

Exercise—Chapter 3

3.1. For each of the problems in Chapter 2, describe in detail what variables or items correspond to stages, states, decisions, transformations, and returns.

Chapter 4

One-dimensional Dynamic Programming: Analytic Solutions

4.1. Introduction

In this chapter we shall apply the principles of dynamic programming to a large number of mathematical problems which have one thing in common, viz., that in the expressions for the recursion relations, the maximization or minimization can be performed without recourse to numerical tabulation of the stage returns and the optimal return functions. Instead, the optimal return functions, $g_s(\lambda_s)$, can be represented by a mathematical formula and, indeed, classical optimization methods can be employed to obtain these representations. We emphasize this class of problem because frequently in certain papers and texts on dynamic programming, one gets the impression that an expression such as

$$g_s(\lambda_s) = \max_{x_s}[f_s(x_s)+g_{s-1}(\lambda_s-x_s)] \tag{4.1.1}$$

can only be calculated by a numerical maximization procedure. While this may be the case for certain functions $f_s(x_s)$, it is not the case for all functions. Hence this chapter will be devoted to explicating the application of dynamic programming to particular classes of problems where the one-dimensional maximization or minimization subproblems can be solved analytically. It will also exhibit plainly the approach of dynamic programming in general. In order to do the latter we shall consider a prototype problem which will be generalized subsequently.

4.2. A Prototype Problem

Consider the problem[†]

$$\min \quad z = x_1^2+x_2^2+x_3^2 \tag{4.2.1}$$

subject to
$$x_1+x_2+x_3 \geqslant b \tag{4.2.2}$$

$$x_1, x_2, x_3 \geqslant 0 \tag{4.2.3}$$

$$b > 0$$

[†] This problem is a special case of an exercise given in Bellman [3]. We shall have a good deal more to say about the general problem.

In order to relate this problem to the concepts we discussed in the last chapter, i.e., stages, state variables, transformations, etc., we shall rewrite (4.2.1)–(4.2.3) as follows:

$$\min \quad z = s_1(\lambda_1, x_1) + s_2(\lambda_2, x_2) + s_3(\lambda_3, x_3) \tag{4.2.4}$$

subject to
$$\lambda_{s-1} = T_s(\lambda_s, x_s(\lambda_s)) \qquad (s = 1, 2, 3)$$

In (4.2.4) we have introduced state variables $(\lambda_0, \lambda_1, \lambda_2, \lambda_3)$ which have enabled us to replace (4.2.2) by the transformations

$$
\begin{aligned}
\lambda_3 &\geqslant b & \lambda_1 &= \lambda_2 - x_2 \\
\lambda_2 &= \lambda_3 - x_3 & \lambda_0 &= \lambda_1 - x_1
\end{aligned}
\tag{4.2.5}
$$

To see that (4.2.5) are equivalent to (4.2.2) we note that by adding the relationships (4.2.5) we obtain

$$x_1 + x_2 + x_3 \geqslant b - \lambda_0 \tag{4.2.6}$$

We set $\lambda_0 = 0^\dagger$ so that (4.2.6) is identical to (4.2.2). This results in $x_1 = \lambda_1$. Since $x_1 \geqslant 0$, we have that $\lambda_1 \geqslant 0$. Similarly, $x_2 \leqslant \lambda_2$ and $x_3 \leqslant \lambda_3$. Let us now restate our original problem in the form of (4.2.4) using the transformations of state variables that we have introduced.

$$\min \quad z = x_1^2 + x_2^2 + x_3^2$$

subject to
$$
\begin{aligned}
\lambda_1 &= \lambda_2 - x_2, & 0 &\leqslant x_1 = \lambda_1 \\
\lambda_2 &= \lambda_3 - x_3, & 0 &\leqslant x_2 \leqslant \lambda_2 \\
\lambda_3 &\geqslant b, & 0 &\leqslant x_3 \leqslant \lambda_3
\end{aligned}
\tag{4.2.7}
$$

It is important to see that (4.2.7) is in the form (4.2.4). This is so because

$$
\begin{aligned}
s_s(\lambda_s, x_s) &= x_s^2 \\
\lambda_{s-1} = T_s(\lambda_s, x_s(\lambda_s)) &= \lambda_s - x_s
\end{aligned}
\qquad (s = 1, 2, 3)
\tag{4.2.8}
$$

Having found the form of the stage returns and the transformations we can now state the original problem in terms of the recursion equations that we use in dynamic programming and which were discussed in the last chapter, i.e.,

$$
\begin{aligned}
g_1(\lambda_1) &= \min_{x_1} \{ f_1[\lambda_1, x_1(\lambda_1)] \} \\
g_s(\lambda_s) &= \min_{x_s} \{ f_s[\lambda_s, x_s(\lambda_s)] + g_{s-1}[T(\lambda_s, x_s(\lambda_s))] \} \qquad (s = 2, 3)
\end{aligned}
\tag{4.2.9}
$$

Equations (4.2.9) are the general form we gave in Chapter 3, except that we are minimizing instead of maximizing. If we now substitute

$$
\begin{aligned}
f_s(x_s) &= x_s^2 \\
\lambda_{s-1} &= \lambda_s - x_s
\end{aligned}
\qquad (s = 1, 2, 3)
\tag{4.2.10}
$$

---

† It is not necessary, nor even correct, in some problems to set $\lambda_0 = 0$. In this problem we will *always* want $x_1 + x_2 + x_3 = b$ so as to minimize $x_1^2 + x_2^2 + x_3^2$. Hence λ_0 was set equal to zero which corresponds to allocating no less than an amount b between x_1, x_2, x_3.

we readily obtain the recurrence relations

$$g_1(\lambda_1) = \min_{x_1=\lambda_1} x_1^2$$

$$g_s(\lambda_s) = \min_{0 \leqslant x_s \leqslant \lambda_s} [x_s^2 + g_{s-1}(\lambda_s - x_s)] \qquad (s = 2, 3) \qquad (4.2.11)$$

Before we proceed to solve the recursion equations it is useful to use a diagrammatic representation of the stagewise process we are employing in the analysis of this problem. The state variable λ_3 can be imagined to be a quantity which must not be less than b and is to be distributed among the three stages so as to minimize $z = x_1^2 + x_2^2 + x_3^2$. This is shown in Fig. 4.2.1.

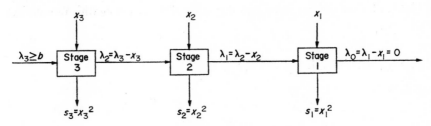

FIG. 4.2.1. Stagewise representation.

The process that is depicted in Fig. 4.2.1 corresponds to what we shall be attempting to perform using equations (4.2.11). We pretend that in order to solve our original problem (4.2.1)–(4.2.3) we are dividing an amount λ_3 (undetermined, except that it must be $\geqslant b$) by a sequential process. In stage 3 an amount λ_3 is available. If we select x_3 then the quantity $\lambda_2 = \lambda_3 - x_3$ is available for subdivision in stages 2 and 1. Hence $\lambda_2 = \lambda_3 - x_3$ enters stage 2 where an amount x_2 is selected or decided upon and hence an amount $\lambda_1 = \lambda_2 - x_2$ is available for stage 1. No more than the remainder must be allocated in stage 1 since we wish to make x_1^2 as small as possible.

It should be noted that the ordering of the variables is arbitrary for two reasons. First, there is symmetry with respect to the occurrence of the variables in both the objective function (4.2.1) and the constraints (4.2.3). Second, even if this was not so the numbering of the stages in Fig. 4.2.1 is arbitrary and x_1 could become x_3 as long as the correct state variable transformation was used.

We shall now solve (4.2.11) and hence solve our original problem. Since

$$g_1(\lambda_1) = \min_{x_1=\lambda_1} x_1^2$$

there is no optimization to be performed here and it is clear that

$$g_1(\lambda_1) = \lambda_1^2 \qquad (4.2.12)$$

The meaning of (4.2.12) should be emphasized. $g_1(\lambda_1)$ is an *optimal* return function. What it says is that no matter how much we have (λ_1), the optimal return is λ_1^2 and $x_1^* = \lambda_1$.

Next we wish to find the second-stage optimal return, $g_2(\lambda_2)$. From (4.2.11) we have that

$$g_2(\lambda_2) = \min_{0 \leqslant x_2 \leqslant \lambda_2} [x_2^2 + g_1(\lambda_2 - x_2)] \tag{4.2.13}$$

From (4.2.12) we can see that

$$g_1(\lambda_2 - x_2) = (\lambda_2 - x_2)^2 \tag{4.2.14}$$

Hence from (4.2.13) and (4.2.14) we have

$$g_2(\lambda_2) = \min_{0 \leqslant x_2 \leqslant \lambda_2} [x_2^2 + (\lambda_2 - x_2)^2] \tag{4.2.15}$$

From (4.2.15) we see that we must find the value of $0 \leqslant x_2 \leqslant \lambda_2$ which minimizes

$$G_2(\lambda_2, x_2) = x_2^2 + (\lambda_2 - x_2)^2 \tag{4.2.16}$$

Taking the partial derivative in (4.2.16) we obtain

$$\frac{\partial G_2}{\partial x_2} = 2x_2 - 2(\lambda_2 - x_2) = 0 \tag{4.2.17}$$

This necessary condition is also sufficient since

$$\frac{\partial G_2^2}{\partial x_2^2} = 4 > 0$$

The solution to (4.2.17) is

$$x_2^* = \frac{\lambda_2}{2} \tag{4.2.18}$$

Therefore, by substituting (4.2.18) into (4.2.15), we obtain

$$g_2(\lambda_2) = \left(\frac{\lambda_2}{2}\right)^2 + \left(\lambda_2 - \frac{\lambda_2}{2}\right)^2 = \frac{\lambda_2^2}{2} \tag{4.2.19}$$

Next we determine $g_3(\lambda_3)$ in precisely the same way as $g_2(\lambda_2)$, i.e.,

$$g_3(\lambda_3) = \min_{0 \leqslant x_3 \leqslant \lambda_3} [x_3^2 + g_2(\lambda_3 - x_3)]$$

$$= \min_{0 \leqslant x_3 \leqslant \lambda_3} \left[x_3^2 + \frac{(\lambda_3 - x_3)^2}{2} \right] \tag{4.2.20}$$

Then

$$G_3(\lambda_3, x_3) = x_3^2 + \frac{(\lambda_3 - x_3)^2}{2} \tag{4.2.21}$$

$$\frac{\partial G_3}{\partial x_3} = 2x_3 - (\lambda_3 - x_3) = 0 \tag{4.2.22}$$

$$\frac{\partial^2 G_3}{\partial x_3^2} = 3 > 0$$

Solving (4.2.22) for x_3 we obtain

$$x_3^* = \frac{\lambda_3}{3} \tag{4.2.23}$$

and, therefore,

$$g_3(\lambda_3) = \left(\frac{\lambda_3}{3}\right)^2 + \frac{[\lambda_3 - (\lambda_3/3)]^2}{2} = \frac{\lambda_3^2}{3} \tag{4.2.24}$$

It is important once again to understand the meaning of equation (4.2.24), i.e.,

$$g_3(\lambda_3) = \frac{\lambda_3^2}{3}$$

This equation tells us that the optimal return for a three-stage process (which we do, in fact, have) is $\lambda_3^2/3$ if the amount to be allocated is λ_3 and all the remaining allocations are optimal. Since the allocations were optimal in stages 1 and 2, $g_3(\lambda_3) = \lambda_3^2/3$ should be the optimal solution for any value λ_3. We know that $\lambda_3 \geqslant b$ and that the optimum will occur when $\lambda_3 = b$. Hence, we have

$$g_3(b) = \frac{b^2}{3} \quad \text{and} \quad x_3^* = \frac{b}{3} \tag{4.2.25}$$

In actual fact it was not necessary to determine (4.2.24) with λ_3, since we knew that the only value we were interested in was b. In this chapter we shall do no more work either way. However, when the optimal return function $g_3(\lambda_3)$ is given by a table of values, we can often save some computation by using the final n-stage value of the state variable.

At this point we have an interesting situation which is characteristic of dynamic programming. We know that the optimal value of $z = x_1^2 + x_2^2 + x_3^2$ is $b^2/3$ and we know that $x_3^* = b/3$. However, we do not yet know what x_2^* and x_1^* are that led to $z^* = b^2/3$. This, however, is easily found by using the definitions of the state variables:

$$\lambda_3 = b, \quad x_3^* = \frac{b}{3}$$

$$\lambda_2 = \lambda_3 - x_3 = b - \frac{b}{3} = \frac{2b}{3}$$

$$x_2^* = \frac{\lambda_2}{2} = \frac{2b}{6} = \frac{b}{3}$$

$$\lambda_1 = \lambda_2 - x_2 = \frac{2b}{3} - \frac{b}{3} = \frac{b}{3}$$

$$x_1^* = \lambda_1 = \frac{b}{3}$$

Hence we have found the optimal solution to our original problem, i.e.,

$$x_1^* = \frac{b}{3}, \quad x_2^* = \frac{b}{3}, \quad x_3^* = \frac{b}{3}, \quad z^* = \frac{b^2}{3}$$

This simple example illustrates the basic approach of dynamic programming. The original problem had to be stated in terms of stages, states, and transformations that were to be carried out at each stage. The definition of state variable and stages had to be such that at each stage it was possible to calculate the return of that stage and, in effect, the total return for an s-stage problem, whatever s might be. In the final nth stage we had the solution to the original problem and then by proceeding backwards through the definitions of state variables and how each state variable was related to the next state variable, we obtained the optimal values of the decision variables.

4.3. Some Variations of the Prototype Problem

Suppose we modify the problem of the previous section as follows:

$$\min \quad z = c_1 x_1^2 + c_2 x_2^2 + c_3 x_3^2$$

subject to
$$x_1 + x_2 + x_3 \geqslant b > 0 \tag{4.3.1}$$
$$x_1, x_2, x_3 \geqslant 0$$
$$c_s > 0, \quad (s = 1, 2, 3)$$

We see that the only difference is that the objective function terms each have different specified coefficients. Nevertheless, the exact same approach will yield the solution, although the algebra will be somewhat more tedious.

We consider that we have a three-stage problem and by analogy with (4.2.7), we see that (4.3.1) can be formulated in terms of state variables $\lambda_1, \lambda_2, \lambda_3$ as follows:

$$\min \quad z = c_1 x_1^2 + c_2 x_2^2 + c_3 x_3^2$$

subject to
$$\lambda_1 = \lambda_2 - x_2, \qquad 0 \leqslant x_1 = \lambda_1$$
$$\lambda_2 = \lambda_3 - x_3, \qquad 0 \leqslant x_2 \leqslant \lambda_2 \tag{4.3.2}$$
$$\lambda_3 = b, \ \lambda_3 \geqslant b \quad 0 \leqslant x_3 \leqslant \lambda_3$$

We note the state variable definitions have not changed. Hence the recursion relations that we must solve are a minor modification of (4.2.11), and are as follows:

$$g_1(\lambda_1) = \min_{x_1 = \lambda_1} c_1 x_1^2$$
$$g_s(\lambda_s) = \min_{0 \leqslant x_s \leqslant \lambda_s} [c_s x_s^2 + g_{s-1}(\lambda_s - x_s)] \qquad (s = 2, 3) \tag{4.3.3}$$

The solution of (4.3.3) is much the same as previously. $g_1(\lambda_1)$ is found from

$$g_1(\lambda_1) = \min_{x_1 = \lambda_1} c_1 x_1^2 = c_1 \lambda_1^2 \tag{4.3.4}$$

Next we solve for $g_2(\lambda_2)$ as follows:

$$g_2(\lambda_2) = \min_{0 \leqslant x_2 \leqslant \lambda_2} [c_2 x_2^2 + g_1(\lambda_2 - x_2)]$$
$$= \min_{0 \leqslant x_2 \leqslant \lambda_2} [c_2 x_2^2 + c_1(\lambda_2 - x_2)^2]$$
$$= \min_{0 \leqslant x_2 \leqslant \lambda_2} G_2(\lambda_2, x_2) \tag{4.3.5}$$

Proceeding to find x_2^*, we differentiate G_2 and set the result equal to zero:

$$\frac{\partial G_2}{\partial x_2} = 2c_2 x_2 - 2c_1(\lambda_2 - x_2) = 0 \tag{4.3.6}$$

Since $[(\partial^2 G_2)/(\partial x_2^2)] = 2(c_1 + c_2) > 0$, we solve (4.3.6) for x_2^* and have that

$$x_2^* = \frac{c_1 \lambda_2}{c_1 + c_2} \tag{4.3.7}$$

Hence, from (4.3.5) and (4.3.7) we have

$$g_2(\lambda_2) = c_2 \left(\frac{c_1 \lambda_2}{c_1 + c_2} \right)^2 + c_1 \left(\lambda_2 - \frac{c_1 \lambda_2}{c_1 + c_2} \right)^2 \tag{4.3.8}$$

Simplifying (4.3.8) we obtain

$$g_2(\lambda_2) = \frac{c_1 c_2}{c_1 + c_2} \lambda_2^2 \tag{4.3.9}$$

Next we solve for $g_3(\lambda_3)$ from

$$\begin{aligned} g_3(\lambda_3) &= \min_{0 \le x_3 \le \lambda_3} [c_3 x_3^2 + g_2(\lambda_3 - x_3)] \\ &= \min_{0 \le x_3 \le \lambda_3} \left[c_3 x_3^2 + \frac{c_1 c_2}{c_1 + c_2} (\lambda_3 - x_3)^2 \right] \\ &= \min_{0 \le x_3 \le \lambda_3} G_3(\lambda_3, x_3) \end{aligned} \tag{4.3.10}$$

Differentiating $G_3(\lambda_3, x_3)$ we have

$$\frac{\partial G_3}{\partial x_3} = 2c_3 x_3 - \frac{2c_1 c_2}{c_1 + c_2}(\lambda_3 - x_3) = 0 \tag{4.3.11}$$

Since

$$\frac{\partial^2 G_3}{\partial x_3^2} = 2c_3 + \frac{2c_1 c_2}{c_1 + c_2} > 0,$$

we solve (4.3.11) for x_3^* and find

$$x_3^* = \frac{c_1 c_2}{c_1 c_2 + c_2 c_3 + c_1 c_3} \lambda_3 \tag{4.3.12}$$

From (4.3.10) and (4.3.12) we have

$$g_3(\lambda_3) = c_3 \left(\frac{c_1 c_2 \lambda_3}{c_1 c_2 + c_2 c_3 + c_1 c_3} \right)^2 + \frac{c_1 c_2}{c_1 + c_2} \left(\lambda_3 - \frac{c_1 c_2 \lambda_3}{c_1 c_2 + c_2 c_3 + c_1 c_3} \right)^2 \tag{4.3.13}$$

After some considerable algebra (4.3.13) can be simplified to

$$g_3(\lambda_3) = \frac{c_1 c_2 c_3}{(c_1 c_2 + c_2 c_3 + c_1 c_3)} \lambda_3^2 \tag{4.3.14}$$

Since $\lambda_3 = b$, we have that

$$z = g_3(b) = \frac{c_1 c_2 c_3}{(c_1 c_2 + c_2 c_3 + c_1 c_3)} b^2 \qquad (4.3.15)$$

and we compute the optimal values of x_1, x_2, x_3 from

$$x_3^* = \frac{c_1 c_2}{c_1 c_2 + c_2 c_3 + c_1 c_3} b$$

$$\lambda_2 = \lambda_3 - x_3 = b - \frac{c_1 c_2}{c_1 c_2 + c_2 c_3 + c_1 c_3} b = \frac{c_2 c_3 + c_1 c_3}{c_1 c_2 + c_2 c_3 + c_1 c_3} b$$

$$x_2^* = \frac{c_1 \lambda_2}{c_1 + c_2} = \left(\frac{c_1}{c_1 + c_2}\right)\left(\frac{c_2 c_3 + c_1 c_3}{c_1 c_2 + c_2 c_3 + c_1 c_3}\right) b = \frac{c_1 c_3 b}{c_1 c_2 + c_2 c_3 + c_1 c_3}$$

$$\lambda_1 = \lambda_2 - x_2 = \frac{c_2 c_3 + c_1 c_3}{c_1 c_2 + c_2 c_3 + c_1 c_3} b - \left(\frac{c_1}{c_1 + c_2}\right)\left(\frac{c_2 c_3 + c_1 c_3}{c_1 c_3 + c_2 c_3 + c_1 c_3}\right) b$$

$$= \left(\frac{c_2}{c_1 + c_2}\right)\left(\frac{c_2 c_3 + c_1 c_3}{c_1 c_2 + c_2 c_3 + c_1 c_3}\right) b = \frac{c_2 c_3 b}{c_1 c_2 + c_2 c_3 + c_1 c_3}$$

$$x_1^* = \lambda_1 = \left(\frac{c_2}{c_1 + c_2}\right)\left(\frac{c_2 c_3 + c_1 c_3}{c_1 c_2 + c_2 c_3 + c_1 c_3}\right) b = \frac{c_2 c_3 b}{c_1 c_2 + c_2 c_3 + c_1 c_3}$$

Hence we have found the solution to the original problem. While the algebra was more tedious than in the problem of the preceding section, the methodology was the same.

In the problem of (4.3.1) while the objective function was changed from the prototype problem of Section 4.2, the state variables were defined in precisely the same way, i.e.,

$$\lambda_{s-1} = T_s[\lambda_s, x_s(\lambda_s)] = \lambda_s - x_s$$

and the state transformation *function* was the same in both problems. Let us now consider another variation of the prototype problem, to exhibit a different (but similar) state transformation function and show that the methodology is quite similar.

Consider the problem

$$\min \quad z = x_1^2 + x_2^2 + x_3^2$$

subject to
$$a_1 x_1 + a_2 x_2 + a_3 x_3 \geqslant b > 0 \qquad (4.3.16)$$

$$x_1, x_2, x_3 \geqslant 0$$

$$a_1, a_2, a_3 > 0$$

If we now carry out an analysis similar to the two preceding problems, it is easily seen that (4.3.16) is equivalent to

$$\min \quad z = x_1^2 + x_2^2 + x_3^2$$

subject to
$$\lambda_1 = \lambda_2 - a_2 x_2, \quad 0 \leqslant x_1 = \frac{\lambda_1}{a_1}$$

$$\lambda_2 = \lambda_3 - a_3 x_3, \quad 0 \leqslant x_2 \leqslant \frac{\lambda_2}{a_2} \qquad (4.3.17)$$

$$\lambda_3 \geqslant b, \quad 0 \leqslant x_3 \leqslant \frac{\lambda_3}{a_3}$$

In (4.3.17) the state transformation relationships are

$$\lambda_{s-1} = T_s(\lambda_s, x_s(\lambda_s)) = \lambda_s - a_s x_s \qquad (s = 1, 2, 3) \tag{4.3.18}$$

and the recurrence relations are easily seen to be

$$g_1(\lambda_1) = \min_{x_1 = (\lambda_1/a_1)} x_1^2$$

$$g_s(\lambda_s) = \min_{0 \le x_s \le (\lambda_s/a_s)} [x_s^2 + g_{s-1}(\lambda_s - a_s x_s)] \qquad (s = 2, 3) \tag{4.3.19}$$

Proceeding to solve (4.3.19) we have

$$g_1(\lambda_1) = \min_{x_1 = (\lambda_1/a_1)} x_1^2 = \left(\frac{\lambda_1}{a_1}\right)^2$$

$$x_1^* = \frac{\lambda_1}{a_1} \tag{4.3.20}$$

Next we solve (4.3.19) for $g_2(\lambda_2)$:

$$g_2(\lambda_2) = \min_{0 \le x_2 \le (\lambda_2/a_2)} [x_2^2 + g_1(\lambda_2 - a_2 x_2)]$$

$$= \min_{0 \le x_2 \le (\lambda_2/a_2)} \left[x_2^2 + \left(\frac{\lambda_2 - a_2 x_2}{a_1}\right)^2\right]$$

$$= \min_{0 \le x_2 \le (\lambda_2/a_2)} G_2(\lambda_2, x_2) \tag{4.3.21}$$

$$\frac{\partial G_2}{\partial x_2} = 2x_2 - \frac{2a_2}{a_1}\left(\frac{\lambda_2 - a_2 x_2}{a_1}\right) = 0 \tag{4.3.22}$$

Since

$$\frac{\partial^2 G_2}{\partial x_2^2} = 2 + 2\left(\frac{a_2}{a_1}\right)^2 > 0$$

or, alternatively, noting that G_2 is a convex function, we can solve (4.3.22) for x_2^*, the optimal value of x_2 as

$$x_2^* = \frac{a_2}{a_1^2 + a_2^2}\lambda_2 < \frac{\lambda_2}{a_2} \tag{4.3.23}$$

Substituting (4.3.23) into (4.3.21) we obtain

$$g_2(\lambda_2) = \left(\frac{a_2\lambda_2}{a_1^2 + a_2^2}\right)^2 + \left[\frac{\lambda_2 - a_2\left(\dfrac{a_2\lambda_2}{a_1^2 + a_2^2}\right)}{a_1}\right]^2$$

which simplifies to

$$g_2(\lambda_2) = \frac{\lambda_2^2}{a_1^2 + a_2^2} \tag{4.3.24}$$

Continuing, we have

$$g_3(\lambda_3) = \min_{0 \leqslant x_3 \leqslant (\lambda_3/a_3)} [x_3^2 + g_2(\lambda_3 - a_3 x_3)]$$

$$= \min_{0 \leqslant x_3 \leqslant (\lambda_3/a_3)} \left[x_3^2 + \frac{(\lambda_3 - a_3 x_3)^2}{a_1^2 + a_2^2} \right]$$

$$= \min_{0 \leqslant x_3 \leqslant (\lambda_3/a_3)} G_3(\lambda_3, x_3) \qquad (4.3.25)$$

$$\frac{\partial G_3}{\partial x_3} = 2x_3 - \frac{2a_3}{a_1^2 + a_2^2}(\lambda_3 - a_3 x_3) = 0 \qquad (4.3.26)$$

Since

$$\frac{\partial^2 G_3}{\partial x_3^2} = 2 + \frac{2a_3^2}{a_1^2 + a_2^2} > 0$$

we can solve (4.3.26) for x_3^*, the optimal value of x_3 as

$$x_3^* = \frac{a_3 \lambda_3}{a_1^2 + a_2^2 + a_3^2} < \frac{\lambda_3}{a_3} \qquad (4.3.27)$$

If we substitute (4.3.27) into (4.3.25) we obtain

$$g_3(\lambda_3) = \left(\frac{a_3 \lambda_3}{a_1^2 + a_2^2 + a_3^2} \right)^2 + \left(\frac{1}{a_1^2 + a_2^2} \right) \left[\lambda_3 - a_3 \left(\frac{a_3 \lambda_3}{a_1^2 + a_2^2 + a_3^2} \right) \right]^2 \qquad (4.3.28)$$

After some manipulation (4.3.28) can be simplified to

$$g_3(\lambda_3) = \frac{\lambda_3^2}{a_1^2 + a_2^2 + a_3^2} \qquad (4.3.29)$$

Since $\lambda_3 = b$, we have that

$$z = g_3(b) = \frac{b^2}{a_1^2 + a_2^2 + a_3^2} \qquad (4.3.30)$$

gives the optimal Soln.

and we can compute the optimal values of x_1, x_2, x_3 from

$$x_3^* = \frac{a_3 b}{a_1^2 + a_2^2 + a_3^2}$$

$$\lambda_2 = \lambda_3 - a_3 x_3 = b - a_3 \left(\frac{a_3 b}{a_1^2 + a_2^2 + a_3^2} \right) = \frac{(a_1^2 + a_2^2)b}{a_1^2 + a_2^2 + a_3^2}$$

$$x_2^* = \frac{a_2}{a_1^2 + a_2^2} \left[\left(\frac{(a_1^2 + a_2^2)b}{a_1^2 + a_2^2 + a_3^2} \right) \right] = \frac{a_2 b}{a_1^2 + a_2^2 + a_3^2}$$

$$\lambda_1 = \lambda_2 - a_2 x_2 = \frac{(a_1^2 + a_2^2)b}{a_1^2 + a_2^2 + a_3^2} - a_2 \left(\frac{a_2 b}{a_1^2 + a_2^2 + a_3^2} \right) = \frac{a_1^2 b}{a_1^2 + a_2^2 + a_3^2}$$

$$x_1^* = \frac{\lambda_1}{a_1} = \frac{a_1^2 b}{a_1(a_1^2 + a_2^2 + a_3^2)} = \frac{a_1 b}{a_1^2 + a_2^2 + a_3^2}$$

Hence we have found the optimal solution.

4.4. Some Generalizations of the Prototype Problem

The problem of 4.2 was actually a special case of the more general problem:

$$\min \quad z = \sum_{j=1}^{n} x_j^p \qquad (p > 0)$$

subject to
$$\sum_{j=1}^{n} x_j \geq b \qquad (b > 0) \qquad (4.4.1)$$

$$x_j \geq 0 \qquad (j = 1, 2, \ldots, n)$$

In our version of the problem we chose $n = 3$ and $p = 2$. We shall now solve the more general version of (4.4.1). However, before doing so, it is useful to first solve (4.4.1) with $p = 2$ and for any n. Hence we wish to solve

$$\min \quad z = \sum_{j=1}^{n} x_j^2$$

subject to
$$\sum_{j=1}^{n} x_j \geq b \qquad (b > 0) \qquad (4.4.2)$$

$$x_j \geq 0 \qquad (j = 1, 2, \ldots, n)$$

Let us examine the values of $x_j(\lambda_j)$ and $g_j(\lambda_j)$ for $j = 1, 2, 3$, which we already know. Table 4.4.1 shows what we have found in Section 4.2.

TABLE 4.4.1

j	$g_j(\lambda_j)$	$x_j^*(\lambda_j)$
1	λ_1^2	λ_1
2	$\lambda_2^2/2$	$\lambda_2/2$
3	$\lambda_3^2/3$	$\lambda_3/3$

The pattern of Table 4.4.1 seems to indicate that a reasonable guess for $j = s$ would be

$$g_s(\lambda_s) = \frac{\lambda_s^2}{s}$$

$$x_s^*(\lambda_s) = \frac{\lambda_s}{s} \qquad (4.4.3)$$

We shall prove that (4.4.3) is correct by induction. We know that the hypothesis is true for $j = 1, 2, 3$. Now we assume that it is true for $j = s$, i.e.,

$$g_s(\lambda_s) = \frac{\lambda_s^2}{s}, \quad x_s^*(\lambda_s) = \frac{\lambda_s}{s}$$

If this is so then

$$g_{s+1}(\lambda_{s+1}) = \min_{0 \le x_{s+1} \le \lambda_{s+1}} [x_{s+1}^2 + g_s(\lambda_{s+1} - x_{s+1})]$$

Therefore

$$g_{s+1}(\lambda_{s+1}) = \min_{0 \le x_{s+1} \le \lambda_{s+1}} \left[x_{s+1}^2 + \frac{(\lambda_{s+1} - x_{s+1})^2}{s} \right]$$

$$= \min_{0 \le x_{s+1} \le \lambda_{s+1}} G_{s+1}(\lambda_{s+1}, x_{s+1}) \tag{4.4.4}$$

The condition for an optimal value of x_{s+1} is

$$\frac{\partial G_{s+1}}{\partial x_{s+1}} = 2x_{s+1} - \frac{2(\lambda_{s+1} - x_{s+1})}{s} = 0 \tag{4.4.5}$$

Solving (4.4.5) yields

$$x_{s+1}^* = \frac{\lambda_{s+1}}{s+1} \tag{4.4.6}$$

The solution of (4.4.6) is a minimum since

$$\frac{\partial^2 G_{s+1}}{\partial x_{s+1}^2} = \frac{2s+2}{s} > 0$$

Hence we have

$$g_{s+1}(\lambda_{s+1}) = \left(\frac{\lambda_{s+1}}{s+1}\right)^2 + \left[\left(\lambda_{s+1} - \frac{\lambda_{s+1}}{s+1}\right)^2 \Big/ s\right] \tag{4.4.7}$$

Simplifying (4.4.7) we have

$$g_{s+1}(\lambda_{s+1}) = \frac{\lambda_{s+1}^2}{s+1} \tag{4.4.8}$$

Therefore, by (4.4.6) and (4.4.8), the induction is complete. Hence we have shown that the solution of (4.4.2) is

$$z^* = \frac{b^2}{n}$$

$$x_j^* = \frac{b}{n} \quad (j = 1, 2, \ldots, n) \tag{4.4.9}$$

Before returning to (4.4.1), let us examine the case of (4.4.1) when $p = 1$. This is a particularly simple case since

$$g_1(\lambda_1) = \min_{x_1 = \lambda_1} x_1 = \lambda_1, \quad x_1^* = \lambda_1 \tag{4.4.10}$$

$$g_2(\lambda_2) = \min_{0 \le x_2 \le \lambda_2} [x_2 + g_1(\lambda_2 - x_2)]$$

$$= \min_{0 \le x_2 \le \lambda_2} [x_2 + (\lambda_2 - x_2)] = \lambda_2 \tag{4.4.11}$$

4.4.1 becomes Min $z = \sum x_j$ s.t $\sum x_j \ge b$

Solution is Min $z = b$ with latitude for x_j

One choice $x_j = \frac{b}{n}$ is "symmetric"

and *any* value of x_2, $0 \leqslant x_2 \leqslant \lambda_2$ will be optimal. Let us choose $x_2^* = \lambda_2/2$. The reason for this choice will become clear later. A proof by induction that $g_s(\lambda_s) = \lambda_s$ is easily established. If we now assume that $g_s(\lambda_s) = \lambda_s$, then we have

$$g_{s+1}(\lambda_{s+1}) = \min_{0 \leqslant x_{s+1} \leqslant \lambda_{s+1}} [x_{s+1} + (\lambda_{s+1} - x_{s+1})]$$

$$= \lambda_{s+1} \tag{4.4.12}$$

and the induction is complete. Again we assume that $x_s^*(\lambda_s) = \lambda_s/s$.

Let us now consider (4.4.1) for all $p \geqslant 1$. We know the solution to (4.4.1) for $p = 1, 2$. It is summarized in Table 4.4.2.

TABLE 4.4.2

p	$g_j(\lambda_j)$	$x_j^*(\lambda_j)$
1	λ_j	$\dfrac{\lambda_j}{j}$
2	$\dfrac{\lambda_j^2}{j}$	$\dfrac{\lambda_j}{j}$

The data given in Table 4.4.2 do not admit of a unique choice for a good guess. We shall not waste time and space choosing the wrong one. Instead let us try to establish that

$$g_j(\lambda_j) = \frac{\lambda_j^p}{j^{p-1}}, \quad x_j^*(\lambda_j) = \frac{\lambda_j}{j}$$

It can be seen that the cases $p = 1, 2$ satisfy this guess. We proceed by induction. Let us assume that for $p \geqslant 1$,

$$g_s(\lambda_s) = \frac{\lambda_s^p}{s^{p-1}}, \quad x_s^*(\lambda_s) = \frac{\lambda_s}{s}$$

Then we have

$$g_{s+1}(\lambda_{s+1}) = \min_{0 \leqslant x_{s+1} \leqslant \lambda_{s+1}} [x_{s+1}^p + g_s(\lambda_{s+1} - x_{s+1})]$$

$$= \min_{0 \leqslant x_{s+1} \leqslant \lambda_{s+1}} \left[x_{s+1}^p + \frac{(\lambda_{s+1} - x_{s+1})^p}{s^{p-1}} \right]$$

$$= \min_{0 \leqslant x_{s+1} \leqslant \lambda_{s+1}} G_{s+1}(\lambda_{s+1}, x_{s+1}) \tag{4.4.13}$$

Differentiating G_{s+1} we obtain

$$\frac{\partial G_{s+1}}{\partial x_{s+1}} = p x_{s+1}^{p-1} - \frac{p}{s^{p-1}} (\lambda_{s+1} - x_{s+1})^{p-1} = 0 \tag{4.4.14}$$

The solution to (4.4.14) is a minimum since

$$\frac{\partial^2 G_{s+1}}{\partial x_{s+1}^2} = p(p-1) x_{s+1}^{p-2} + p(p-1) (\lambda_{s+1} - x_{s+1})^{p-2} > 0$$

for $0 \leqslant x_{s+1} \leqslant \lambda_{s+1}$.

5*

Solving (4.4.14) yields

$$x_{s+1}^* = \frac{\lambda_{s+1}}{s+1} \tag{4.4.15}$$

and

$$g_{s+1}(\lambda_{s+1}) = \left(\frac{\lambda_{s+1}}{s+1}\right)^p + \left[\left(\lambda_{s+1} - \frac{\lambda_{s+1}}{s+1}\right)^p \middle/ s^{p-1}\right]$$

which simplifies to

$$g_{s+1}(\lambda_{s+1}) = \frac{\lambda_{s+1}^p}{(s+1)^{p-1}} \tag{4.4.16}$$

and this completes the induction.

Therefore we have established that the solution to (4.4.1) for $p \geqslant 1$ is

$$z = g_n(b) = \frac{b^p}{n^{p-1}}$$

and

$$x_j^*(b) = \frac{b}{n} \qquad (j = 1, 2, \ldots, n)$$

It will be noted that we have solved our original problem (4.4.1) for $p \geqslant 1$. We restricted p to be $\geqslant 1$ because under these conditions x_j^p and hence $\sum_j x_j^p$ is a convex function. This is easily shown. Actually, for $p = 1$, x_j is both convex and concave. It is the dividing line. In our dynamic programming subproblems, e.g.,

$$g_s(\lambda_s) = \min_{0 \leqslant x_s \leqslant \lambda_s} [x_s^p + g_{s-1}(\lambda_s - x_s)] \tag{4.4.17}$$

we are minimizing a convex function such as

$$x_s^p + \frac{(\lambda_s - x_s)^p}{s^{p-1}}$$

over the convex set $0 \leqslant x_s \leqslant \lambda_s$. Hence we know (Proposition 1.4.1 in Chapter 1) that any local optimum will be a global optimum. Therefore we were able to use the calculus to find that optimum.

We turn now to the case where $0 < p < 1$. For this case, it can be shown that x^p is a concave function and since the sum of concave functions is concave, the objective function is concave. It is also known (Proposition 1.4.4) that at least one global minimum of a concave function over a closed convex set will be one of the extreme points of the convex set. The convex set we will be dealing with is

$$X_s = \{x_s \,|\, 0 \leqslant x_s \leqslant \lambda_s\} \qquad (s = 1, 2, \ldots, n)$$

a particularly simple set with two extreme points, viz., zero and λ_s.

Let us examine a special case first to get some insight into the nature of the solution. Consider the problem

$$\min \quad z = x_1^{1/2} + x_2^{1/2} + x_3^{1/2}$$

subject to
$$x_1 + x_2 + x_3 \geqslant b \tag{4.4.18}$$

$$x_1, x_2, x_3 \geqslant 0$$

By analogy with the previous examples, it is clear that

$$g_1(\lambda_1) = \min_{x_1 = \lambda_1} x_1^{1/2} = \lambda_1^{1/2} \tag{4.4.19}$$

$$g_2(\lambda_2) = \min_{0 \leqslant x_2 \leqslant \lambda_2} [x_2^{1/2} + g_1(\lambda_2 - x_2)]$$

$$= \min_{0 \leqslant x_2 \leqslant \lambda_2} [x_2^{1/2} + (\lambda_2 - x_2)^{1/2}] \tag{4.4.20}$$

Since we know that the global minimum for (4.4.20) will occur at one (or both) of $x_2 = 0$, $x_2 = \lambda_2$, we can restrict our attention to these values. Therefore

$$g_2(\lambda_2) = \min[0 + \lambda_2^{1/2}, \lambda_2^{1/2} + 0] = \lambda_2^{1/2} \tag{4.4.21}$$

and $x_2^*(\lambda_2) = 0$ or λ_2, since both lead to a global optimum.

Similarly, we find that

$$g_3(\lambda_3) = \min_{0 \leqslant x_3 \leqslant \lambda_3} [x_3^{1/2} + g_2(\lambda_3 - x_3)]$$

$$= \min_{0 \leqslant x_3 \leqslant \lambda_3} [x_3^{1/2} + (\lambda_3 - x_3)^{1/2}]$$

$$= \min[0 + \lambda_3^{1/2}, \lambda_3^{1/2} + 0] = \lambda_3^{1/2} \tag{4.4.22}$$

and $x_3^*(\lambda_3) = 0$ or λ_3.

Therefore, we have that

$$z = g_3(b) = b^{1/2}$$

$$x_3^* = \lambda_3 = b$$

$$\lambda_2 = \lambda_3 - x_3 = b - b = 0; \quad x_2^* = 0$$

$$\lambda_1 = \lambda_2 - x_2 = 0 - 0 = 0; \quad x_1^* = 0$$

It should be noted that since there are alternate optimal solutions at stages 2 and 3, there are other optimal solutions. For example, $x_1^* = 0$, $x_2^* = b$, $x_3^* = 0$ is such a solution.

We shall guess, without much difficulty, that the general solution to (4.4.1) for $0 < p < 1$ is

$$g_j(\lambda_j) = \lambda_j^p$$

$$x_j^* = 0 \quad (j < n)$$

$$x_n^* = b$$

The proof is by induction on j. It is clearly true for $j = 1$. Now suppose for $j = s$, $g_s(\lambda_s) = \lambda_s^p$. Then

$$g_{s+1}(\lambda_{s+1}) = \min_{0 \leqslant x_{s+1} \leqslant \lambda_{s+1}} [x_{s+1}^p + g_s(\lambda_{s+1} - x_{s+1})]$$

$$= \min_{0 \leqslant x_{s+1} \leqslant \lambda_{s+1}} [x_{s+1}^p + (\lambda_{s+1} - x_{s+1})^p]$$

$$= \min_{0 \leqslant x_{s+1} \leqslant \lambda_{s+1}} [\lambda_{s+1}^p, \lambda_{s+1}^p]$$

Therefore

$$g_{s+1}(\lambda_{s+1}) = \lambda_{s+1}^p$$

and

$$x_{s+1}^* = 0 \text{ or } \lambda_{s+1}$$

and the induction is complete.

We have therefore shown that the solution to (4.4.1) for $0 < p < 1$ is given by

$$z^* = g_n(b) = b^p$$
$$x_n^* = b, \quad x_{n-1}^* = x_{n-2}^* = \ldots = x_1^* = 0 \qquad (4.4.23)$$

There are, of course, many other alternate optimal solutions.

4.5. Some Generalizations

In the previous section we considered, in (4.4.1) when $0 < p < 1$, a problem in which we minimized a concave function over a closed convex set in each of the one-dimensional subproblems we solved. For variety, we shall maximize a convex function (which is equivalent to minimizing a concave function) in considering a more general problem than (4.4.1). However, we shall again find a considerable simplification in the solution of the recurrence relations.

The problem we wish to consider is

$$\max \quad z = \sum_{j=1}^{n} \phi(x_j) \qquad (4.5.1)$$

subject to

$$\sum_{j=1}^{n} x_j = b, \qquad (b > 0)$$

$$x_j \geqslant 0, \qquad (j = 1, 2, \ldots, n)$$

The first case we shall consider is when $\phi(x)$ is assumed to be convex. The analysis is similar to the problems in Sections 4.2–4.4. We define state variables as before, since the constraint $\Sigma x_j = b$, $x_j \geqslant 0$ is the same. It is a simple matter to see that the recurrence relations are

$$g_1(\lambda_1) = \max_{x_1 = \lambda_1} \phi(x_1)$$
$$g_j(\lambda_j) = \max_{0 \leqslant x_j \leqslant \lambda_j} [\phi(x_j) + g_{j-1}(\lambda_j - x_j)], \qquad (j = 2, 3, \ldots, n) \qquad (4.5.2)$$

However, since $\phi(x)$ is a convex function, we know by Proposition 1.4.3 that the global maximum is at either or both of the extreme points of the convex set

$$X_j = \{x_j \mid 0 \leqslant x_j \leqslant \lambda_j\}$$

Therefore, we can easily evaluate (4.5.2) as

$$g_1(\lambda_1) = \max_{x_1 = \lambda_1} \phi(x_1) = \phi(\lambda_1), \quad x_1^*(\lambda_1) = \lambda_1$$

$$g_2(\lambda_2) = \max_{0 \leqslant x_2 \leqslant \lambda_2} [\phi(x_2) + g_1(\lambda_2 - x_2)]$$

$$= \max_{0 \leqslant x_2 \leqslant \lambda_2} [\phi(x_2) + \phi(\lambda_2 - x_2)]$$

$$= \max[\phi(0) + \phi(\lambda_2), \phi(\lambda_2) + \phi(0)]$$

$$= \phi(0) + \phi(\lambda_2) \tag{4.5.3}$$

and $x_2^*(\lambda_2) = 0$ or λ_2.

$$g_3(\lambda_3) = \max_{0 \leqslant x_3 \leqslant \lambda_3} [\phi(x_3) + g_2(\lambda_3 - x_3)]$$

$$= \max_{0 \leqslant x_3 \leqslant \lambda_3} [\phi(x_3) + \phi(0) + \phi(\lambda_3 - x_3)]$$

$$= \max[\phi(0) + \phi(0) + \phi(\lambda_3), \phi(\lambda_3) + \phi(0) + \phi(0)]$$

$$= \phi(\lambda_3) + 2\phi(0)$$

and $x_3^*(\lambda_3) = 0$ or λ_3.

It seems reasonable from (4.5.3) that the general solution to (4.5.2) is

$$g_j(\lambda_j) = \phi(\lambda_j) + (j-1)\phi(0) \quad \text{and} \quad x_j^*(\lambda_j) = 0 \text{ or } \lambda_j$$

The proof is by induction on j. It is clear that for $j = 1, 2, 3$ the general solution is satisfied. Suppose it is true for $j = s$. Then we have that $g_s(\lambda_s) = \phi(\lambda_s) + (s-1)\phi(0)$. Then

$$g_{s+1}(\lambda_{s+1}) = \max_{0 \leqslant x_{s+1} \leqslant \lambda_{s+1}} [\phi(x_{s+1}) + g_s(\lambda_{s+1} - x_{s+1})]$$

$$= \max_{0 \leqslant x_{s+1} \leqslant \lambda_{s+1}} [\phi(x_{s+1}) + \phi(\lambda_{s+1} - x_{s+1}) + (s-1)\phi(0)]$$

$$= \max[\phi(0) + \phi(\lambda_{s+1}) + (s-1)\phi(0), \phi(\lambda_{s+1}) + \phi(0) + (s-1)\phi(0)]$$

$$= \phi(\lambda_{s+1}) + s\phi(0)$$

where $x_{s+1}^*(\lambda_{s+1}) = 0$ or λ_{s+1}. Therefore the induction is complete. Hence we see that when maximizing convex functions in the recurrence relations, the analysis of the problem is simpler and more general.

It is now clear that the general solution to (4.5.1) when $\phi(x)$ is convex is

$$z^* = g_n(b) = \phi(b) + (n-1)\phi(0)$$

$$x_n^* = \lambda_n = b$$

$$\lambda_{n-1} = \lambda_n - x_n^* = 0, \qquad x_{n-1}^* = \lambda_{n-1} \quad \text{or} \quad 0$$

$$\lambda_{n-2} = \lambda_{n-1} - x_{n-1}^* = 0, \qquad x_{n-2}^* = \lambda_{n-2} \quad \text{or} \quad 0$$

$$\begin{array}{ccccccc} & \cdot & & \cdot & & \cdot & \\ & \cdot & & \cdot & & \cdot & \\ & \cdot & & \cdot & & \cdot & \end{array}$$

$$\lambda_1 = \lambda_2 - x_2^* = 0, \qquad x_1^* = \lambda, \qquad \text{or} \quad 0$$

Let us now consider the problem (4.5.1) when $\phi(x)$ is a monotonically increasing function which is strictly and twice differentially concave. For this case we know that any local maximum is a global maximum and we can attempt to use the tools of analysis to determine the solution. Let us examine the first few state functions for this problem. The recurrence relations are, as usual,

$$g_1(\lambda_1) = \max_{x_1 = \lambda_1} \phi(x_1) = \phi(\lambda_1), \quad x_1^*(\lambda_1) = \lambda_1 \tag{4.5.4}$$

$$\begin{aligned} g_2(\lambda_2) &= \max_{0 \leqslant x_2 \leqslant \lambda_2} [\phi(x_2) + g_1(\lambda_2 - x_2)] \\ &= \max_{0 \leqslant x_2 \leqslant \lambda_2} [\phi(x_2) + \phi(\lambda_2 - x_2)] \\ &= \max_{0 \leqslant x_2 \leqslant \lambda_2} G_2(\lambda_2, x_2) \end{aligned} \tag{4.5.5}$$

Differentiating G_2 we have that

$$\frac{\partial G_2}{\partial x_2} = \phi'(x_2) - \phi'(\lambda_2 - x_2) = 0 \tag{4.5.6}$$

Since $\phi(x)$ is assumed to be strictly concave, we know that $(\partial^2 G_2)/(\partial \overset{2}{x_2}) < 0$ and the solution to (4.5.6) will be a local and therefore a global maximum. From (4.5.6) we see that

$$\phi'(x_2) = \phi'(\lambda_2 - x_2)$$

which implies that

$$x_2 = \lambda_2 - x_2 \qquad \left(\text{See note } p\,62\right)$$

and therefore

$$x_2^*(\lambda_2) = \frac{\lambda_2}{2} \tag{4.5.7}$$

From (4.5.5) and (4.5.7) we see that

$$g_2(\lambda_2) = \phi\left(\frac{\lambda_2}{2}\right) + \phi\left(\lambda_2 - \frac{\lambda_2}{2}\right) = 2\phi\left(\frac{\lambda_2}{2}\right) \tag{4.5.8}$$

If we continue our analysis we find

$$\begin{aligned} g_3(\lambda_3) &= \max_{0 \leqslant x_3 \leqslant \lambda_3} [\phi(x_3) + g_2(\lambda_3 - x_3)] \\ &= \max_{0 \leqslant x_3 \leqslant \lambda_3} \left[\phi(x_3) + 2\phi\left(\frac{\lambda_3 - x_3}{2}\right)\right] \\ &= \max_{0 \leqslant x_3 \leqslant \lambda_3} G_3(\lambda_3, x_3) \end{aligned} \tag{4.5.9}$$

$$\frac{\partial G_3}{\partial x_3} = \phi'(x_3) - \phi'\left(\frac{\lambda_3 - x_3}{2}\right) = 0 \tag{4.5.10}$$

and

$$x_3 = \frac{\lambda_3 - x_3}{2}$$

Therefore

$$x_3^*(\lambda_3) = \frac{\lambda_3}{3} \tag{4.5.11}$$

Hence from (4.5.9) and (4.5.11) we have

$$g_3(\lambda_3) = \phi\left(\frac{\lambda_3}{3}\right) + 2\phi\left(\frac{\lambda_3 - \dfrac{\lambda_3}{3}}{2}\right)$$

$$= \phi\left(\frac{\lambda_3}{3}\right) + 2\phi\left(\frac{\lambda_3}{3}\right) = 3\phi\left(\frac{\lambda_3}{3}\right) \tag{4.5.12}$$

From these results, it is plausible to guess that the general solution is

$$g_j(\lambda_j) = j\phi\left(\frac{\lambda_j}{j}\right) \quad \text{and} \quad x_j^* = \frac{\lambda_j}{j} \tag{4.5.13}$$

Equation (4.5.13) certainly holds for $j = 1, 2, 3$. Suppose it holds for $j = s$. Then $g_s(\lambda_s) = s\phi(\lambda_s/s)$. We then have

$$g_{s+1}(\lambda_{s+1}) = \max_{0 \leqslant x_{s+1} \leqslant \lambda_{s+1}} [\phi(x_{s+1}) + g_s(\lambda_{s+1} - x_{s+1})]$$

$$= \max_{0 \leqslant x_{s+1} \leqslant \lambda_{s+1}} \left[\phi(x_{s+1}) + s\phi\left(\frac{\lambda_{s+1} - x_{s+1}}{s}\right)\right]$$

$$= \max_{0 \leqslant x_{s+1} \leqslant \lambda_{s+1}} G_{s+1}(\lambda_{s+1}, x_{s+1}) \tag{4.5.14}$$

$$\frac{\partial G_{s+1}}{\partial x_{s+1}} = \phi'(x_{s+1}) - \phi'\left(\frac{\lambda_{s+1} - x_{s+1}}{s}\right) = 0 \tag{4.5.15}$$

and

$$x_{s+1} = \frac{\lambda_{s+1} - x_{s+1}}{s}$$

Therefore

$$x_{s+1}^*(\lambda_{s+1}) = \frac{\lambda_{s+1}}{s+1} \tag{4.5.16}$$

From (4.5.14) and (4.5.16) we have

$$g_{s+1}(\lambda_{s+1}) = \phi\left(\frac{\lambda_{s+1}}{s+1}\right) + s\phi\left(\frac{\lambda_{s+1} - \dfrac{\lambda_{s+1}}{s+1}}{s}\right)$$

$$= \phi\left(\frac{\lambda_{s+1}}{s+1}\right) + s\phi\left(\frac{\lambda_{s+1}}{s+1}\right) = (s+1)\,\phi\left(\frac{\lambda_{s+1}}{s+1}\right)$$

and the induction is complete.

The general solution to (4.5.1) when $\phi(x)$ is a monotonically increasing strictly concave function and twice differentiable is then

$$z = g_n(b) = n\phi\left(\frac{b}{n}\right)$$

$$x_n^* = \frac{\lambda_n}{n} = \frac{b}{n}$$

$$\lambda_{n-1} = \lambda_n - x_n^* = b - \frac{b}{n} = \frac{(n-1)b}{n}$$

$$x_{n-1}^* = \frac{\lambda_{n-1}}{n-1} = \frac{(n-1)b}{(n-1)n} = \frac{b}{n}$$

and in general

$$\lambda_{n-r} = \frac{(n-r)b}{n} \qquad (r = 1, 2, \ldots, n)$$

$$x^*_{n-r} = \frac{\lambda_{n-r}}{n-r} = \frac{(n-r)b}{n(n-r)} = \frac{b}{n} \qquad (r = 1, 2, \ldots, n-1)$$

We have in this result a fairly general set of relationships. For any particular function $\phi(x)$, the solution can be obtained by simple substitution.

4.6. A Problem in Renewable Resources

We shall now consider a problem concerned with the optimal management of what might be termed a "renewable" resource. An example might be the raising of cattle, some of which are sold and some of which are retained for breeding. Another would be the breeding of fish under the same circumstances. Still a third example would be a grower of corn who sells part of his crop and retains part of it as seed for the following year's crop. For descriptive purposes we will refer to the "grower," his "crop," and the portion of the crop retained as "seed."

Suppose that in a given year, q units of the crop have been grown, some of which will be retained as seed for the succeeding year and the remainder of which will be sold. The yield from each unit of the seed crop is $\alpha > 1$ units and the income from y units of crop which are sold is $\phi(y)$. In each of the years that follow, the grower again decides to keep some of his crop for seed and to sell the remainder. If we assume that at the end of n years he sells the entire crop, what is the selling policy which maximizes his total income over n years?

S is number of years to final sell off $S = n, n-1, \ldots, K, \ldots 2, 1$

λ_s is seed at start of stage S

x_s is seed sold at end of stage S

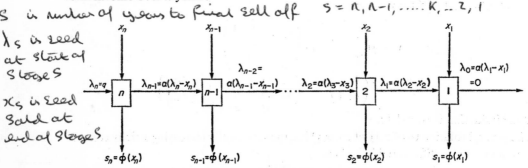

FIG. 4.6.1. Stagewise representation.

See Notes p57

Figure 4.6.1 will help to understand the notation we shall use. We shall define the state variables λ_s as the amount of seed available at the beginning of year s (or the end of year $s-1$). The decision variable x_s is the amount sold at the end of year s.

As long as we bear in mind that the state variables and state transformation functions are given by

$$\lambda_{s-1} = T_s(\lambda_s, x_s(\lambda_s)) = \alpha(\lambda_s - x_s) \qquad (s = 1, 2, \ldots, n) \qquad (4.6.1)$$

then the optimal return functions follow readily. We have numbered the stages backwards so that $g_1(\lambda_1)$ corresponds to the year n state function. We have then

$$g_1(\lambda_1) = \max_{x_1 = \lambda_1} \phi(x_1) = \phi(\lambda_1) \qquad (4.6.2)$$

and
$$g_s(\lambda_s) = \max_{0 \leqslant x_s \leqslant \lambda_s} [\phi(x_s) + g_{s-1}(\alpha(\lambda_s - x_s))] \qquad (s = 2, 3, \ldots, n) \qquad (4.6.3)$$

In brief, (4.6.2) gives the optimal return when an amount λ_1 is available (in the nth year). Since at the end of the last year, all of the crop is sold, $x_1 = \lambda_1$. Equation (4.6.3) gives the optimal return when an amount of crop λ_s is available for investment and there are s stages remaining [year $n - (s-1)$].

Let us now examine the optimal policy for the grower under various assumptions on the amount of money he can sell the crop for, $\phi(y)$.

CASE 1: $\qquad\qquad\qquad \phi(y) = cy \quad (c > 0)$

If the return is linear, we obtain

$$g_1(\lambda_1) = \max_{x_1 = \lambda_1} c x_1 = c \lambda_1 \qquad (4.6.4)$$

$$g_2(\lambda_2) = \max_{0 \leqslant x_2 \leqslant \lambda_2} [c x_2 + g_1(\alpha(\lambda_2 - x_2))]$$

$$= \max_{0 \leqslant x_2 \leqslant \lambda_2} [c x_2 + c\alpha(\lambda_2 - x_2)] \qquad (4.6.5)$$

Since $\alpha > 1$, it is clear that

$$G_2 = c x_2 + c\alpha(\lambda_2 - x_2) = c(1-\alpha)x_2 + c\alpha\lambda_2$$

takes on its maximum value when $x_2 = 0$ and therefore

$$g_2(\lambda_2) = c\alpha\lambda_2 \qquad (4.6.6)$$

It is reasonable to guess that

$$g_j(\lambda_j) = c\alpha^{j-1}\lambda_j \qquad (j = 1, 2, \ldots, n) \qquad (4.6.7)$$

and that
$$x_1^*(\lambda_1) = c\lambda_1 \quad \text{and} \quad x_j^*(\lambda_j) = 0 \quad (j = 2 \ldots n) \qquad (4.6.8)$$

We prove this by induction. We see that (4.6.7) and (4.6.8) are satisfied by $j = 1, 2$. Suppose $j = s$. Then

$$g_s(\lambda_s) = c\alpha^{s-1}\lambda_s \quad \text{and} \quad x_s^*(\lambda_s) = 0 \quad (s > 1)$$

Then
$$g_{s+1}(\lambda_{s+1}) = \max_{0 \leqslant x_{s+1} \leqslant \lambda_{s+1}} [c x_{s+1} + g_s(\alpha(\lambda_{s+1} - x_{s+1}))]$$

$$= \max_{0 \leqslant x_{s+1} \leqslant \lambda_{s+1}} [c x_{s+1} + c\alpha^{s-1}(\alpha(\lambda_{s+1} - x_{s+1}))]$$

$$= \max_{0 \leqslant x_{s+1} \leqslant \lambda_{s+1}} [c\alpha^s \lambda_{s+1} + c(1 - \alpha^s) x_{s+1}]$$

$$= \max_{0 \leqslant x_{s+1} \leqslant \lambda_{s+1}} G_{s+1}(\lambda_{s+1}, x_{s+1}) \qquad (4.6.9)$$

The maximum value of G_{s+1} occurs when $x_{s+1} = 0$ since $\alpha > 1$. Therefore we have

$$g_{s+1}(\lambda_{s+1}) = c\alpha^s \lambda_{s+1}, \quad x_{s+1}^*(\lambda_{s+1}) = 0$$

and the induction is complete.

The solution to the grower's problem when $\phi(y) = cy$, a linear return function, is simple. Since $x_1^* = \lambda_1^*$, and $x_2^* = x_3^* = \ldots = x_n^* = 0$, this means that we sell nothing until the final year (one-stage solution) and then sell everything. This will give us the optimal return which is

See
notes
p 58

$$g_n(q) = c\alpha^{n-1}q \qquad (4.6.10)$$

and $x_1^* = q$, $x_2^* = x_3^* = \ldots = x_n^* = 0$.

CASE 2: $\qquad\qquad \phi(y) = cy^2 \quad (c > 0)$

We assume here that the return when the crop is sold is a quadratic function of the amount sold. Since $\phi(y) = cy^2$ is a convex function and the recurrence equations involve maximizing a convex function over a convex set $0 \leq x_s \leq \lambda_s$, we know that the optimal solution will be at one or the other of the extreme points of

$$X_s = \{x_s \mid 0 \leq x_s \leq \lambda_s\} \qquad (4.6.11)$$

We then calculate

$$g_1(\lambda_1) = \max_{x_1 = \lambda_1} cx_1^2 = c\lambda_1^2 \quad \text{and} \quad x_1^*(\lambda_1) = \lambda_1 \qquad (4.6.12)$$

$$g_2(\lambda_2) = \max_{0 \leq x_2 \leq \lambda_2} [cx_2^2 + g_1(\alpha(\lambda_2 - x_2))]$$

$$= \max_{0 \leq x_2 \leq \lambda_2} [cx_2^2 + c(\alpha(\lambda_2 - x_2))^2]$$

$$= \max [0 + c\alpha^2\lambda_2^2, \ c\lambda_2^2 + 0]$$

$$= c\alpha^2\lambda_2^2, \quad x_2^*(\lambda_2) = 0 \qquad (4.6.13)$$

It is plausible to assume that the general solution to our problem is

$c\alpha^{2j-2}\lambda_j^2 \qquad$ ←

$$g_j(\lambda_j) = c\alpha\lambda_j^2 \quad \text{and} \quad x_j^*(\lambda_j) = 0 \quad (j > 1) \qquad (4.6.14)$$

We proceed by induction. If the solution for $j = s$ is $g_s(\lambda_s) = c\alpha\lambda_s^2$, then $\quad c\alpha^{2s-2}\lambda_s^2$

$$g_{s+1}(\lambda_{s+1}) = \max_{0 \leq x_{s+1} \leq \lambda_{s+1}} [cx_{s+1}^2 + g_s(\alpha(\lambda_{s+1} - x_{s+1}))]$$
$${}^{2s-2}$$
$$= \max_{0 \leq x_{s+1} \leq \lambda_{s+1}} [cx_{s+1}^2 + c\alpha^s(\alpha(\lambda_{s+1} - x_{s+1}))^2]$$
^{2s}
$$= \max[0 + c\alpha^{s+1}\lambda_{s+1}^2, \ c\lambda_{s+1}^2 + 0]$$
^{2s}
$$= c\alpha^{s+1}\lambda_{s+1}^2 \quad \text{and} \quad x_{s+1}^*(\lambda_{s+1}) = 0$$

Therefore the induction is proven.

The solution to our problem is very similar to the previous case. When the return is quadratic, $x_1^* = \lambda_1$, $x_2^* = x_3^* = \ldots = x_n^* = 0$. This means again that we sell nothing until the final year and then sell everything. This policy will yield the maximum return which is

$$g_n(q) = c\alpha^q \quad c\alpha^{2n-2}q^2 \tag{4.6.15}$$

and $x_1^* = q$, $x_2^* = x_3^* = \ldots = x_n^* = 0$.

See result 59

CASE 3:
$$\phi(y) = cy^p, \quad c > 0, \quad p \geqslant 1$$

Again we note that $\phi(y) = cy^p, c > 0, p \geqslant 1$ is a convex function. Hence the maximization in the recurrence equations will be simplified. We can then calculate

$$g_1(\lambda_1) = \max_{x_1 = \lambda_1} cx_1^p = c\lambda_1^p \tag{4.6.16}$$

$$g_2(\lambda_2) = \max_{0 \leqslant x_2 \leqslant \lambda_2} \left[cx_2^p + g_1(\alpha(\lambda_2 - x_2))\right]$$

$$= \max_{0 \leqslant x_2 \leqslant \lambda_2} \left[cx_2^p + c(\alpha(\lambda_2 - x_2))^p\right]$$

$$= \max[0 + c\alpha^p\lambda_2^p, \ c\lambda_2^p + 0]$$

$$= c\alpha^p\lambda_2^p \quad \text{and} \quad x_2^*(\lambda_2) = 0 \tag{4.6.17}$$

We can proceed to the general proof, since it seems clear that $g_j(\lambda_j) = c\alpha^{(j-1)p}\lambda_j^p$, $x_j^*(\lambda_j) = 0$, $j > 1$. We see that the hypothesis is satisfied for $j = 1, 2$. Suppose that for $j = s$, $g_s(\lambda_s) = c\alpha^{(s-1)p}\lambda_s^p$. Then we have

$$g_{s+1}(\lambda_{s+1}) = \max_{0 \leqslant x_{s+1} \leqslant \lambda_{s+1}} \left[cx_{s+1}^p + g_s(\alpha(\lambda_{s+1} - x_{s+1}))\right]$$

$$= \max_{0 \leqslant x_{s+1} \leqslant \lambda_{s+1}} \left[cx_{s+1}^p + c\alpha^{(s-1)p}(\alpha(\lambda_{s+1} - x_{s+1}))^p\right]$$

$$= \max[0 + c\alpha^{sp}\lambda_{s+1}^p, \ c\lambda_{s+1}^p + 0]$$

$$= c\alpha^{sp}\lambda_{s+1}^p \quad \text{and} \quad x_{s+1}^*(\lambda_{s+1}) = 0 \tag{4.6.18}$$

This completes the proof.

The solution to the grower's problem with $\phi(y) = cy^p, c > 0, p \geqslant 1$ is to again follow the policy of selling nothing until the final year. The return will then be

$$g_n(q) = c\alpha^{(n-1)p}q^p \tag{4.6.19}$$

and $x_1^* = q$, $x_2^* = x_3^* = \ldots = x_n^* = 0$.

CASE 4:
$$\phi(y) = cy^p, \quad c > 0, \quad 0 < p < 1$$

For this case it is a simple matter to show that cy^p is a concave function and the sub-problems that are solved in the recurrence equations will involve the maximization of a concave function, as we shall see. We have that

$$g_1(\lambda_1) = \max_{x_1 = \lambda_1} cx_1^p = c\lambda_1^p \tag{4.6.20}$$

$$g_2(\lambda_2) = \max_{0 \leqslant x_2 \leqslant \lambda_2} \left[cx_2^p + g_1(\alpha(\lambda_2 - x_2))\right]$$

$$= \max_{0 \leqslant x_2 \leqslant \lambda_2} \left[cx_2^p + c(\alpha(\lambda_2 - x_2))^p\right]$$

$$= \max_{0 \leqslant x_2 \leqslant \lambda_2} G_2(\lambda_2, x_2) \tag{4.6.21}$$

Since G_2 is the sum of concave functions it is also concave. Therefore any local maximum will be a global maximum. Hence

$$\frac{\partial G_2}{\partial x_2} = pcx_2^{p-1} - p\alpha^p c(\lambda_2 - x_2)^{p-1} = 0 \qquad (4.6.22)$$

But G_2 Concave
so not necessary

$$\frac{\partial^2 G}{\partial x_2^2} = p(p-1)cx_2^{p-2} + p(p-1)\,\alpha^p c(\lambda_2 - x_2)^{p-2} < 0 \qquad (4.6.23)$$

since $p-1 < 0$ and $0 < x_2 \leqslant \lambda_2$. Hence we will find a maximum. Solving (4.6.22) we find

$$pcx_2^{p-1} = p\alpha^p c(\lambda_2 - x_2)^{p-1}$$

which simplifies to

$$x_2^*(\lambda_2) = \frac{\alpha^{[p/(p-1)]}\lambda_2}{1 + \alpha^{[p/(p-1)]}} \qquad (4.6.24)$$

Since

$$0 < \frac{\alpha^{[p/(p-1)]}}{1 + \alpha^{[p/(p-1)]}} < 1,$$

we can see from (4.6.24) that $0 < x_2^* < \lambda_2$. Substituting (4.6.24) into (4.6.21) we have

$$g_2(\lambda_2) = c\left(\frac{\alpha^{[p/(p-1)]}}{1+\alpha^{[p/(p-1)]}}\right)^p \lambda_2^p + c\alpha^p\left(\lambda_2 - \frac{\alpha^{[p/(p-1)]}\lambda_2}{1+\alpha^{[p/(p-1)]}}\right)^p$$

which simplifies to

$$g_2(\lambda_2) = \frac{c\alpha^p}{(1+\alpha^{[p/(p-1)]})^{p-1}}\lambda_2^p \qquad (4.6.25)$$

Next we examine

$$g_3(\lambda_3) = \max_{0 \leqslant x_3 \leqslant \lambda_3}\ [cx_3^p + g_2(\alpha(\lambda_3 - x_3))]$$

$$= \max_{0 \leqslant x_3 \leqslant \lambda_3}\ \left[cx_3^p + \frac{c\alpha^p}{(1+\alpha^{[p/(p-1)]})^{p-1}}\,(\alpha(\lambda_3-x_3))^p\right]$$

$$= \max_{0 \leqslant x_3 \leqslant \lambda_3}\ G_3(\lambda_3, x_3) \qquad (4.6.26)$$

$$\frac{\partial G_3}{\partial x_3} = pcx_3^{p-1} - \frac{pc\alpha^{2p}}{(1+\alpha^{[p/(p-1)]})^{p-1}}(\lambda_3-x_3)^{p-1} = 0 \qquad (4.6.27)$$

G_3 concave $\rightarrow$
$$\frac{\partial^2 G_3}{\partial x_3^2} = p(p-1)cx_3^{p-2} + \frac{p(p-1)c\alpha^{2p}}{(1+\alpha^{[p/(p-1)]})^{p-1}}(\lambda_3-x_3)^{p-2} < 0$$

for $0 < p < 1$ and $0 \leqslant x_3 \leqslant \lambda_3$. We find a maximum by solving (4.6.27) for x_3

$$pcx_3^{p-1} = \frac{pc\alpha^{2p}}{(1+\alpha^{[p/(p-1)]})^{p-1}}(\lambda_3-x_3)^{p-1}$$

which simplifies to

$$x_3^*(\lambda_3) = \frac{\alpha^{[2p/(p-1)]}}{1+\alpha^{[p/(p-1)]}+\alpha^{[2p/(p-1)]}}\lambda_3 < \lambda_3 \qquad (4.6.28)$$

Substituting (4.6.28) into (4.6.26) we obtain

$$g_3(\lambda_3) = c\left(\frac{\alpha^{[2p/(p-1)]}}{1+\alpha^{[p/(p-1)]}+\alpha^{[2p/(p-1)]}}\right)^p \lambda_3^p + \frac{c\alpha^{2p}}{(1+\alpha^{[2p/(p-1)]})^{p-1}}$$

$$\times\left(\lambda_3 - \frac{\alpha^{[2p/(p-1)]}}{1+\alpha^{[p/(p-1)]}+\alpha^{[p/(2p-1)]}}\,\lambda_3\right)^p$$

which, after considerable simplification, reduces to

$$g_3(\lambda_3) = \frac{c\alpha^{2p}}{(1+\alpha^{[p/(p-1)]}+\alpha^{[2p/(p-1)]})^{p-1}}\,\lambda_3^p \tag{4.6.29}$$

Now we can hazard a guess as to the general form of the solution. It seems reasonable to guess that

$$g_j(\lambda_j) = \frac{c\alpha^{(j-1)p}}{(1+\alpha^{[p/(p-1)]}+\ \ldots\ +\alpha^{\{[(j-1)p]/(p-1)\}})^{p-1}}\,\lambda_j^p \tag{4.6.30}$$

and

$$x_j^*(\lambda_j) = \frac{\alpha^{(j-1)p}}{1+\alpha^{[p/(p-1)]}+\ \ldots\ +\alpha^{\{[(j-1)p]/(p-1)\}}}\,\lambda_j \tag{4.6.31}$$

Suppose it is true for $j = s$. Then

$$g_s(\lambda_s) = \frac{c\alpha^{(s-1)p}}{(1+\alpha^{[p/(p-1)]}+\ \ldots\ +\alpha^{\{[(s-1)p]/(p-1)\}})^{p-1}}\,\lambda_s^p \tag{4.6.32}$$

Then we have

$$g_{s+1}(\lambda_{s+1}) = \max_{0\le x_{s+1}\le\lambda_{s+1}}\ \left[cx_{s+1}^p+g_s(\alpha(\lambda_{s+1}-x_{s+1}))\right]$$

$$= \max_{0\le x_{s+1}\le\lambda_{s+1}}\ \left[cx_{s+1}^p+\frac{c\alpha^{(s-1)p}}{(1+\alpha^{[p/(p-1)]}+\ \ldots\ +\alpha^{\{[(s-1)p]/(p-1)\}})^{p-1}}\,(\alpha(\lambda_{s+1}-x_{s+1}))^p\right]$$

$$= \max_{0\le x_s\le\lambda_{s+1}}\ G_{s+1}(\lambda_{s+1},\,x_{s+1}) \tag{4.6.33}$$

$$\frac{\partial G_{s+1}}{\partial x_{s+1}} = pcx_{s+1}^{p-1}-\frac{pc\alpha^{(s-1)p+p}(\lambda_{s+1}-x_{s+1})^{p-1}}{(1+\alpha^{[p/(p-1)]}+\ \ldots\ +\alpha^{\{[(s-1)p]/(p-1)\}})^{p-1}} = 0 \tag{4.6.34}$$

$$\frac{\partial^2 G_{s+1}}{\partial x_{s+1}^2} = p(p-1)cx_{s+1}^{p-2}+p(p-1)c\alpha^{sp}(\lambda_{s+1}-x_{s+1})^{p-2} < 0 \tag{4.6.35}$$

for $0 < p < 1$ and $0 \le x_{s+1} \le \lambda_{s+1}$. Solving (4.6.34) we have

$$pcx_{s+1}^p = \frac{pc\alpha^{sp}(\lambda_{s+1}-x_{s+1})^{p-1}}{(1+\alpha^{[p/(p-1)]}+\ \ldots\ +\alpha^{\{[(s-1)p]/(p-1)\}})^{p-1}} \tag{4.6.36}$$

which simplifies to

$$x_{s+1}^*(\lambda_{s+1}) = \frac{\alpha^{[sp/(p-1)]}}{1+\alpha^{[p/(p-1)]}+\ \ldots\ +\alpha^{[sp/(p-1)]}}\,\lambda_{s+1} < \lambda_{s+1} \tag{4.6.37}$$

Upon substituting (4.6.37) into (4.6.33) it can be verified, after some algebra, that

$$g_{s+1}(\lambda_{s+1}) = \frac{c\alpha^{sp}}{(1+\alpha^{[p/(p-1)]}+\ \ldots\ +\alpha^{[sp/(p-1)]})^{p-1}}\,\lambda_{s+1}^p \qquad (4.6.38)$$

which completes the induction.

We can now state the general solution to our problem when $\phi(y) = cy^p$, $c > 0$, $0 < p < 1$. It is

$$g_n(q) = \frac{c\alpha^{(n-1)p}}{\left[\sum_{j=1}^{n}\alpha^{\{[(j-1)p]/(p-1)\}}\right]^{p-1}}\,q^p \qquad (4.6.39)$$

and

$$x_n^* = \frac{\alpha^{(n-1)p}}{\sum_{j=1}^{n}\alpha^{\{[(j-1)p]/(p-1)\}}}\,q \qquad (4.6.40)$$

Then

$$\lambda_{n-1} = \alpha(q-x_n^*) = \alpha q\,\frac{\sum_{j=1}^{n-1}\alpha^{\{[(j-1)p]/(p-1)\}}}{\sum_{j=1}^{n}\alpha^{\{[(j-1)p]/(p-1)\}}}$$

yielding

$$x_{n-1}^* = \frac{\alpha^{(n-2)p+1}}{\sum_{j=1}^{n}\alpha^{\{[(j-1)p]/(p-1)\}}}\,q \qquad (4.6.41)$$

Then

$$\lambda_{n-2} = \alpha(\lambda_{n-1}-x_{n-1}^*) = \alpha^2 q\,\frac{\sum_{j=1}^{n-2}\alpha^{\{[(j-1)p]/(p-1)\}}}{\sum_{j=1}^{n}\alpha^{\{[(j-1)p]/(p-1)\}}}$$

which yields

$$x_{n-2}^* = \frac{\alpha^{(n-3)p+2}}{\sum_{n=1}^{n}\alpha^{\{[(j-1)p]/(p-1)\}}}\,q \qquad (4.6.42)$$

and in general, it is easy to show that

$$x_{n-k}^* = \frac{\alpha^{(n-k-1)p+k}}{\sum_{j=1}^{n}\alpha^{\{[(j-1)p]/(p-1)\}}}\,q \qquad (k = 0, 1, \ldots, n-1) \qquad (4.6.43)$$

Hence, we have found the general solution for this case.

4.7. Multiplicative Constraints and Functions

A problem which arises in engineering design is to minimize the total energy to compress a gas in a multistage process, with initial pressure p_0 to a final pressure p_n, both of which are known. The energy E_n for the n-stage process is given by

$$E_n = (NRT) \left(\frac{\gamma}{\gamma-1} \right) \left[\left(\frac{p_1}{p_0} \right)^\alpha + \left(\frac{p_2}{p_1} \right)^\alpha + \cdots + \left(\frac{p_n}{p_{n-1}} \right)^\alpha - n \right]$$

where p_j = discharge pressure at the jth stage;
N = number of moles of gas;
R = universal gas constant;
T = temperature;
$\alpha = (\gamma-1)/\gamma$;
$\gamma = C_p/C_v$ = ratio of specific heats.

We can simplify the expression of our problem by defining

$$K = (NRT)(\gamma/(\gamma-1)) \quad \text{i.e} \quad NRT \left(\frac{\gamma}{\gamma-1} \right)$$

$$x_j = \frac{p_j}{p_{j-1}} > 1 \quad (j = 1, 2, \ldots, n)$$

Then the problem we wish to solve is given by

$$\min \quad E_n = K \left[\sum_{j=1}^n x_j^\alpha - n \right]$$

subject to
$$\prod_{j=1}^n x_j = b = \frac{p_n}{p_0} \qquad (4.7.1)$$

$$x_j \geqslant 1 \quad (j = 1, 2, \ldots, n)$$

Before considering the solution to (4.7.1), let us consider the general problem

$$\min \quad z = \sum_{j=1}^n \phi(x_j) \qquad (4.7.2)$$

subject to
$$\prod_{j=1}^n x_j = b$$

$$x_j \geqslant 0 \quad (j = 1, 2, \ldots, n)$$

It will be noted that (4.7.1) and (4.7.2) contain a *multiplicative* rather than an additive constraint. Hence we need to consider anew what the state transformation function and state variables are for $\prod_j x_j = b$.

We define

$$\lambda_{s-1} = T_s(\lambda_s, x_s(\lambda_s)) = \frac{\lambda_s}{x_s} \quad (s = 2, \ldots, n) \qquad (4.7.3)$$

$$x_1 = \lambda_1$$

6

In effect, what we have done in (4.7.3) is to consider that $\lambda_n = b$ is to be subdivided sequentially into n quantities $x_1, x_2, \ldots, x_n$ so that $\prod_{j=1}^{n} x_j = \lambda_n$. If we choose x_n at stage n, then we obtain a stage return of $s_n = \phi(x_n)$ and the amount remaining for further division in the successive stages is

$$\lambda_{n-1} = \frac{\lambda_n}{x_n} \tag{4.7.4}$$

We continue this process and quite clearly obtain

$$\lambda_{s-1} = \frac{\lambda_s}{x_s} \qquad (s = 2, \ldots, n)$$

and, finally $\qquad x_1 = \lambda_1$

Using these relationships, we obtain the recurrence relations

$$g_1(\lambda_1) = \min_{x_1 = \lambda_1} \phi(x_1)$$

$$g_s(\lambda_s) = \min_{x_s \geq 0} \left[\phi(x_s) + g_{s-1}\left(\frac{\lambda_s}{x_s}\right) \right] \qquad (s = 2, \ldots, n) \tag{4.7.5}$$

If we specialize $\phi(y)$ we can obtain similar solutions to all the cases we examined in the earlier sections of this chapter.

Let us now return to (4.7.1). It is clear that (4.7.1) has the same form as (4.7.2) with the trivial exception of lower bound on the variables, which is easily handled. Using the notation of (4.7.2) and (4.7.5) and applying it to (4.7.1), we have

$$\phi(x_j) = K(x_j^\alpha - 1)$$

$$\lambda_{j-1} = \frac{\lambda_j}{x_j} \qquad (j = 1, 2, \ldots, n) \tag{4.7.6}$$

and the recurrence relations are

$$g_1(\lambda_1) = \min_{x_1 = \lambda_1} K(x_1^\alpha - 1) = K(\lambda_1^\alpha - 1) \tag{4.7.7}$$

$$g_2(\lambda_2) = \min_{1 \leq x_2 \leq \lambda_2} \left[K(x_2^\alpha - 1) + g_1\left(\frac{\lambda_2}{x_2}\right) \right]$$

$$= \min_{1 \leq x_2 \leq \lambda_2} \left[K(x_2^\alpha - 1) + K\left(\left(\frac{\lambda_2}{x_2}\right)^\alpha - 1 \right) \right]$$

$$= \min_{1 \leq x_2 \leq \lambda_2} G_2(\lambda_2, x_2) \tag{4.7.8}$$

It can be shown that for the appropriate values of α for most cases, $G_2(\lambda_2, x_2)$ has a global minimum in the interval $1 \leq x_2 \leq \lambda_2$. Hence, we have

$$\frac{\partial G_2}{\partial x_2} = K\alpha x_2^{\alpha-1} - K\alpha\lambda_2^\alpha x_2^{-\alpha-1} = 0 \tag{4.7.9}$$

$$\frac{\partial^2 G_2}{\partial x_2^2} = 2\alpha^2 K \lambda_2^{\frac{\alpha-2}{2}} = \beta K \text{ say}, \quad \beta > 0$$

$$\text{at } (\lambda_2, \lambda_2^{1/2})$$

K is function of α \qquad \qquad From 4.7.10

$\therefore$ true for appropriate values of α

Solving (4.7.9) we have that

$$x_2^*(\lambda_2) = \lambda_2^{1/2} \tag{4.7.10}$$

Substituting (4.7.10) into (4.7.8) yields

$$g_2(\lambda_2) = 2K(\lambda_2^{\alpha/2} - 1) \tag{4.7.11}$$

From (4.7.11) we might surmise that the general solution is

$$g_j(\lambda_j) = jK(\lambda_j^{\alpha/j} - 1)$$

and

$$x_j^*(\lambda_j) = \lambda_j^{1/j} \tag{4.7.12}$$

Let us prove this. Equation (4.7.12) is true for $j = 1, 2$. Suppose it is true for $j = s$. Then

$$g_s(\lambda_s) = sK(\lambda_s^{\alpha/s} - 1)$$

Then

$$g_{s+1}(\lambda_{s+1}) = \min_{1 \le x_{s+1} \le \lambda_{s+1}} \left[K(x_{s+1}^\alpha - 1) + g_s\left(\frac{\lambda_{s+1}}{x_{s+1}}\right) \right]$$

$$= \min_{1 \le x_{s+1} \le \lambda_{s+1}} \left[K(x_{s+1}^\alpha - 1) + sK\left(\left(\frac{\lambda_{s+1}}{x_{s+1}}\right)^{\alpha/s} - 1\right) \right]$$

$$= \min_{1 \le x_{s+1} \le \lambda_{s+1}} G_{s+1}(\lambda_{s+1}, x_{s+1}) \tag{4.7.13}$$

$$\frac{\partial G_{s+1}}{\partial x_{s+1}} = K\alpha x_{s+1}^{\alpha-1} - sK\lambda_{s+1}^{\alpha/s}\left(\frac{\alpha}{s}\right)x_{s+1}^{-(\alpha/s)-1} = 0 \tag{4.7.14}$$

Solving (4.7.14) we obtain

$$x_{s+1}^*(\lambda_{s+1}) = \lambda_{s+1}^{1/(s+1)} \tag{4.7.15}$$

See notes p60 for 2nd derivative test (handwritten)

Substituting (4.7.15) into (4.7.13) yields

$$g_{s+1}(\lambda_{s+1}) = (s+1) K(\lambda_{s+1}^{\alpha/(s+1)} - 1) \tag{4.7.16}$$

which completes the induction.

Let us now find the solution to our problem, (4.7.1). We have that

$$E_n = g_n(b) = nK(b^{\alpha/n} - 1)$$
$$x_n^*(b) = b^{1/n}$$
$$\lambda_{n-1} = \frac{\lambda_n}{x_n} = \frac{b}{b^{1/n}} = b^{(n-1)/n}$$
$$x_{n-1}^*(\lambda_{n-1}) = (b^{(n-1)/n})^{1/(n-1)} = b^{1/n}$$

and in general, it is easy to show by induction that

$$x_j^* = b^{1/n} \qquad (j = 1, 2, \ldots, n)$$

In Chapter 2 we gave an example of a problem with a multiplicative objective function. Let us now consider a more general problem with such an objective function.

6*

Consider the problem

$$\max \quad z = x_1^{P_1} x_2^{P_2} \ldots x_n^{P_n}, \quad p_j \geqslant 1$$

subject to
$$x_1 + x_2 + \ldots + x_n = b \tag{4.7.17}$$

$$x_j \geqslant 0$$

From the constraint it is clear that the state transformation function is

$$\lambda_{s-1} = T_s(\lambda_s, x_s(\lambda_s)) = \lambda_s - x_s \quad (s = 2 \ldots n)$$

$$x_1 = \lambda_1 \tag{4.7.18}$$

From these state variables and the form of the objective function, it follows that

$$g_1(\lambda_1) = \max_{x_1 = \lambda_1} x_1^{P_1} \qquad x_s^{P_s}$$

$$g_s(\lambda_s) = \max_{0 \leqslant x_s \leqslant \lambda_s} [x_s^{P_s} g_{s-1}(\lambda_s - x_s)] \quad (s = 2 \ldots n) \tag{4.7.19}$$

Let us now compute the first few terms:

$$g_1(\lambda_1) = \max_{x_1 = \lambda_1} x_1^{P_1} = \lambda_1^{P_1} \tag{4.7.20}$$

$$g_2(\lambda_2) = \max_{0 \leqslant x_2 \leqslant \lambda_2} [x_2^{P_2} g_1(\lambda_2 - x_2)]$$

$$= \max_{0 \leqslant x_2 \leqslant \lambda_2} [x_2^{P_2}(\lambda_2 - x_2)^{P_1}]$$

$$= \max_{0 \leqslant x_2 \leqslant \lambda_2} G_2(\lambda_2, x_2) \tag{4.7.21}$$

Differentiating G_2 yields

$$\frac{\partial G_2}{\partial x_2} = -x_2^{P_2} p_1(\lambda_2 - x_2)^{P_1 - 1} + (\lambda_2 - x_2)^{P_1} p_2 x_2^{P_2 - 1} = 0 \tag{4.7.22}$$

It can be shown that the solution to (4.7.22) is the maximum we seek. The solution to (4.7.22) is easily found to be

$$x_2^*(\lambda_2) = \frac{p_2}{p_1 + p_2} \lambda_2 \quad \left(\begin{array}{c} \text{other soln} \\ x_2 = 0, \ x_2 = \lambda_2 \end{array} \right) \tag{4.7.23}$$

Substituting (4.7.23) into (4.7.21) we have

$$g_2(\lambda_2) = x_2^{P_2}(\lambda_2 - x_2)^{P_1}$$

$$= \left(\frac{p_2}{p_1 + p_2} \lambda_2 \right)^{P_2} \left(\lambda_2 - \frac{p_2}{p_1 + p_2} \lambda_2 \right)^{P_1}$$

which simplifies to

$$g_2(\lambda_2) = \frac{p_1^{P_1} p_2^{P_2}}{(p_1 + p_2)^{P_1 + P_2}} \lambda_2^{P_1 + P_2} \tag{4.7.24}$$

From (4.7.24) we might guess that the general form of the solution was

$$g_j(\lambda_j) = \frac{p_1^{p_1} p_2^{p_2} \cdots p_j^{p_j}}{(p_1+p_2+ \cdots +p_j)^{p_1+p_2+ \cdots +p_j}} \lambda_j^{p_1+p_2+ \cdots +p_j} \qquad (4.7.25)$$

and

$$x_j^*(\lambda_j) = \frac{p_j}{p_1+p_2+ \cdots +p_j} \lambda_j$$

It can be seen that (4.7.25) holds for $j = 1, 2$. Suppose it holds for $j = s$. Then

$$g_s(\lambda_s) = \frac{p_1^{p_1} p_2^{p_2} \cdots p_s^{p_s}}{(p_1+p_2+ \cdots +p_s)^{p_1+p_2+ \cdots +p_s}} \lambda_s^{p_1+p_2+ \cdots +p_s}$$

Then

$$g_{s+1}(\lambda_{s+1}) = \max_{0 \le x_{s+1} \le \lambda_{s+1}} [x_{s+1}^{p_{s+1}} g_s(\lambda_{s+1} - x_{s+1})] \qquad \leftarrow \quad p_1^{p_1} p_2^{p_2} \cdots p_s^{p_s}$$

$$= \max_{0 \le x_{s+1} \le \lambda_{s+1}} \left[x_{s+1}^{p_{s+1}} \left(\frac{p_1^{p_1} p_2^{p_2} p_s^{p_s}}{(p_1+p_2+ \cdots +p_s)^{p_1+p_2+ \cdots +p_s}} \right) (\lambda_{s+1} - x_{s+1})^{p_1+p_2+ \cdots +p_s} \right]$$

$$= \max_{0 \le x_{s+1} \le \lambda_{s+1}} G_{s+1}(\lambda_{s+1}, x_{s+1}) \qquad (4.7.26)$$

$$\frac{\partial G_{s+1}}{\partial x_{s+1}} = \left(\frac{p_1^{p_1} p_2^{p_2} \cdots p_s^{p_s}}{(p_1+p_2+ \cdots +p_s)^{p_1+p_2+ \cdots +p_s}} \right)$$
$$\times [-x_{s+1}^{p_{s+1}}(p_1+p_2+ \cdots +p_s)(\lambda_{s+1} - x_{s+1})^{p_1+p_2+ \cdots +p_s-1}$$
$$+ (\lambda_{s+1} - x_{s+1})^{p_1+p_2+ \cdots +p_s} p_{s+1} x_{s+1}^{p_{s+1}-1}] = 0 \qquad (4.7.27)$$

Solving (4.7.27) we obtain

$$x_{s+1}^*(\lambda_{s+1}) = \frac{p_{s+1}}{p_1+p_2+ \cdots +p_{s+1}} \lambda_{s+1} \quad \left(\begin{array}{l} \text{Other soln} \\ x_{s+1} = 0 \\ \ni \lambda_{s+1} \end{array} \right) \qquad (4.7.28)$$

Substituting (4.7.28) into (4.7.26), we have

$$g_{s+1}(\lambda_{s+1}) = \left(\frac{p_{s+1}}{p_1+p_2+ \cdots +p_{s+1}} \lambda_{s+1} \right)^{p_{s+1}}$$

$$\times \left(\frac{p_1^{p_1} p_2^{p_2} \cdots p_s^{p_s}}{(p_1+p_2+ \cdots +p_s)^{p_1+p_2+ \cdots +p_s}} \right)$$

$$\times \left(\lambda_{s+1} - \frac{p_{s+1}}{p_1+p_2+ \cdots +p_{s+1}} \lambda_{s+1} \right)^{p_1+p_2+ \cdots +p_s} \qquad (4.7.29)$$

Simplifying (4.7.29) we obtain

$$g_{s+1}(\lambda_{s+1}) = \frac{p_1^{p_1} p_2^{p_2} \cdots p_{s+1}^{p_{s+1}}}{(p_1+p_2+ \cdots +p_{s+1})^{p_1+p_2+ \cdots +p_{s+1}}} \lambda_{s+1}^{p_1+p_2+ \cdots +p_{s+1}} \qquad (4.7.30)$$

and the induction is complete.

The solution to (4.7.17) is therefore

$$z = g_n(b) = \frac{p_1^{p_1} p_2^{p_2} \cdots p_n^{p_n}}{(p_1+p_2+ \cdots +p_n)^{p_1+p_2+ \cdots +p_n}} b^{p_1+p_2+ \cdots +p_n}$$

and

$$x_n^*(b) = \frac{p_n}{p_1+p_2+ \cdots +p_n} b$$

$$\lambda_{n-1} = \lambda_n - x_n = b - \frac{p_n}{p_1+p_2+ \cdots +p_n} b = \frac{p_1+p_2+ \cdots +p_{n-1}}{p_1+p_2+ \cdots +p_n} b$$

$$x_{n-1}^* = \left(\frac{p_{n-1}}{p_1+p_2+ \cdots +p_{n-1}}\right) \left(\frac{p_1+p_2+ \cdots +p_{n-1}}{p_1+p_2+ \cdots +p_n}\right) b = \frac{p_{n-1}}{p_1+p_2+ \cdots +p_n} b$$

and it is easy to show, by induction, that

$$x_{n-k}^* = \frac{p_{n-k}}{p_1+p_2+ \cdots +p_n} b \qquad (k = 0, 1, \ldots, n-1)$$

which completes the solution.

Exclude

4.8. Some Variations on State Functions

Let us consider how we might solve the following problem by dynamic programming:

$$\min z = \sum_{j=1}^{n} \phi_j(x_j - r_j) + \sum_{j=1}^{n} \psi_j(x_j - x_{j-1}) \tag{4.8.1}$$

where $x_0 = b$, $\{r_j\}$ is a known sequence, and ϕ_j and ψ_j are continuous functions. Problems of the form (4.8.1) are often called "smoothing" problems and arise in production and inventory processes in which one desires to smooth out large variations in the behavioral characteristics of a production process or in the inventories of products under control. Quadratic smoothing functions are often used, and we shall examine this case after developing the general recurrence relations.

Let us proceed to develop the recurrence relations that can be used to solve this problem. In the course of doing so the correct form of the state variables and state transformations will become apparent. From (4.8.1) it is clear that we can write

$$z = \min_{x_1} [\phi_1(x_1 - r_1) + \psi_1(x_1 - b)] + \min_{x_2, \ldots, x_n} \sum_{j=2}^{n} [\phi_j(x_j - r_j) + \psi_j(x_j - x_{j-1})] \tag{4.8.2}$$

and

$$\min_{x_2, \ldots, x_n} \sum_{j=2}^{n} [\phi_j(x_j - r_j) + \psi_j(x_j - x_{j-1})]$$

$$= \min_{x_2} [\phi_2(x_2 - r_2) + \psi_2(x_2 - x_1)] + \min_{x_3, \ldots, x_n} \sum_{j=3}^{n} [\phi_j(x_j - r_j) + \psi_j(x_j - x_{j-1})] \tag{4.8.3}$$

It is obvious that this decomposition can be continued. An examination of (4.8.2) indicates that the minimization of the summation, in the second term, is over $x_2, \ldots, x_n$.

Yet there remains an x_1 in the first term of the summation. In (4.8.3) a similar situation exists with respect to x_2. This suggests that if we define a state variable $\lambda_j = x_{j-1}$ we can avoid this problem. More precisely we can define

$$g_s(\lambda_s) = \min_{x_s \ldots x_n} \sum_{j=s}^{n} [\phi_j(x_j - r_j) + \psi_j(x_j - x_{j-1})] \qquad (s = 2, \ldots n) \qquad (4.8.4)$$

where $x_{s-1} = \lambda_s$.

Using (4.8.4) we can obtain the recurrence relations

$$g_n(\lambda_n) = \min_{x_n} [\phi_n(x_n - r_n) + \psi_n(x_n - \lambda_n)]$$

$$g_s(\lambda_s) = \min_{x_s} [\phi_s(x_s - r_s) + \psi_s(x_s - \lambda_s) + g_{s+1}(x_s)] \qquad (s = 1, 2, \ldots, n-1) \qquad (4.8.5)$$

It should be noted that we are using a "forward" recursion in (4.8.5). We have reversed the order in which we move from stage to stage. Equation (4.8.6) is the reason for calling this a forward recursion. In deriving (4.8.5) we have implicitly used the state transformation

$$\lambda_{s+1} = T_s(\lambda_s, x_s(\lambda_s)) = \lambda_s + (x_s - x_{s-1}) \qquad (4.8.6)$$

Let us now consider a specific example where

$$\begin{aligned} \phi_j(x_j - r_j) &= \alpha_j(x_j - r_j)^2 \qquad (\alpha_j > 0) \\ \psi_j(x_j - x_{j-1}) &= \beta_j(x_j - x_{j-1})^2 \qquad (\beta_j > 0) \end{aligned} \qquad (4.8.7)$$

where $\{\alpha_j\}$, $\{\beta_j\}$ are known sequences. The calculation begins with

$$g_n(\lambda_n) = \min_{x_n} [\alpha_n(x_n - r_n)^2 + \beta_n(x_n - \lambda_n)^2]$$

$$= \min_{x_n} G_n(\lambda_n, x_n) \qquad (4.8.8)$$

It is evident that G_n is a convex function of x_n. Therefore we have

$$\frac{\partial G_n}{\partial x_n} = 2\alpha_n(x_n - r_n) + 2\beta_n(x_n - \lambda_n) = 0$$

$$\frac{\partial^2 G_n}{\partial x_n^2} = 2\alpha_n + 2\beta_n > 0 \qquad (4.8.9)$$

Then we can solve (4.8.9) for x_n^*, obtaining

$$x_n^*(\lambda_n) = \frac{\beta_n \lambda_n}{\alpha_n + \beta_n} + \frac{\alpha_n r_n}{\alpha_n + \beta_n} \qquad (4.8.10)$$

In order to keep the algebra manageable, we define

$$c_n \equiv \frac{\beta_n}{\alpha_n + \beta_n}$$

$$d_n \equiv \frac{\alpha_n r_n}{\alpha_n + \beta_n} \qquad (4.8.11)$$

which gives us

$$x_n^*(\lambda_n) = c_n\lambda_n + d_n \tag{4.8.12}$$

Substituting (4.8.12) into (4.8.8) yields

$$g_n(\lambda_n) = \alpha_n(c_n\lambda_n + d_n - r_n)^2 + \beta_n(c_n\lambda_n + d_n - \lambda_n)^2 \tag{4.8.13}$$

Simplifying (4.8.13) gives

$$g_n(\lambda_n) = [\alpha_n c_n^2 + \beta_n(c_n - 1)^2]\lambda_n^2 + [2\alpha_n c_n(d_n - r_n) + 2\beta_n(c_n - 1)d_n]\lambda_n + \alpha_n(d_n - r_n)^2 + \beta_n d_n^2 \tag{4.8.14}$$

We now define

$$
\begin{aligned}
u_n &\equiv \alpha_n c_n^2 + \beta_n(c_n - 1)^2 \\
v_n &\equiv 2\alpha_n c_n(d_n - r_n) + 2\beta_n(c_n - 1)d_n \\
w_n &\equiv \alpha_n(d_n - r_n)^2 + \beta_n d_n^2
\end{aligned}
\tag{4.8.15}
$$

which enables us to write (4.8.14) as

$$g_n(\lambda_n) = u_n\lambda_n^2 + v_n\lambda_n + w_n \tag{4.8.16}$$

Next we calculate $g_{n-1}(\lambda_n)$ from $\quad g_{n-1}(\lambda_{n-1})$

$$
\begin{aligned}
g_{n-1}(\lambda_{n-1}) &= \min_{x_{n-1}} [\alpha_{n-1}(x_{n-1} - r_{n-1})^2 + \beta_{n-1}(x_{n-1} - \lambda_{n-1})^2 + g_n(x_{n-1})] \\
&= \min_{x_{n-1}} [\alpha_{n-1}(x_{n-1} - r_{n-1})^2 + \beta_{n-1}(x_{n-1} - \lambda_{n-1})^2 + u_n x_{n-1}^2 + v_n x_{n-1} + w_n] \\
&= \min_{x_{n-1}} G_{n-1}(\lambda_{n-1}, x_{n-1}) \tag{4.8.17}
\end{aligned}
$$

Differentiating (4.8.17) we obtain

$$\frac{\partial G_{n-1}}{\partial x_{n-1}} = 2\alpha_{n-1}(x_{n-1} - r_{n-1}) + 2\beta_{n-1}(x_{n-1} - \lambda_{n-1}) + 2u_n x_{n-1} + v_n = 0 \tag{4.8.18}$$

Assuming that $[(\partial^2 g_{n-1})/(\partial x_{n-1}^2)] > 0$, we solve (4.8.18) for x_{n-1}^*, which yields

$$x_{n-1}^*(\lambda_{n-1}) = \frac{\beta_{n-1}\lambda_{n-1}}{\alpha_{n-1} + \beta_{n-1} + u_n} + \frac{\alpha_{n-1}r_{n-1} + \dfrac{v_n}{2}}{\alpha_{n-1} + \beta_{n-1} + u_n} \tag{4.8.19}$$

Defining

$$c_{n-1} \equiv \frac{\beta_{n-1}}{\alpha_{n-1} + \beta_{n-1} + u_n} \tag{4.8.20}$$

$$d_{n-1} \equiv \frac{\alpha_{n-1}r_{n-1} + \dfrac{v_n}{2}}{\alpha_{n-1} + \beta_{n-1} + u_n}$$

We now have

$$x_{n-1}^*(\lambda_{n-1}) = c_{n-1}\lambda_{n-1} + d_{n-1} \tag{4.8.21}$$

Substituting (4.8.21) into (4.8.17), we have

$$g_{n-1}(\lambda_{n-1}) = \alpha_{n-1}(c_{n-1}\lambda_{n-1}+d_{n-1}-r_{n-1})^2$$
$$+\beta_{n-1}(c_{n-1}\lambda_{n-1}+d_{n-1}-\lambda_{n-1})^2$$
$$+u_n(c_{n-1}^2\lambda_{n-1}^2+2c_{n-1}d_{n-1}\lambda_{n-1}+d_{n-1}^2)$$
$$+v_n(c_{n-1}\lambda_{n-1}+d_{n-1})+w_n \tag{4.8.22}$$

We can simplify (4.8.22), to obtain

$$g_{n-1}(\lambda_{n-1}) = [\alpha_{n-1}c_{n-1}^2+\beta_{n-1}(c_{n-1}-1)^2+u_nc_{n-1}^2]\lambda_{n-1}^2$$
$$+[2\alpha_{n-1}c_{n-1}(d_{n-1}-r_{n-1})+2\beta_{n-1}(c_{n-1}-1)d_{n-1}+2u_nc_{n-1}d_{n-1}+v_nc_{n-1}]\lambda_{n-1}$$
$$+[\alpha_{n-1}(d_{n-1}-r_{n-1})^2+\beta_{n-1}d_{n-1}^2+u_nd_{n-1}^2+v_nd_{n-1}+w_n] \tag{4.8.23}$$

Defining

$$u_{n-1} \equiv \alpha_{n-1}c_{n-1}^2+\beta_{n-1}(c_{n-1}-1)^2+u_nc_{n-1}^2$$
$$v_{n-1} \equiv 2\alpha_{n-1}c_{n-1}(d_{n-1}-r_{n-1})+2\beta_{n-1}(c_{n-1}-1)d_{n-1}+2u_nc_{n-1}d_{n-1}+v_nc_{n-1} \tag{4.8.24}$$
$$w_{n-1} \equiv \alpha_{n-1}(d_{n-1}-r_{n-1})^2+\beta_{n-1}d_{n-1}^2+u_nd_{n-1}^2+v_nd_{n-1}+w_n$$

we can rewrite (4.8.23) as

$$g_{n-1}(\lambda_{n-1}) = u_{n-1}\lambda_{n-1}^2+v_{n-1}\lambda_{n-1}+w_{n-1} \tag{4.8.25}$$

We can now find the general form of the $x_j^*(\lambda_j)$ and $g_j(\lambda_j)$. (4.8.24) gives us u_{n-1}, v_{n-1}, w_{n-1} in terms of u_n, v_n, and w_n and known constants. We shall now show that

$$g_j(\lambda_j) = u_j\lambda_j^2+v_j\lambda_j+w_j \tag{4.8.26}$$

where
$$u_j = \alpha_jc_j^2+\beta_j(c_j-1)^2+u_{j+1}c_j^2$$
$$v_j = 2\alpha_jc_j(d_j-r_j)+2\beta_j(c_j-1)d_j+2u_{j+1}c_jd_j+v_{j+1}c_j$$
$$w_j = \alpha_j(d_j-r_j)^2+\beta_jd_j^2+u_{j+1}d_j^2+v_{j+1}d_j+w_{j+1}$$

$$c_j = \frac{\beta_j}{\alpha_j+\beta_j+u_{j+1}}$$

$$d_j = \frac{\alpha_jr_j+\dfrac{v_{j+1}}{2}}{\alpha_j+\beta_j+u_{j+1}}$$

and
$$x_j^*(\lambda_j) = c_j\lambda_j+d_j \tag{4.8.27}$$

It is clear that (4.8.26) and (4.8.27) hold for $j = n-1$. The case of $j = n$ is a special case, which is known. We shall proceed by backwards induction, i.e., we assume that (4.8.26) holds for $j = s$. Then we have

$$g_s(\lambda_s) = u_s\lambda_s^2+v_s\lambda_s+w_s \tag{4.8.28}$$

$$u_s = \alpha_s c_s^2 + \beta_s (c_s - 1)^2 + u_{s+1} c_s^2$$

$$v_s = 2\alpha_s c_s (d_s - r_s) + 2\beta_s (c_s - 1)d_s + 2u_{s+1} c_s d_s + v_{s+1} c_s$$

$$w_s = \alpha_s (d_s - r_s)^2 + \beta_s d_s^2 + u_{s+1} d_s^2 + v_{s+1} d_s + w_{s+1}$$

$$c_s = \frac{\beta_s}{\alpha_s + \beta_s + u_{s+1}}$$

$$d_s = \frac{\alpha_s r_s + \dfrac{v_{s+1}}{2}}{\alpha_s + \beta_s + u_{s+1}}$$

$$x_s^*(\lambda_s) = c_s \lambda_s + d_s \tag{4.8.29}$$

We now evaluate

$$g_{s-1}(\lambda_{s-1}) = \min_{x_{s-1}} [\alpha_{s-1}(x_{s-1} - r_{s-1})^2 + \beta_{s-1}(x_{s-1} - \lambda_{s-1})^2 + g_s(x_{s-1})]$$

$$= \min_{x_{s-1}} [\alpha_{s-1}(x_{s-1} - r_{s-1})^2 + \beta_{s-1}(x_{s-1} - \lambda_{s-1})^2 + u_s x_{s-1}^2 + v_s x_{s-1} + w_s]$$

$$= \min_{x_{s-1}} G_{s-1}(\lambda_{s-1}, x_{s-1}) \tag{4.8.30}$$

$$\frac{\partial G_{s-1}}{\partial x_{s-1}} = 2\alpha_{s-1}(x_{s-1} - r_{s-1}) + 2\beta_{s-1}(x_{s-1} - \lambda_{s-1}) + 2u_s x_{s-1} + v_s = 0 \tag{4.8.31}$$

Solving (4.8.31) we obtain

$$x_{s-1}^*(\lambda_{s-1}) = \frac{\beta_{s-1}\lambda_{s-1}}{\alpha_{s-1} + \beta_{s-1} + u_s} + \frac{\alpha_{s-1} r_{s-1} + \dfrac{v_s}{2}}{\alpha_{s-1} + \beta_{s-1} + u_s} \tag{4.8.32}$$

Then

$$x_{s-1}^*(\lambda_{s-1}) = c_{s-1}\lambda_{s-1} + d_{s-1} \tag{4.8.33}$$

where

$$c_{s-1} \equiv \frac{\beta_{s-1}}{\alpha_{s-1} + \beta_{s-1} + u_s}$$

$$d_{s-1} \equiv \frac{\alpha_{s-1} r_{s-1} + \dfrac{v_s}{2}}{\alpha_{s-1} + \beta_{s-1} + u_s}$$

Substituting (4.8.33) into (4.8.30), we have

$$g_{s-1}(\lambda_{s-1}) = \alpha_{s-1}(c_{s-1}\lambda_{s-1} + d_{s-1} - r_{s-1})^2 + \beta_{s-1}(c_{s-1}\lambda_{s-1} + d_{s-1} - \lambda_{s-1})^2$$
$$+ u_s(c_{s-1}\lambda_{s-1} + d_{s-1})^2 + v_s(c_{s-1}\lambda_{s-1} + d_{s-1}) + w_s \tag{4.8.34}$$

After simplification, we obtain

$$g_{s-1}(\lambda_{s-1}) = u_{s-1}\lambda_{s-1}^2 + v_{s-1}\lambda_{s-1} + w_{s-1} \tag{4.8.35}$$

where

$$u_{s-1} \equiv \alpha_{s-1} c_{s-1}^2 + \beta_{s-1}(c_{s-1} - 1)^2 + u_s c_{s-1}^2$$

$$v_{s-1} \equiv 2\alpha_{s-1} c_{s-1}(d_{s-1} - r_{s-1}) + 2\beta_{s-1}(c_{s-1} - 1)d_{s-1} + 2u_s c_{s-1} d_{s-1} + v_s c_{s-1}$$

$$w_{s-1} \equiv \alpha_{s-1}(d_{s-1} - r_{s-1})^2 + \beta_{s-1} d_{s-1}^2 + u_s d_{s-1}^2 + v_s d_{s-1} + w_s$$

This completes the induction.

We shall not take an inordinate amount of space and repetitious proofs by induction to develop general formulae for the values of the coefficients in the final solution to our problem. Instead we shall discuss how the x_j^* and z^* are obtained.

The values of c_n, d_n, u_n, v_n, w_n are calculated from (4.8.11) and (4.8.15). Then, using (4.8.29), we can compute all successive values of $c_s, d_s, u_s, v_s, w_s, s = n-1,$ $n-2, \ldots, 1$. Next we compute $z^* = g_1(b) = u_1b^2 + v_1b + w_1$ and $x_1^* = b$. Then we use $x_j^*(\lambda_j) = c_j\lambda_j + d_j$ with $\lambda_j = x_{j-1}^*$ for $j = 2 \ldots n$.

4.9. A Minimax Objective Function

There are many activities where it makes sense to consider minimizing a maximum value of some measure rather than a pure minimization of some objective. For example, if one wished to optimally locate an emergency ambulance station in some community, rather than minimize a sum of distances to all possible fixed locations, a preferable objective function might be to minimize the maximum distance to any of the locations. The results of these two approaches are quite different. Other activities where such mini-max criteria are used are in problems in numerical analysis (the theory of approximation) and also in certain areas of control theory, where the amount of a deviation from exact or ideal specifications is minimized.

The problem we are addressing is as follows:

$$z = \min_{x_1, x_2, \ldots, x_n} [\max(\phi(x_1), \phi(x_2), \ldots, \phi(x_n))]$$

subject to

$$\sum_{j=1}^{n} x_j = b$$

$$x_j \geq 0 \quad (j = 1, 2, \ldots, n) \tag{4.9.1}$$

We also assume that the function $\phi(y)$ is a monotone increasing function.

In order to see easily how to determine the recursion equations for this case, let us compare the objective function of (4.9.1) with the case of

$$\min \sum_{j=1}^{n} \phi(x_j) \tag{4.9.2}$$

subject to the constraints of (4.9.1). We already know the recursion relations for this problem, viz.,

$$g_1(\lambda_1) = \min_{x_1 = \lambda_1} \phi(x_1) \tag{4.9.3}$$

$$g_s(\lambda_s) = \min_{0 \leq x_s \leq \lambda_s} [\phi(x_s) + g_{s-1}(\lambda_s - x_s)] \quad (s = 2 \ldots n)$$

If we consider the meaning of (4.9.3), what the recurrence relation says is that the optimal return for an s-stage process is the minimum of the sum of the return $\phi(x_s)$ plus the optimal return for an $(s-1)$-stage process, when the state variable is $\lambda_s - x_s$. Therefore we need to transliterate this statement to the problem of (4.9.1). This is easily done since the state transformation function is the same, i.e.,

$$\lambda_{s-1} = T_s(\lambda_s, x_s(\lambda_s)) = \lambda_s - x_s \tag{4.9.4}$$

The return from s stages in (4.9.1) is the maximum of the returns at each of the stages, i.e.,

$$\max[\phi(x_1), \phi(x_2), \ldots, \phi(x_s)] \tag{4.9.5}$$

Therefore, if stages 1, 2, ..., $s-1$ are optimal with respect to the state λ_{s-1}, then we should be able to replace (4.9.5) by

$$\max(g_{s-1}(\lambda_{s-1}), \phi(x_s)) \tag{4.9.6}$$

From (4.9.6) and the form of the objective function (4.9.1), we see that the analog of (4.9.3) is

$$g_1(\lambda_1) = \min_{x_1 = \lambda_1} \phi(x_1)$$

$$g_s(\lambda_s) = \min_{0 \leqslant x_s \leqslant \lambda_s} [\max(\phi(x_s), g_{s-1}(\lambda_s - x_s))] \qquad (s = 2 \ldots n) \tag{4.9.7}$$

Let us now use these recursion relations to solve (4.9.1). We have that

$$g_1(\lambda_1) = \min_{x_1 = \lambda_1} \phi(x_1) = \phi(\lambda_1)$$

$$g_2(\lambda_2) = \min_{0 \leqslant x_2 \leqslant \lambda_2} [\max(\phi(x_2), g_1(\lambda_2 - x_2))]$$

$$= \min_{0 \leqslant x_2 \leqslant \lambda_2} [\max(\phi(x_2), \phi(\lambda_2 - x_2))]$$

$$= \min_{0 \leqslant x_2 \leqslant \lambda_2} G_2(\lambda_2, x_2) \tag{4.9.8}$$

INCORRECT
See Notes
p 62
Since $G_2(\lambda_2, x_2) = \max[\phi(x_2), \phi(\lambda_2 - x_2)]$, the minimum of the maximum will occur when $\phi(x_2) = \phi(\lambda_2 - x_2)$. A proof by contradiction is obvious. Suppose $\phi(x_2) < \phi(\lambda_2 - x_2)$ and x_2 is the minimum. Then, since they are both increasing functions, there is some value α such that

$$\phi(x_2) < \phi(x_2 + \alpha) = \phi(\lambda_2 - (x_2 + \alpha)) < \phi(\lambda_2 - x_2)$$

which is a contradiction. Therefore, we have proven that

$$\phi(x_2) = \phi(\lambda_2 - x_2)$$
$$x_2 = \lambda_2 - x_2$$

or

$$x_2^*(\lambda_2) = \frac{\lambda_2}{2} \tag{4.9.9}$$

Substituting (4.9.9) into (4.9.8) we have

$$g_2(\lambda_2) = \max\left[\phi\left(\frac{\lambda_2}{2}\right), \phi\left(\frac{\lambda_2}{2}\right)\right] = \phi\left(\frac{\lambda_2}{2}\right) \tag{4.9.10}$$

We might guess that

$$g_j(\lambda_j) = \phi\left(\frac{\lambda_j}{j}\right)$$

and

$$x_j^*(\lambda_j) = \frac{\lambda_j}{j} \tag{4.9.11}$$

The proof is by induction. Equation (4.9.11) is true for $j = 1, 2$. If (4.9.11) is true for $j = s$,

$$g_s(\lambda_s) = \phi\left(\frac{\lambda_s}{s}\right)$$

and

$$g_{s+1}(\lambda_{s+1}) = \min_{0 \leq x_{s+1} \leq \lambda_{s+1}} [\max(\phi(x_{s+1}), g_s(\lambda_{s+1} - x_{s+1}))]$$

$$= \min_{0 \leq x_{s+1} \leq \lambda_{s+1}} \left[\max\left(\phi(x_{s+1}), \phi\left(\frac{\lambda_{s+1} - x_{s+1}}{s}\right)\right)\right]$$

$$= \min_{0 \leq x_{s+1} \leq \lambda_{s+1}} G_{s+1}(\lambda_{s+1}, x_{s+1}) \tag{4.9.12}$$

The same argument that we used to show that $\phi(x_2) = \phi(\lambda_2 - x_2)$ will be valid here. Hence we can show that

$$\phi(x_{s+1}) = \phi\left(\frac{\lambda_{s+1} - x_{s+1}}{s}\right)$$

and therefore

$$x_{s+1} = \frac{\lambda_{s+1} - x_{s+1}}{s}$$

$$x_{s+1}^*(\lambda_{s+1}) = \frac{\lambda_{s+1}}{s+1} \tag{4.9.13}$$

and

$$g_{s+1}(\lambda_{s+1}) = \max\left[\phi\left(\frac{\lambda_{s+1}}{s+1}\right)\right], \left[\phi\left(\lambda_{s+1} - \frac{\lambda_{s+1}}{s+1}\right)\bigg/s\right]$$

$$= \phi\left(\frac{\lambda_{s+1}}{s+1}\right) \tag{4.9.14}$$

which completes the induction.

The solution to (4.9.1) can now be obtained:

$$z = g_n(b) = \phi\left(\frac{b}{n}\right) \quad \text{and} \quad x_n^* = \frac{b}{n}$$

$$\lambda_{n-1} = \lambda_n - x_n = b - \frac{b}{n} = \left(\frac{n-1}{n}\right)b$$

$$x_{n-1}^* = \left(\frac{n-1}{n}\right)b/n - 1 = \frac{b}{n}$$

and it is easily established that

$$x_j^* = \frac{b}{n} \quad (j = 1, 2, \ldots, n) \tag{4.9.15}$$

Exercises—Chapter 4

4.1. Solve the following problem by dynamic programming and obtain the general solution:

$$\min \quad z = \sum_{j=1}^{n} c_j x_j^2$$

subject to

$$\sum_{j=1}^{n} a_j x_j \geqslant b$$

$$x_j \geqslant 0 \qquad (j = 1, 2, \ldots, n)$$

4.2. Obtain the general solution for

$$\min \quad z = \sum_{j=1}^{n} c_j x_j^p$$

subject to

$$\sum_{j=1}^{n} x_j \geqslant b$$

$$x_j \geqslant 0 \qquad (j = 1, 2, \ldots, n)$$

4.3. Obtain the general solution for

$$\max \quad z = \sum_{j=1}^{n} \phi_j(x_j)$$

subject to

$$\sum_{j=1}^{n} x_j = b$$

$$x_j \geqslant 0 \qquad (j = 1, 2, \ldots, n)$$

and the $\phi_j(x_j)$ are convex functions.

4.4. Obtain the general solution for

$$\min \quad z = \sum_{j=1}^{n} (a x_j^2 + x_j)$$

subject to

$$\sum_{j=1}^{n} x_j = b$$

$$x_j \geqslant 0 \qquad (j = 1, 2, \ldots, n)$$

4.5. Suppose we have b dollars to be used for producing varying amounts of n different products. If we produce an amount x_j of the jth product we incur the following costs:

r_j = unit cost of raw materials for product j;

s_j = unit cost of equipment for product j;

t_j = unit cost of labor for product j;

C_j = fixed cost, independent of amount of product j if $x_j > 0$.

The cost of producing an amount x_j of product j is then

$$f_j(x_j) = (r_j + s_j + t_j) x_j + C_j, \qquad x_j > 0$$
$$= 0 \qquad\qquad\qquad , \qquad x_j = 0$$

If p_j is the selling price of product j, then we wish to maximize total profit. Therefore we wish to solve:

$$\max \quad P = \sum_{j=1}^{n} p_j x_j$$

subject to

$$\sum_{j=1}^{n} f_j(x_j) \leqslant b$$

$$x_j \geqslant 0$$

Find the recurrence relations for solving this problem by dynamic programming and exhibit the solution.

4.6. Obtain the solution for

$$\min \quad z = \prod_{j=1}^{n} x_j^p$$

subject to

$$\sum_{j=1}^{n} x_j^q \geqslant b$$

$$x_j \geqslant 0 \qquad (j = 1, 2, \ldots, n)$$

for

(a) $p > q$;   (b) $p = q$;   (c) $p < q$.

4.7. Obtain the solution for

$$\min_{x_1, x_2, \ldots, x_n} \quad [\max(\phi_j(x_j))]$$

subject to

$$\sum_{j=1}^{n} x_j = b$$

$$x_j \geqslant 0 \qquad (j = 1, 2, \ldots, n)$$

Chapter 5

One-dimensional Dynamic Programming: Computational Solutions

5.1. Introduction

In Chapter 4 we considered problems with one state variable at each stage (λ_j), and such that the optimal return functions $[g_j(\lambda_j)]$ and the decision variables $[x_j^*(\lambda_j)]$ corresponding to the optimal return functions could be determined by the use of methods of classical analysis. In order for this to be possible, what is necessary is that the objective function terms (stagewise return functions) consist of either continuous functions and/or functions with some special property such as convexity, monotonicity, etc. One further requirement, and the most important one, is that the application of first-order necessary conditions for the determination of the maximum or minimum leads to an equation which can be solved for the decision variable x_j. If that was not the case, then we could not have obtained an analytic representation of $g_j(\lambda_j)$ and $x_j^*(\lambda_j)$.

A second complication that can arise would be in problems where the decision variables x_j are not continuous, but instead, are required to take on only integer values. For such problems, the methods of Chapter 4 are clearly inapplicable.

In order to handle problems which have either of the characteristics alluded to in the foregoing paragraphs, we shall resort to the use of tables to represent the optimal return functions and the optimal decision variable functions. A table is a perfectly acceptable representation of a function of a real variable, since it satisfies, in every way, the definition of a function.

A rather interesting thing happens when we resort to the use of tables for functional representations. Integer-valued problems become easy and exact solutions are readily obtainable. On the other hand, problems with continuous variables can only be solved approximately, since we must approximate (even if it is as close as we wish) a continuous variable with a table or grid of discrete variables.

Another class of problems exists for which we must resort to tabular representation of $g_j(\lambda_j)$ and $x_j^*(\lambda_j)$. This is the class of problems for which the stage returns themselves, $s_j(\lambda_j, x_j)$, are given to us as tables of values. For example, a problem could be given as

$$\max \quad z = \sum_{j=1}^{n} \phi_j(x_j)$$

subject to
$$\sum_{j=1}^{n} x_j = b \tag{5.1.1}$$

$$x_j \geq 0 \qquad (j = 1, 2, \ldots, n)$$

where each of the $\phi_j(x_j)$ are given as tables. For example, $\phi_1(x_1)$ might be

x_1	0	1	2	3	4	...
$\phi_1(x_1)$	2	3	3.8	4.6	5.2	...

It is obvious that the analytic representation of a function is much more compact, in terms of computer storage (or any other kind), than a tabulation. For example, suppose we had an optimal solution represented by

$$x_s^*(\lambda_s) = \alpha_s \lambda_s^2 + \beta_s \lambda_s + \gamma_s \tag{5.1.2}$$

To store this function requires only that the coefficients α_s, β_s, and γ_s be stored. Then for any value of λ_s, $x_s^*(\lambda_s)$ can be computed. On the other hand, a tabular representation of $x_s^*(\lambda_s)$ for $\lambda_s = 0, 1, \ldots, 100$ would require 101 values to be stored (assuming equal increments of λ_s). The savings is very clear. For larger tables the savings is even greater. We shall have occasion to discuss this matter in greater detail when we discuss multidimensional problems in Chapter 6.

In this chapter we shall discuss the use of tabular function representation, both for the original problem statement as well as the optimal return functions and optimal solution functions.

5.2. A Prototype Problem

Consider the following nonlinear programming problem:

$$\max \quad z = \sum_{j=1}^{n} \phi_j(x_j)$$

subject to
$$\sum_{j=1}^{n} a_j x_j \leqslant b, \qquad a_j > 0 \tag{5.2.1}$$

$$x_j \geqslant 0, \quad \text{integers} \quad (j = 1, 2, \ldots, n)$$

We shall assume further that the a_j and b are integers. This is not an essential restriction because one can always make this true by a choice of a scaling factor.

If we compare (5.2.1) with (4.3.16), they are equivalent if $\phi_j(x_j) = x_j^2$. Hence it can readily be seen that the recurrence relations are similar to (4.3.19) with $\phi_j(x_j)$ substituting for x_j^2. Hence we have the state transformation function

$$\lambda_s = \lambda_{s+1} - a_{s+1} x_{s+1} \qquad (s = 1, 2, \ldots, n-1) \tag{5.2.2}$$

Since the constraint of (5.2.1) is $\sum_{j=1}^{n} a_j x_j \leqslant b$ and x_j must be integer, we have for $g_1(\lambda_1)$ that

$$g_1(\lambda_1) = \max_{0 \leqslant x_1 \leqslant [\lambda_1/a_1]} \phi_1(x_1) \tag{5.2.3}$$

The notation $[\lambda_1/a_1]$ indicates the greatest integer less than or equal to λ_1/a_1. Equation (5.2.3) restricts $x_1 \leqslant [\lambda_1/a_1]$ because the constraint $\sum_{j=1}^{n} a_j x_j \leqslant b$ is an inequality and x_1

7

must be an integer. Next we have

$$g_2(\lambda_2) = \max_{0 \leqslant x_2 \leqslant [\lambda_2/a_2]} [\phi_2(x_2) + g_1(\lambda_2 - a_2 x_2)] \qquad (5.2.4)$$

and in general

$$g_s(\lambda_s) = \max_{0 \leqslant x_s \leqslant [\lambda_s/a_s]} [\phi_s(x_s) + g_{s-1}(\lambda_s - a_s x_s)] \qquad (s = 2, \ldots, n) \qquad (5.2.5)$$

Let us now consider how we actually employ (5.2.3) and (5.2.5) to find the solution to (5.2.1).

We begin by computing $g_1(\lambda_1)$ for a range of values of λ_1. We must allow λ_1 to vary over the integers $0, 1, \ldots, b$. For any given value of λ_1, we suitably restrict the range over which x_1 may vary. In short, we would need to compute $g_1(\lambda_1)$ for $\lambda_1 = 0, 1, \ldots, b$. For each λ_1, we would also record the value of x_1, i.e., x_1^*, that led to the maximum value of $\phi_1(x_1)$. This maximum value may *not* be unique. Several values of x_1 may give the same value of $\phi_1(x_1)$. If one is interested in *all* possible optimal solutions, then all values of $x_1^*(\lambda_1)$ would be recorded. Otherwise, any one of the values is tabulated. The result of this calculation is shown in Table 5.2.1.

TABLE 5.2.1

λ_1	$g_1(\lambda_1)$	$x_1^*(\lambda_1)$
0	$g_1(0)$	$x_1^*(0)$
1	$g_1(1)$	$x_1^*(1)$
.	.	.
.	.	.
.	.	.
b	$g_1(b)$	$x_1^*(b)$

Having calculated $g_1(\lambda_1)$ we proceed to determine $g_2(\lambda_2)$ for $\lambda_2 = 0, 1, \ldots, b$ using (5.2.4):

$$g_2(\lambda_2) = \max_{0 \leqslant x_2 \leqslant [\lambda_2/a_2]} [\phi_2(x_2) + g_1(\lambda_2 - a_2 x_2)] \qquad (5.2.4)$$

In order to carry out the maximization indicated in (5.2.4) we must evaluate

$$G_2(\lambda_2, x_2) = \phi_2(x_2) + g_1(\lambda_2 - a_2 x_2) \qquad (5.2.6)$$

for $x_2 = 0, 1, \ldots, [\lambda_2/a_2]$. This means we must evaluate $g_1(\lambda_2)$, $g_1(\lambda_2 - a_2)$, $g_1(\lambda_2 - 2a_2), \ldots, g_1(\lambda_2 - a_2[\lambda_2/a_2])$. We can find the values of these functions by consulting Table 5.2.1 where $g_1(\lambda_1)$ is evaluated for all integer arguments in the range $[0, b]$. Hence $G_2(\lambda_2, x_2)$ can be evaluated for all arguments required in (5.2.4) and the maximum values of $g_2(\lambda_2)$ can be determined and tabulated in a second table which has precisely the same form as Table 5.2.1 except that we tabulate $g_2(\lambda_2)$ and $x_2^*(\lambda_2)$. $x_2^*(\lambda_2)$ was noted as the value of x_2 that led to the maximum value $g_2(\lambda_2)$ for each value of λ_2. Since a_2 was assumed to be an integer, $y_2 - a_2 x_2$ will be an integer for integer values of λ_2 and x_2. Hence the values of $g_1(\lambda_2 - a_2 x_2)$ will all be available in the table of $g_1(\lambda_1)$.

The process we have described can obviously be continued, using

$$g_s(\lambda_s) = \max_{0 \leqslant x_s \leqslant [\lambda_s/a_s]} [\phi_s(x_s) + g_{s-1}(\lambda_s - a_s x_s)] \qquad (s = 2, \ldots, n) \qquad (5.2.7)$$

to compute a table for each of the succeeding values of $g_s(y_s)$. Finally, we are ready to compute $g_n(b)$. It is not necessary to compute a table for $g_n(\lambda_n)$ since for the complete n-stage process we know that $\lambda_n = b$. Hence the single value, $g_n(b)$ is all that is required. This is given by

$$g_n(b) = \max_{0 \leqslant x_n \leqslant [b/a_n]} [\phi_n(x_n) + g_{n-1}(b - a_n x_n)] \qquad (5.2.8)$$

Therefore $z^* = g_n(b)$ and we note the value of x_n that led to the maximum value in (5.2.8). This then gives us x_n^* (or several values of x_n^* if the optimum is not unique). To determine the remaining optimal values $x_{n-1}^*, x_{n-2}^*, \ldots, x_1^*$, it is necessary to use the tables we have prepared. Since we know the value x_n^*, we know that the remaining values must satisfy

$$\sum_{j=1}^{n-1} a_j x_j \leqslant b - a_n x_n^* \qquad (5.2.9)$$

Hence $\sum_{j=1}^{n} \phi_j(x_j)$ must be maximized for nonnegative integers x_j which satisfy (5.2.9). However, this maximum is, by definition, $g_{n-1}(b - a_n x_n^*)$ and the value (or values) of x_{n-1} that lead to this maximum are $x_{n-1}^*(b - a_n x_n^*)$. These values can be found in the table for the $(n-1)$st stage, i.e., in the table for $g_{n-1}(\lambda_{n-1})$. Hence we look in that table for an argument equal to $b - a_n x_n^*$ and at the line for that entry we find the optimal value x_{n-1}^*. We obviously can continue this process and at the next stage $(n-2)$, we enter the table for the argument

$$b - a_n x_n^* - a_{n-1} x_{n-1}^*$$

and hence we determine x_{n-2}^* as

$$x_{n-2}^*(b - a_n x_n^* - a_{n-1} x_{n-1}^*)$$

It is clear that in general

$$x_{n-k}^* = x_{n-k}^*\left(b - \sum_{i=0}^{k-1} a_{n-i} x_{n-i}^*\right) \qquad (k = 1, 2, \ldots, n-1) \qquad (5.2.10)$$

Hence we have described a complete procedure for obtaining the optimal solution.

It will readily be seen that we need to calculate each table for the full range of each $\lambda_s = 0, 1, \ldots, b$, since we do not know which arguments we shall need until the "backward pass" to determine the optimal values of $x_{n-1}^*, x_{n-2}^*, \ldots, x_1^*$. After considering alternate optimal solutions and an example of the computational process, we shall return to the matter of the computational efficiency of the tabular representation of functions.

7*

In the course of calculating any table which represents $g_s(\lambda_s)$ for all values of λ_s, we may note *all* possible optimal values $x_s^*(\lambda_s)$, if there are more than one that lead to the same maximal value $g_s(\lambda_s)$. If we should do so, then it is a relatively straightforward matter (although possibly tedious) to find all alternate optimal solutions to the original problem, if we desire to know them all. Instead of tracing one path backwards through the tables, we would need to trace a tree of backward paths. Suppose, for example, that we have a final optimal value x_n^*. (If there were more than one, we can repeat the process we are about to describe, for each of them.) Suppose x_{n-1}^* is not unique but there are two such values. We designate them $x_{n-1,1}^*$ and $x_{n-1,2}^*$. Then, if we examine Fig. 5.2.1,

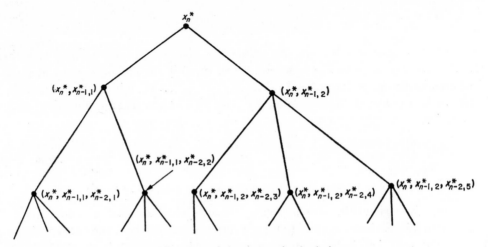

FIG. 5.2.1. Tree of alternate optimal solutions.

we see that we can trace out all solutions by making many backward passes to find all solutions. The final set of values of the x_s^* at the terminal branches of the tree each correspond to different optimal solutions.

5.3. An Example of the Computational Process

Consider the problem

$$\text{max} \quad z = \sum_{j=1}^{3} \phi_j(x_j) \tag{5.3.1}$$

subject to

$$2x_1 + 3x_2 + x_3 \leqslant 10$$

$$x_1, x_2, x_3 \geqslant 0, \quad \text{integer}$$

where the $\phi_j(x_j)$ are given in Table 5.3.1.

We first calculate $g_1(\lambda_1)$ from

$$g_1(\lambda_1) = \max_{0 \leqslant x_1 \leqslant [\lambda_1/2]} \phi_1(x_1) \tag{5.3.2}$$

TABLE 5.3.1

x_j	$\phi_1(x_1)$	$\phi_2(x_2)$	$\phi_3(x_3)$
0	2	5	8
1	4	10	12
2	7	15	17
3	11	20	22
4	13	24	19
5	15	18	16
6	18	12	14
7	22	9	11
8	18	5	9
9	15	3	7
10	11	1	4

Therefore we have

$$g_1(0) = \max_{x_1=0} \phi_1(x_1) = 2, \quad x_1^*(0) = 0$$

$$g_1(1) = \max_{x_1=0} \phi_1(x_1) = 2, \quad x_1^*(1) = 0$$

$$g_1(2) = \max_{0 \leq x_1 \leq 1} \phi_1(x_1) = \max[\phi_1(0), \phi_1(1)] \qquad = 4, \quad x_1^*(2) = 1$$

$$g_1(3) = \max_{0 \leq x_1 \leq 1} \phi_1(x_1) = \max[\phi_1(0), \phi_1(1)] \qquad = 4, \quad x_1^*(3) = 1$$

$$g_1(4) = \max_{0 \leq x_1 \leq 2} \phi_1(x_1) = \max[\phi_1(0), \phi_1(1), \phi_1(2)] = 7, \quad x_1^*(4) = 2$$

and so forth. The complete table of $g_1(\lambda_1)$ is given in Table 5.3.2.

TABLE 5.3.2

λ_1	$g_1(\lambda_1)$	$x_1^*(\lambda_1)$
0	2	0
1	2	0
2	4	1
3	4	1
4	7	2
5	7	2
6	11	3
7	11	3
8	13	4
9	13	4
10	15	5

Next we compute $g_2(\lambda_2)$ from

$$g_2(\lambda_2) = \max_{0 \leq x_2 \leq [\lambda_2/3]} [\phi_2(x_2) + g_1(\lambda_2 - 3x_2)] \qquad (5.3.3)$$

We then have

$$g_2(0) = \max_{x_2=0} [\phi_2(0)+g_1(0)] = 5+2 = 7, \quad x_2^*(0) = 0$$

$$g_2(1) = \max_{x_2=0} [\phi_2(0)+g_1(1)] = 5+2 = 7, \quad x_2^*(1) = 0$$

$$g_2(2) = \max_{x_2=0} [\phi_2(0)+g_1(2)] = 5+4 = 9, \quad x_2^*(2) = 0$$

$$g_2(3) = \max_{0 \leqslant x_2 \leqslant 1} [\phi_2(x_2)+g_1(3-3x_2)] = \max[5+4,\ 10+2] = 12, \quad x_2^*(3) = 1$$

$$g_2(4) = \max_{0 \leqslant x_2 \leqslant 1} [\phi_2(x_2)+g_1(4-3x_2)] = \max[5+7,\ 10+2] = 12, \quad x_2^*(4) = 0,1$$

and so forth. The complete table of $g_2(\lambda_2)$ is given in Table 5.3.3.

TABLE 5.3.3

λ_2	$g_2(\lambda_2)$	$x_2^*(\lambda_2)$
0	7	0
1	7	0
2	9	0
3	12	1
4	12	0,1
5	14	1
6	17	2
7	17	1,2
8	19	2
9	22	3
10	22	2,3

Finally, we compute

$$z^* = g_3(10) = \max_{0 \leqslant x_3 \leqslant 10} [\phi_3(x_3)+g_2(10-x_3)] \qquad (5.3.4)$$

Therefore

$$g_3(10) = \max[8+22,\ 12+22,\ 17+19,\ 22+17,\ 19+17,\ 16+14,$$
$$14+12,\ 11+12,\ 9+9,\ 7+7,\ 4+7]$$
$$g_3(10) = 39 \quad \text{and} \quad x_3^* = 3$$

Since $x_3^* = 3$, $\lambda_2 = 10-x_3^* = 10-3 = 7$. Therefore, $x_2^* = 1, 2$ and we have alternate optimal solutions. We will trace both solutions. For $x_3^* = 3$, $x_2^* = 1$, $\lambda_1 = \lambda_2-3x_2^* = 7-3 = 4$ and $x_1^* = 2$. For $x_3^* = 3$, $x_2^* = 2$, $\lambda_1 = \lambda_2-3x_2^* = 7-6 = 1$ and $x_1^* - 0$. Hence we have two optimal solutions. They are

$$x_1^* = 0, \quad x_2^* = 2, \quad x_3^* = 3 \quad \text{and} \quad z^* = 39$$
$$x_1^* = 2, \quad x_2^* = 1, \quad x_3^* = 3 \quad \text{and} \quad z^* = 39$$

There are a number of matters concerning this computational process which require discussion. It is clear that for problems with a large number of stages and a large number of values in each table, one will have to use a digital computer for calculations. In a computer, in order to minimize the total time for the computation, it is desirable (although not necessary) to store all the required quantities in high speed (random access) memory. Hence it is useful to store only what is absolutely required. It will be noted that the minimum required in any table consists of the values of λ_s and the corresponding values of $x_s^*(\lambda_s)$. These must be retained for each stage because in the backward pass through the tables we shall require the table of each stage. In very large problems, these tables can be stored on magnetic tape or disk and read into memory as required. Note that it is not necessary to ever save more than one table of $g_s(\lambda_s)$ at any stage. This is true because

$$g_{s+1}(\lambda_{s+1}) = \max_{0 \leqslant x_{s+1} \leqslant [\lambda_{s+1}/a_{s+1}]} [\phi_{s+1}(x_{s+1}) + g_s(\lambda_{s+1} - a_{s+1}x_{s+1})] \qquad (5.3.5)$$

and once $g_{s+1}(\lambda_{s+1})$ is calculated, we no longer need $g_s(\lambda_s)$. What we do need are the values of λ_{s+1} and the $x_{s+1}(\lambda_{s+1})$ that led to the maximum value. A problem with 100 variables (stages) and 1000 entries per table would require 100,000 words of storage. If the $\phi_j(x_j)$ were given analytically they would require a few hundred words of storage. However, if they were given by tables, as in the example just examined, we would require another 100,000 words of storage for the original data. In problems of this type, auxiliary computer storage would probably be used.

5.4. The Computational Effectiveness of Dynamic Programming

One might be tempted, especially in dealing with a problem such as the one we solved in Section 5.3, to wonder whether it might not be just as efficient to solve that problem by complete enumeration of all feasible solutions. For problems with two or three variables, there would not be a major difference. However, the effectiveness of dynamic programming as compared with enumeration of all feasible solutions becomes very significant as the number of variables (stages) increases. Suppose we consider the problem given by (5.2.1). It is difficult to make a direct comparison for the general case. Hence let us take a special case of (5.2.1), viz.,

$$\max \quad z = \sum_{j=1}^{n} \phi_j(x_j)$$

subject to
$$\sum_{j=1}^{n} x_j = b \qquad (5.4.1)$$

$$x_j \geqslant 0 \qquad (j = 1, 2, \ldots, n)$$

Let us first consider total enumeration of all feasible solutions. The number of possible values that the x_j can take on and still satisfy the constraint of (5.4.1) is given by the well-known combinatorial problem of finding the number of combinations of b objects with repetition out of n distinct objects and is given by [17]

$$\binom{n+b-1}{b} = \frac{(n+b-1)!}{b!\,(n-1)!} \qquad (5.4.2)$$

Let us now consider the dynamic programming approach. To evaluate $g_s(\lambda_s)$ for a given λ_s, we compare λ_s+1 values. To determine all the entries in the $g_s(\lambda_s)$ table we must compute

$$\sum_{\lambda_s=0}^{b} (\lambda_s+1) = \frac{(b+1)(b+2)}{2} \tag{5.4.3}$$

We must evaluate (5.4.3) for the first $n-1$ $g_s(\lambda_s)$. Therefore this requires

$$\frac{(n-1)(b+1)(b+2)}{2}$$

comparisons. Finally, we calculate $g_n(b)$ and this requires $b+1$ comparisons. Therefore the total number of comparisons is

$$C_{DP} = \frac{(n-1)(b+1)(b+2)}{2}+b+1 \tag{5.4.4}$$

Let us now compare (5.4.2) and (5.4.4) for some reasonable values of b and n. Table 5.4.1 shows these comparisons. We see that the amount of computation for dynamic

TABLE 5.4.1

	Enumeration	Dynamic programming
$b = 25$ $n = 5$	23,751	1,430
$b = 50$ $n = 5$	316,251	5,355
$b = 100$ $n = 10$	4.26×10^{12}	46,460
$b = 100$ $n = 20$	4.91×10^{21}	97,970
$b = 200$ $n = 40$	1.05×10^{45}	791,940

programming is quite modest whereas the increase in the number of computations for enumeration is disastrous. A computer could carry out the computations for the largest dynamic programming problem in the table in a matter of a minute or two. For the case of enumeration, at the rate of 10^9 evaluations per second, it would take approximately 10^{37} years! The advantage of dynamic programming for these kinds of problems is extremely significant.

5.5. An Integer Nonlinear Programming Problem

We shall now consider a problem which is impossible to solve, in general, except by dynamic programming. Consider the problem

$$\max \quad z = \sum_{j=1}^{n} \phi_j(x_j)$$

subject to
$$\sum_{j=1}^{n} h_j(x_j) \leqslant b \tag{5.5.1}$$

$$x_j \geqslant 0, \quad \text{integer} \quad (j = 1, 2, \ldots, n)$$

where $h_j(\cdot)$ are assumed to be increasing functions.

The $h_j(x_j)$ in (5.5.1) may be given in tabular form or any other mode of representation. Problems of the type (5.5.1), where the variables x_j are constrained to be integers, are notoriously difficult to solve, even if the $\phi_j(x_j) = c_j x_j$ and $h_j(x_j) = a_j x_j$, i.e., for linear problems. Let us now consider the solution of (5.5.1).

It can be seen that it is no more difficult to derive functional equations to solve (5.5.1) than it was to do the same for (5.2.1). We consider the problem as a multistage decision process with state variables and state transformations given by

$$\lambda_{s-1} = T_s(\lambda_s, x_s(\lambda_s)) = \lambda_s - h_s(x_s) \tag{5.5.2}$$

This is analogous to

$$\lambda_{s-1} = \lambda_s - a_s x_s$$

in the problem given by (5.2.1). Using (5.5.2) and the principle of optimality we can readily derive the recurrence relations

$$g_1(\lambda_1) = \max_{0 \leqslant x_1 \leqslant [\xi_1]} \phi_1(x_1)$$
$$g_s(\lambda_s) = \max_{0 \leqslant x_s \leqslant [\xi_s]} [\phi_s(x_s) + g_{s-1}[\lambda_s - h_s(x_s)]] \qquad (s = 2 \ldots n) \tag{5.5.3}$$

and where ξ_s is a solution to (root of)

$$\lambda_s - h_s(\xi_s) = 0 \tag{5.5.4}$$

The condition $0 \leqslant x_s \leqslant [\xi_s]$ is similar to the condition for (5.2.1) which was $0 \leqslant x_s \leqslant [\lambda_s/a_s]$ since λ_s/a_s is the solution to

$$\lambda_s - a_s x_s = 0$$

Since $h_s(x_s)$ is in general a nonlinear function, it may be necessary to determine, numerically, a root of (5.5.4). Aside from this rather small complication, we use (5.5.3) to calculate the tables of $g_s(\lambda_s)$ and $x_s^*(\lambda_s)$ and then find the solution to the original problem, just as we did in Sections 5.2 and 5.3.

As an example, consider the following problem

$$\max \quad z = \sum_{j=1}^{3} \phi_j(x_j)$$

subject to $x_1^2 + 3x_2^2 + 2x_3^2 \leqslant 20$ (5.5.5)

$$x_j \geqslant 0, \quad \text{integer} \quad (j = 1, 2, 3)$$

where the $\phi_j(x_j)$ are given by Table 5.3.1. We calculate $g_1(\lambda_1)$ using

$$g_1(\lambda_1) = \max_{0 \leqslant x_1 \leqslant [\xi_1]} \phi_1(x_1)$$ (5.5.6)

Since $\xi_1^2 - \lambda_1 = 0$, $\xi_1 = \lambda_1^{1/2}$. Therefore

$$g_1(0) = \max_{x_1=0} \phi_1(x_1) = 2, \qquad\qquad x_1^*(0) = 0$$

$$g_1(1) = \max_{0 \leqslant x_1 \leqslant 1} \phi_1(x_1) = \max(2, 4) = 4, \qquad x_1^*(1) = 1$$

$$g_1(2) = \max_{0 \leqslant x_1 \leqslant 1} \phi_1(x_1) = \max(2, 4) = 4, \qquad x_1^*(2) = 1$$

$$g_1(3) = \max_{0 \leqslant x_1 \leqslant 1} \phi_1(x_1) = \max(2, 4) = 4, \qquad x_1^*(3) = 1$$

$$g_1(4) = \max_{0 \leqslant x_1 \leqslant 2} \phi_1(x_1) = \max(2, 4, 7) = 7, \quad x_1^*(4) = 2$$

and so forth. The complete table for $g_1(\lambda_1)$ is given in Table 5.5.1. The calculation of $g_2(\lambda_2)$ is made from

$$g_2(\lambda_2) = \max_{0 \leqslant x_2 \leqslant [\xi_2]} [\phi_2(x_2) + g_1(\lambda_2 - 3x_2^2)]$$ (5.5.7)

where $$\xi_2 = \left(\frac{\lambda_2}{3}\right)^{1/2}$$

TABLE 5.5.1

λ_1	$g_1(\lambda_1)$	$x_1^*(\lambda_1)$	λ_1	$g_1(\lambda_1)$	$x_1^*(\lambda_1)$
0	2	0	11	11	3
1	4	1	12	11	3
2	4	1	13	11	3
3	4	1	14	11	3
4	7	2	15	11	3
5	7	2	16	13	4
6	7	2	17	13	4
7	7	2	18	13	4
8	7	2	19	13	4
9	11	3	20	13	4
10	11	3			

Hence we have

$$g_2(0) = \max_{x_2=0}(5+2) = 7, \qquad\qquad x_2^*(0) = 0$$

$$g_2(1) = \max_{x_2=0}(5+4) = 9, \qquad\qquad x_2^*(1) = 0$$

$$g_2(2) = \max_{x_2=0}(5+4) = 9, \qquad\qquad x_2^*(2) = 0$$

$$g_2(3) = \max_{0 \leqslant x_2 \leqslant 1}(5+4,\ 10+2) = 12, \quad x_2^*(3) = 1$$

$$g_2(4) = \max_{0 \leqslant x_2 \leqslant 1}(5+7,\ 10+4) = 14, \quad x_2^*(4) = 1$$

and so forth. The results of the complete calculation are given in Table 5.5.2. Finally, we calculate

$$g_3(20) = \max_{0 \leqslant x_3 \leqslant 3}[\phi_3(x_3)+g_2(20-2x_3^2)]$$

$$= \max(8+23,\ 12+22,\ 17+21,\ 22+9)$$

$$= \max(31,\ 34,\ 38,\ 31) = 38$$

TABLE 5.5.2

λ_2	$g_2(\lambda_2)$	$x_2^*(\lambda_2)$	λ_2	$g_2(\lambda_2)$	$x_2^*(\lambda_2)$
0	7	0	11	17	1
1	9	0	12	21	1
2	9	0	13	21	1
3	12	1	14	21	1
4	14	1	15	21	1
5	14	1	16	22	2
6	14	1	17	22	2
7	17	1	18	22	2
8	17	1	19	23	1
9	17	1	20	23	1
10	17	1			

and $x_3^* = 2$. Then $\lambda_2 = 20-8 = 12$ and $x_2^*(12) = 1$. $\lambda_1 = 12-3 = 9$ and $x_1^*(9) = 3$. Therefore the optimal solution to (5.5.5) is $x_1^* = 3$, $x_2^* = 1$, $x_3^* = 2$ and $z^* = 38$.

5.6. Computation with Continuous Variables

We have already noted that problems with continuous variables, whose subproblems cannot be optimized analytically, are more difficult to solve than problems with integer variables. Let us see why that is so.

Consider the problem

$$\max \quad z = \sum_{j=1}^{n} \phi_j(x_j)$$

subject to

$$\sum_{j=1}^{n} a_j x_j \leqslant b, \qquad a_j > 0 \qquad\qquad (5.6.1)$$

$$x_j \geqslant 0$$

It is apparent that (5.6.1) is identical to (5.2.1) except that the variables are no longer restricted to be integers. The derivation of the recurrence equations, except for the upper bound restriction on the x_j, is exactly as it was for the problem given by (5.2.1). The state transformation functions are

$$\lambda_s = \lambda_{s+1} - a_{s+1} x_{s+1} \qquad (s = 1, 2, \ldots, n-1) \tag{5.6.2}$$

and the recurrence relations are

$$g_1(\lambda_1) = \max_{0 \leq x_1 \leq (\lambda_1/a_1)} \phi_1(x_1)$$

$$g_s(\lambda_s) = \max_{0 \leq x_s \leq (\lambda_s/a_s)} [\phi_s(x_s) + g_{s-1}(\lambda_s - a_s x_s)] \qquad (s = 2, 3, \ldots, n) \tag{5.6.3}$$

There are significant differences between how we use (5.6.3) and how we used (5.2.7) when the x_j were restricted to take on integral values. First of all we need to consider for how many values of λ_s in the range $[0, b]$ we must evaluate $g_s(\lambda_s)$. Having established a grid of points for λ_s, we then may consider how to determine $g_s(\lambda_s)$ for a particular value of λ_s, say $\bar{\lambda}_s$. We have

$$g_s(\bar{\lambda}_s) = \max_{0 \leq x_s \leq (\bar{\lambda}_s/a_s)} G_s[\bar{\lambda}_s, x_s(\bar{\lambda}_s)] \tag{5.6.4}$$

where

$$G_s[\bar{\lambda}_s, x_s(\bar{\lambda}_s)] = \phi_s(x_s) + g_{s-1}(\bar{\lambda}_s - a_s x_s) \tag{5.6.5}$$

We assume in using (5.6.4) and (5.6.5) that the optimal return function $g_{s-1}(\lambda_{s-1})$ is known. Then $G_s[\bar{\lambda}_s, x_s(\bar{\lambda}_s)]$ is defined over all values in the range $0 \leq x_s \leq (\bar{\lambda}_s/a_s)$. We need to determine the value of x_s in this range at which G_s attains its maximum value. In order to do this we would divide the interval $[0, (\bar{\lambda}_s/a_s)]$ into a discrete set of points and evaluate the function G_s at each of the discrete set of values between 0 and $\bar{\lambda}_s/a_s$. Typically, one would impose a relatively coarse spacing on the points chosen such that

$$x_{sl} = x_{s, l-1} + \Delta x_s \qquad l = 1, 2, \ldots, \frac{\bar{\lambda}_s}{a_s \Delta x_s} \tag{5.6.6}$$

assuming that $\bar{\lambda}_s/(a_s \Delta x_s)$ is an integer. Such a set of points is shown in Fig. 5.6.1. At each of these points $G_s(\bar{\lambda}_s, x_{sl})$ is evaluated and an approximate maximum is obtained from

$$g_s(\bar{\lambda}_s) \approx \max_l G_s(\bar{\lambda}_s, x_{sl}) \tag{5.6.7}$$

Then a finer grid might be tried, say $\Delta x_s/2$, and the entire procedure can be repeated. If the new value(s) of $G_{s, \max}$ is close to the previous value(s), we would stop. Otherwise, a finer grid of points would be used again. Alternatively, one might use the finer grid of points only in the neighborhood of $x_s = A$ and $x_s = B$, in Fig. 5.6.1, since these are the locations of approximate local maxima.

It is clear that the general procedure we have discussed for finding the maximum value of $G_s(\bar{\lambda}_s, x_s)$ and the value of x_s^* at which it occurs is not "exact" in the sense of always finding the true maximum. However, too much can be made of this theoretical short-

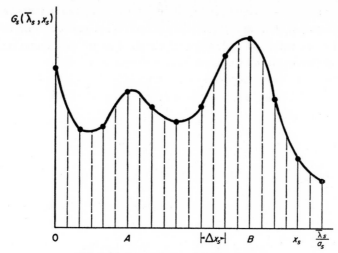

FIG. 5.6.1. Dependence of $G_s(\bar{\lambda}_s, x_s)$ on x_s.

coming. If one uses a sufficiently fine grid of points one can ascertain the maximal value of G_s to any arbitrary accuracy. Since, in any case, the value of a continuous function of a continuous variable must be expressed in terms of decimal approximations, it is not clear that, except in a theoretical sense, one is severely handicapped by using a search method to maximize G_s. The total amount of computation required is great for extreme accuracy but using a computer can and does alleviate this problem. We shall consider the matter of the determination of the maximum G_s for convex or concave functions ϕ_j in the next section. For these cases, the determination of $G_{s,\,max}$ is much simpler than the procedure given above.

There are additional problems that we will encounter in solving (5.6.4). We have assumed that $g_{s-1}(\lambda_{s-1})$ was available to us in trying to calculate the maximum value of $G_s(\bar{\lambda}_s, x_s)$. This may not be true. We can see this as follows. Suppose $g_{s-1}(\lambda_{s-1})$ was tabulated for values $\lambda_{s-1} = 0, \Delta_{s-1}, 2\Delta_{s-1}, \ldots, b$. Now suppose we wish to calculate $g_s(\bar{\lambda}_s)$. Then we need to know $g_{s-1}(\bar{\lambda}_s - a_s x_s)$. Suppose, as an example, $x_s = \bar{x}_s$. Then we need to have available to us $g_{s-1}(\bar{\lambda}_s - a_s \bar{x}_s)$. This implies that $\bar{\lambda}_s - a_s \bar{x}_s$ equals some value of λ_{s-1} in the tabulation of g_{s-1}. This can very easily fail to be the case. For example, if g_{s-1} was tabulated for $\lambda_{s-1} = 0, .2, .4, \ldots, 5$ and $\bar{\lambda}_s = 4, a_s = 3, \bar{x}_s = 1$. Then we need to know $g_{s-1}(\lambda_{s-1})$ for $\lambda_{s-1} = 4 - 3(.1) = 3.7$. However, while we know g_{s-1} for $\bar{\lambda}_{s-1} = 3.6$ and 3.8, we will not have a value tabulated for $\bar{\lambda}_{s-1} = 3.7$. It can readily be seen that this situation will be quite common. The only recourse we have is to make use of some interpolation procedure. We can use interpolation providing that the $g_s(\lambda_s)$ are continuous functions. It is a straightforward matter to show that if the $\phi_j(x_j)$ are continuous functions of x_j, then the $g_s(\lambda_s)$ will also be continuous functions of λ_s.

There is one further complication that may arise. Even if the $g_s(\lambda_s)$ are continuous, the $x_s^*(\lambda_s)$ need not be continuous, as Bellman [3] has shown. Since we may be forced to interpolate between values of λ_s to determine $g_s(\lambda_s)$, we shall have a problem if, say $x_s^*(\lambda_s) \neq x_s^*(\lambda_s + \Delta_s)$. We cannot interpolate to determine $x_s^*[\bar{\lambda}_s + (\Delta_s/2)]$ under these conditions.

There is a way to avoid having to interpolate for x_s^* but there is a penalty of increased storage and computation time attached to its use. What can be done is to compute $x_s^*(\lambda_s)$ directly for the values of λ_s that are required. If we do this, then we do not tabulate $x_s^*(\lambda_s)$ in the tables of $g_s(\lambda_s)$. However, we must store the $g_s(\lambda_s)$ tables for all s. We can see this as follows. Suppose we calculate a complete set of tables $g_s(\lambda_s)$, $s = 1, 2 \ldots, n$. At the last stage we calculate $g_n(b)$ and in so doing we also determine $x_n^*(b)$. Then we have that

$$\lambda_{n-1} = \lambda_n - a_n x_n = b - a_n x_n^*(b) \tag{5.6.8}$$

then we compute $g_{n-1}(\lambda_{n-1})$ where λ_{n-1} is given by (5.6.8), i.e.,

$$g_{n-1}(b - a_n x_n^*) = \max_{0 \leqslant x_{n-1} \leqslant ((b - a_n x_n^*)/(a_{n-1}))} [\phi_{n-1}(x_{n-1}) + g_{n-2}(b - a_n x_n^* - a_{n-1} x_{n-1})] \tag{5.6.9}$$

In carrying out the maximization in (5.6.9) we shall also find the value of x_{n-1}^* that led to the maximum value. We can continue this process to find $x_{n-2}^*, x_{n-3}^*, \ldots, x_1^*$. By performing these calculations we can avoid the problem posed by the discontinuous nature of $x_s^*(\lambda_s)$.

5.7. Convex and Concave $\phi_j(x_j)$

Let us now reconsider (5.6.1) but under the assumption that the $\phi_j(x_j)$ are either convex or concave, in addition to being continuous functions. We shall see that the computational process for solving (5.6.1) under these conditions is considerably simpler. Since convex and concave functions arise frequently in applications, these cases are considered in more detail. Consider first the case where the $\phi_j(x_j)$ are convex functions. In [3] Bellman has shown that if the $\phi_j(x_j)$ are convex functions then $g_s(\lambda_s)$ are also convex functions of x_s. When the $g_s(\lambda_s)$ are convex then the task of finding the maximum value of $G_s(\bar{\lambda}_s, x_s)$ is quite simple. For fixed $\bar{\lambda}_s$, G_s is convex in x_s. Then by Proposition 1.4.3, the maximum value of $G_s(\bar{\lambda}_s, x_s)$ is taken on at either or both of the extreme points of the closed convex set $0 \leqslant x_s \leqslant (\bar{\lambda}_s/a_s)$. Therefore we have that

$$g_s(\bar{\lambda}_s) = G_s(\bar{\lambda}_s, 0) \quad \text{or} \quad G_s\left(\bar{\lambda}_s, \frac{\bar{\lambda}_s}{a_s}\right) \tag{5.7.1}$$

From (5.7.1) we see that we need no search method at all if the $\phi_j(x_j)$ are convex functions. We need only compare $G_s(\bar{\lambda}_s, x_s)$ at two values of x_s and choose the largest of the corresponding values of G_s.

When the $\phi_j(x_j)$ are concave functions we shall see that we still require that a search method be used. However, in contrast to the case when nothing can be said about the nature of the $\phi_j(x_j)$, for concave functions the search method is more efficient and we can be certain about finding an approximate global optimum in the search process.

If the $\phi_j(x_j)$ are concave functions then one can show that the optimal return functions $g_s(\lambda_s)$ is a concave function of x_s for a fixed value $\bar{\lambda}_s$. Therefore, we know that in maximizing $G_s(\bar{\lambda}_s, x_s)$ any local maximum will also be a global maximum (Proposition 1.4.2).

We know further that we must perform a one-dimensional maximization of a continuous concave function, i.e.,

$$g_s(\bar{\lambda}_s) = \max_{0 \leqslant x_s \leqslant (\lambda_s/a_s)} G_s(\bar{\lambda}_s, x_s) \tag{5.7.2}$$

where $G_s(\bar{\lambda}_s, x_s)$ is a concave function of x_s.

There are a great many methods available for dealing with solving (5.7.2), and a discussion of their properties is outside the scope of this book. However, mention of one of the simplest is in order. If we can assume that G_s is a differentiable function of x_s, then one can consider fitting a quadratic function to $G_s(x_s)$ from a Taylor's series expansion. For simplicity in notation we shall consider minimizing $F(x)$.[†] We can approximate $F(x)$ by

$$Q(x) = F(x_k) + F'(x_k)(x - x_k) + \frac{F'(x_k) - F'(x_{k-1})}{x_k - x_{k-1}} \frac{(x - x_k)^2}{2} \tag{5.7.3}$$

where $F' \equiv dF/dx$. We can then estimate x_{k+1} by finding the point where the derivative of Q is zero. This gives us

$$\frac{dQ}{dx} = F'(x_k) + \frac{F'(x_k) - F'(x_{k-1})}{x_k - x_{k-1}}(x - x_k) = 0 \tag{5.7.4}$$

Solving (5.7.4) for $x = x_{k+1}$ gives us

$$x_{k+1} = x_k - F'(x_k) \left[\frac{x_k - x_{k-1}}{F'(x_k) - F'(x_{k-1})} \right] \tag{5.7.5}$$

Figure 5.7.1 depicts this approximation method which is usually called the method of false position *(regula falsi)*.

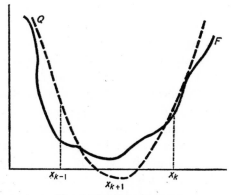

FIG. 5.7.1. False position.

If one always chooses x_{k-1} and x_k so that $F'(x_k)$ and $F'(x_{k-1})$ have opposite signs, then this method for finding the optimal value of x can be shown to be globally convergent

[†] Instead of maximizing $G(x)$ we shall minimize $F(x) = -G(x)$.

and the order of the convergence is ~ 1.6. It should be noted that the usual context in which the method of false position is presented is that of finding a root of $f(x) = 0$. If $f = dQ/dx$, then we see that is precisely what we are doing.

5.8. Equipment Replacement Problems

In this section we shall discuss an equipment replacement model to further illustrate the nature of computational solutions when the original problem data are more conveniently expressed in terms of functions which are given as tables. A simple version of an equipment replacement problem was given in Section 2.5. We shall now consider a more elaborate and more realistic version of such problems.

The necessity to replace obsolete or obsolescent equipment, machines, automobiles, etc., is commonly observed in many areas of our heavily industrialized society. For example, as a digital computer ages its performance compared with more recent models can no longer accommodate the increased demands being made on it. Even though a large outlay of capital will have to be made for a new computer, and there will be costs attendant to interruptions because of installation of the computer as well as conversion of computer programs, a time inevitably comes when these costs are more than balanced by a decrease in operating costs (e.g., maintenance and utilities) and a substantial increase in productivity. There are many other kinds of machines and equipment which have similar characteristics.

The approach we shall take is to determine optimal replacement policies, given certain basic data on costs of replacement, operating costs, and the income or revenue derived from operating the machine. Each of these costs is assumed to vary with time. In general the yearly income $I(t)$ is, as indicated, a function of t, the age of the machine. $I(t)$ is clearly a decreasing function of t. The yearly operating costs $O(t)$ are an increasing function of t since older machines require more maintenance, consume more power or supplies, etc. Finally, the cost of replacing a machine $C(t)$ is an increasing cost of t because we assume that the older the machine to be replaced is, the less is its salvage value. Hence the net cost of replacement increases as a function of t.

One further aspect of the model we consider, which is based on the work of Bellman and Dreyfus [4], is that we allow for technological change. In other words, the income we can expect $I(t)$, the operating cost $O(t)$, and replacement cost $C(t)$ are all themselves functions of t. What this means, e.g., is that the income we can expect from a machine made in year t is generally less than the income we can expect from a machine made in year $t+k$, where $k > 0$. Therefore, our data for the problem will give $I(t)$, $O(t)$, and $C(t)$ for machines that were made in all possible years of the planning period.

We shall also assume that all future incomes are discounted. This means that a unit of income one period hence is considered to be worth α units in the current period. We shall suppose that the decision x_j to keep (K) or replace (R) a machine is made only at times $t = 0, 1, 2, \ldots$.

Let us now define the notation we shall use:

$I_j(t)$ = income in period j from a machine that was made in year $j-t$ and is t years old at the start of period j.

$O_j(*)$ = operating cost in period j for a machine made in year $j-t$ and is t years old at the start of period j.

$C_j(t)$ = replacement cost for a machine made in year $j-t$ and is t years old at the start of period j.

α = discount factor $(0 \leqslant \alpha \leqslant 1)$.

T = age of the incumbent machine at the beginning of the first period.

N = total number of periods of plan.

$g_j(t)$ = optimal return for periods j, $j+1$, $\ldots$, N when the jth period is started with a machine that is t years old.

$x_j(t)$ = decision (K or R) at the beginning of period j that will yield $g_j(t)$.

In order to derive the optimal decision rule, we observe the following. If a new machine is purchased at the beginning of period j, the total return from periods j, $j+1$, $\ldots$, N would be the income from a new machine in period j minus the operating expense of the new machine in period j minus the cost of replacing a machine that is t years old at the beginning of period j plus the *optimal* return from periods $j+1$, $j+2$, $\ldots$, N starting with a machine that is one year old discounted to the beginning of period j. Similarly, if a machine that is t years old is kept (not replaced) during the jth period, the total return from periods j, $j+1$, $\ldots$, N would be the income from a machine that is t years old in period j minus the operating expense of the machine that is t years old in period j plus the *optimal* return from periods $j+1$, $j+2$, $\ldots$, N starting with a machine that is $t+1$ years old and discounted to the beginning of period j.

A transliteration of the preceding paragraph, with the addition of choosing whichever total return is greater, gives us a set of recurrence relations which solve the problem of maximizing total return over a total time of N periods. These recurrence relations are

$$g_j(t) = \max \begin{bmatrix} (R): & I_j(0) - O_j(0) - C_j(t) + \alpha g_{j+1}(1) \\ (K): & I_j(t) - O_j(t) + \alpha g_{j+1}(t+1) \end{bmatrix} \tag{5.8.1}$$

$$(j = 1, 2, \ldots, N; \quad t = 1, 2, \ldots, j-1, j+T-1)$$

We also require the relationship that

$$g_{N+1}(t) = 0 \qquad (j = 1, 2, \ldots, N) \tag{5.8.2}$$

as well as the fact that for $g_1(\cdot)$, the only allowable value of t is T since when we enter the planning process we must have a machine of age T.

In order to exhibit the use of these relationships, let us suppose we wish to decide in each of the next five years including this year whether to keep or replace a machine which is currently two years old. We also assume that $\alpha = 1$. We have the following data available to us.

Machine made in year 1

Age	0	1	2	3	4
Income	20	19	18	16	14
Operating cost	4	4	6	6	8
Replacement cost	25	27	30	32	35

8

Machine made in year 2

Age	0	1	2	3
Income	25	23	22	20
Operating cost	3	4	6	7
Replacement cost	27	29	32	34

Machine made in year 3

Age	0	1	2
Income	27	24	22
Operating cost	3	3	4
Replacement cost	29	30	31

Machine made in year 4

Age	0	1
Income	28	26
Operating cost	2	3
Replacement cost	30	31

Machine made in year 5

Age	0
Income	30
Operating cost	2
Replacement cost	32

Incumbent machine [year (−1)]

Age	2	3	4	5	6
Income	16	14	14	12	12
Operating cost	6	6	7	7	8
Replacement cost	30	32	34	34	36

The way the calculation proceeds is to begin with the fifth year. We can reach the fifth year with a machine that is 1, 2, 3, 4, or 6 years old. We therefore have

$$g_5(t) = \max \begin{bmatrix} (R): & I_5(0) - O_5(0) - C_5(t) + 1 \cdot g_6(1) \\ (K): & I_5(t) - O_5(t) + 1 \cdot g_6(t+1) \end{bmatrix}$$

$$g_5(1) = \max \begin{bmatrix} (R): & 30 - 2 - 31 + 0 = -3 \\ (K): & 26 - 3 + 0 = 23 \end{bmatrix} = 23$$

$$x_5(1) = K$$

$$g_5(2) = \max \begin{bmatrix} (R): & 30 - 2 - 31 + 0 = -3 \\ (K): & 22 - 4 + 0 = 18 \end{bmatrix} = 18$$

$$x_5(2) = K$$

$$g_5(3) = \max \begin{bmatrix} (R): & 30-2-34+0 = -6 \\ (K): & 20-7+0 = 13 \end{bmatrix} = 13$$

$$x_5(3) = K$$

$$g_5(4) = \max \begin{bmatrix} (R): & 30-2-35+0 = -7 \\ (K): & 14-8+0 = 6 \end{bmatrix} = 6$$

$$x_5(4) = K$$

$$g_5(6) = \max \begin{bmatrix} (R): & 30-2-36+0 = -8 \\ (K): & 12-8+0 = 4 \end{bmatrix} = 4$$

$$x_5(6) = K$$

We can begin the fourth year with a machine that is 1, 2, 3, or 5 years old. We then have for our recurrence relationship:

$$g_4(t) = \max \begin{bmatrix} (R): & I_4(0)-O_4(0)-C_4(t)+1 \cdot g_5(1) \\ (K): & I_4(t)-O_4(t)+1 \cdot g_5(t+1) \end{bmatrix}$$

We then have for the allowable values of t:

$$g_4(1) = \max \begin{bmatrix} (R): & 28-2-30+23 = 19 \\ (K): & 24-3+18 = 39 \end{bmatrix} = 39$$

$$x_4(1) = K$$

$$g_4(2) = \max \begin{bmatrix} (R): & 28-2-32+23 = 17 \\ (K): & 22-6+13 = 29 \end{bmatrix} = 29$$

$$x_4(2) = K$$

$$g_4(3) = \max \begin{bmatrix} (R): & 28-2-32+23 = 17 \\ (K): & 16-6+6 = 16 \end{bmatrix} = 17$$

$$x_4(3) = R$$

$$g_4(5) = \max \begin{bmatrix} (R): & 28-2-34+23 = 14 \\ (K): & 12-7+4 = 9 \end{bmatrix} = 14$$

$$x_4(5) = R$$

In the third year we can start with a machine that is 1, 2, or 4 years old. We then have:

$$g_3(t) = \max \begin{bmatrix} (R): & I_3(0)-O_3(0)-C_3(t)+1 \cdot g_4(1) \\ (K): & I_3(t)-O_3(t)+1 \cdot g_4(t+1) \end{bmatrix}$$

$$g_3(1) = \max \begin{bmatrix} (R): & 27-3-29+39 = 34 \\ (K): & 23-4+29 = 48 \end{bmatrix} = 48$$

$$x_3(1) = K$$

$$g_3(2) = \max \begin{bmatrix} (R): & 27-3-30+39 = 33 \\ (K): & 18-6+17 = 29 \end{bmatrix} = 33$$

$$x_3(2) = R$$

$$g_3(4) = \max \begin{bmatrix} (R): & 27-3-34+39 = 29 \\ (K): & 14-7+14 = 21 \end{bmatrix} = 29$$

$$x_3(4) = R$$

8*

For the second year we have $t = 1, 3$.

$$g_2(t) = \max \begin{bmatrix} (R): & I_2(0)-O_2(0)-C_2(t)+1\cdot g_3(1) \\ (K): & I_2(t)-O_2(t)+1\cdot g_3(t+1) \end{bmatrix}$$

$$g_2(1) = \max \begin{bmatrix} (R): & 25-3-27+48 = 43 \\ (K): & 19-4+33 = 48 \end{bmatrix} = 48$$

$$x_2(1) = K$$

$$g_2(3) = \max \begin{bmatrix} (R): & 25-3-32+48 = 38 \\ (K): & 14-6+29 = 37 \end{bmatrix} = 38$$

$$x_2(3) = R$$

In year 1 we have a two-year-old machine and we calculate

$$g_1(t) = \max \begin{bmatrix} (R): & I_1(0)-O_1(0)-C_1(t)+g_2(1) \\ (K): & I_1(t)-O_1(t)+g_2(t+1) \end{bmatrix}$$

$$g_1(2) = \max \begin{bmatrix} (R): & 20-4-30+48 = 34 \\ (K): & 16-6+38 = 48 \end{bmatrix} = 48$$

$$x_1(2) = K$$

We now summarize our results in Table 5.8.1.

TABLE 5.8.1. Optimal policy for years 1–5

Age of incumbent machine	$g_5(t)$	$x_5(t)$	$g_4(t)$	$x_4(t)$	$g_3(t)$	$x_3(t)$	$g_2(t)$	$x_2(t)$	$g_1(t)$	$x_1(t)$
1	23	K	39	K	48	K	48	K		
2	18	K	29	K	33	R			48	K
3	13	K	17	R			38	R		
4	6	K			29	R				
5			14	R						
6	4	K								

We know that we wish to enter the first year with a machine that is two years old. Hence the optimal policy is to keep the machine since $x_1(2) = K$. Therefore we enter the second year with a machine that is three years old. We see that $x_2(3) = R$. Therefore we purchase a new machine and we then proceed to the third year with a machine that is one year old. We see that the optimal policy is $x_3(1) = K$. We then enter the fourth year with a two-year-old machine and the optimal policy is $x_4(2) = K$. So we keep the machine. We enter the fifth year with a three-year-old machine and the optimal policy $x_5(3) = K$ and we again keep the machine.

We can now express the optimal policy and the optimal return. The optimal return is $g_1(2) = 48$ units. The optimal policy is shown in Table 5.8.2.

TABLE 5.8.2

Year	Age of machine	Optimal policy
1	2	K
2	3	R
3	1	K
4	2	K
5	3	K

It is worth noting that even very large problems can be very rapidly solved without extensive computations. In fact, more complicated and realistic conditions may be assumed and solved with very little more effort.

5.9. Some Integer Constrained Problems

We shall return to a consideration of some problems where the variables are constrained to be integers in one or more unusual ways in order to illustrate the versatility of the tabular approach to solving problems via dynamic programming.

Consider the following problem:

$$\max \quad z = \sum_{j=1}^{n} \phi_j(x_j)$$

subject to
$$\sum_{j=1}^{n} x_j \leqslant b \tag{5.9.1}$$

$$x_j = 0 \quad \text{or} \quad 1 \qquad (j = 1, 2, \ldots, n)$$

We define the state transformation functions as

$$\lambda_s = \lambda_{s+1} - x_{s+1} \qquad (s = 1, 2, \ldots, n-1) \tag{5.9.2}$$

from which the usual recurrence relations follow:

$$g_s(\lambda_s) = \max_{x_s = 0, 1} [\phi_s(x_s) + g_{s-1}(\lambda_s - x_s)] \tag{5.9.3}$$

Therefore

$$g_s(\lambda_s) = \max[\phi_s(0) + g_{s-1}(\lambda_s), \ \phi_s(1) + g_{s-1}(\lambda_s - 1)] \tag{5.9.4}$$

Equation (5.9.4) is valid only for $s > 1$, $\lambda_s > 0$. It is clear that

$$g_1(\lambda_1) = \max[\phi_1(0), \ \phi_1(1)], \quad \lambda_1 \geqslant 1 \tag{5.9.5}$$

and

$$g_s(0) = \sum_{j=1}^{s} \phi_j(0) \qquad (s = 1, 2, \ldots, n) \tag{5.9.6}$$

Even though other methods exist for solving this problem we shall employ dynamic programming. The solution method will form a foundation for certain complications of this basic problem which we shall consider subsequently.

Consider the following numerical example. We are given a set of functions $\phi_j(x_j)$ $j = 1, 2, \ldots, 6$ as in Table 5.9.1. We let $b = 3$.

TABLE 5.9.1. The functions $\phi_j(x_j)$

x_j	$\phi_1(x_1)$	$\phi_2(x_2)$	$\phi_3(x_3)$	$\phi_4(x_4)$	$\phi_5(x_5)$	$\phi_6(x_6)$
0	15	30	30	10	25	10
1	20	20	40	40	20	15

First we compute $g_1(\lambda_1)$. We have

$$g_1(0) = \phi_1(0) = 15, \quad x_1^*(0) = 0$$
$$g_1(1) = \max[\phi_1(0), \ \phi_1(1)] = \max(15, 20) = 20, \quad x_1^*(1) = 1$$
$$g_1(2) = g_1(3) = \max[\phi_1(0), \ \phi_1(1)] = 20, \quad x_1^*(2) = x_1^*(3) = 1$$

We then compute $g_2(\lambda_2)$ as follows:

$$g_2(0) = \phi_1(0) + \phi_2(0) = 15 + 30 = 45, \quad x_2^*(0) = 0$$
$$g_2(1) = \max[\phi_2(0) + g_1(1), \ \phi_2(1) + g_1(0)]$$
$$= \max(30 + 20, \ 20 + 15) = 50, \quad x_2^*(1) = 0$$
$$g_2(2) = \max[\phi_2(0) + g_1(2), \ \varphi_2(1) + g_1(1)]$$
$$= \max(30 + 20, \ 20 + 20) = 50, \quad x_2^*(2) = 0$$
$$g_2(3) = \max[\phi_2(0) + g_1(3), \ \phi_2(1) + g_1(2)]$$
$$= \max(30 + 20, \ 20 + 20) = 50, \quad x_2^*(3) = 0$$

Similarly, we have:

$$g_3(0) = \sum_{j=1}^{3} \phi_j(0) = 75, \quad x_3^*(0) = 0$$

$$g_3(1) = \max(30 + 50, \ 40 + 45) = 85, \quad x_3^*(1) = 1$$
$$g_3(2) = \max(30 + 50, \ 40 + 50) = 90, \quad x_3^*(2) = 1$$
$$g_3(3) = \max(30 + 50, \ 40 + 50) = 90, \quad x_3^*(3) = 1$$
$$g_4(0) = 85, \quad x_4^*(0) = 0$$
$$g_4(1) = \max(10 + 85, \ 40 + 75) = 115, \quad x_4^*(1) = 1$$
$$g_4(2) = \max(10 + 90, \ 40 + 85) = 125, \quad x_4^*(2) = 1$$
$$g_4(3) = \max(10 + 90, \ 40 + 90) = 130, \quad x_4^*(3) = 1$$
$$g_5(0) = 110, \quad x_5^*(0) = 0$$
$$g_5(1) = \max(25 + 115, \ 20 + 85) = 140, \quad x_5^*(1) = 0$$

$$g_5(2) = \max(25+125,\ 20+115) = 150, \quad x_5^*(2) = 0$$
$$g_5(3) = \max(25+130,\ 20+125) = 155, \quad x_5^*(3) = 0$$
$$g_6(0) = 120, \quad x_6^*(0) = 0$$
$$g_6(1) = \max(10+140,\ 15+110) = 150, \quad x_6^*(1) = 0$$
$$g_6(2) = \max(10+150,\ 15+140) = 160, \quad x_6^*(2) = 0$$
$$g_6(3) = \max(10+155,\ 15+150) = 165, \quad x_6^*(3) = 0,1$$

The calculations are summarized in Table 5.9.2.

TABLE 5.9.2. Summary of optimal returns

λ_j	$g_1(\lambda_1)$	$x_1^*(\lambda_1)$	$g_2(\lambda_2)$	$x_2^*(\lambda_2)$	$g_3(\lambda_3)$	$x_3^*(\lambda_3)$	$g_4(\lambda_4)$	$x_4^*(\lambda_4)$	$g_5(\lambda_5)$	$x_5^*(\lambda_5)$	$g_6(\lambda_6)$	$x_6^*(\lambda_6)$
0	15	0	45	0	75	0	85	0	110	0	120	0
1	20	1	50	0	85	1	115	1	140	0	150	0
2	20	1	50	0	90	1	125	1	150	0	160	0
3	20	1	50	0	90	1	130	1	155	0	165	0,1

We see that the solution we are interested in is $g_6(3)$. We really did not need the rest of the g_6 table. We see that since both $x_6 = 0$ and $x_6 = 1$ yielded the same value, $g_6(3) = 165$, there are two alternate optimal solutions, which are easily traced in Table 5.9.2. Hence we have the two optimal solutions

$$\left\{ \begin{array}{l} x_1, x_3, x_4 = 1, \\ x_2, x_5, x_6 = 0, \end{array} \right\}, \quad \left\{ \begin{array}{l} x_3, x_4, x_6 = 1 \\ x_1, x_2, x_5 = 0 \end{array} \right\}$$

both of which yield a maximum value of 165.

Let us now complicate (5.9.1) as follows. We now wish to solve

$$\max \quad z = \sum_{j=1}^{n} \phi_j(x_j)$$

subject to

$$\sum_{j=1}^{n} x_j \leqslant b \tag{5.9.7}$$

$$x_j = 0, 1 \quad (j = 1, 2, \ldots, n) \tag{5.9.8}$$

$$x_j x_{j+1} = 0 \quad (j = 1, 2, \ldots, n-1) \tag{5.9.9}$$

The $n-1$ constraints, $x_j x_{j+1} = 0$, would seem at first glance to hopelessly complicate matters. However, by formulating the state variables carefully, we can solve (5.9.7) by two sequences of single-state variable problems. The formulation of this as well as the previous problem is due to Bellman [18].

As in the previous problem, if we ignored the constraints $x_j x_{j+1} = 0$, the state transformation would be

$$\lambda_s = \lambda_{s+1} - x_{s+1} \quad (s = 1, 2, \ldots, n-1) \tag{5.9.10}$$

However, we do have the constraints. Let us then add a *label*,[†] which we shall call μ, to each optimal return function. This means that instead of $g_s(\lambda_s)$ we shall have $g_s(\lambda_s, \mu)$. μ will be 0 or 1 and will tell us whether x_{s+1} was 0 or 1. In other words we will define

$$g_s(\lambda_s, \mu) = \max_{R_s} \sum_{j=1}^{s} \phi_s(x_s) \qquad (s = 1, 2, \ldots, n) \qquad (5.9.11)$$

where the region R_s is given by

$$\sum_{j=1}^{s} x_j \leq \lambda_s$$

$$x_j = 0, 1 \qquad (j = 1, 2, \ldots, s) \qquad (5.9.12)$$

$$x_j x_{j+1} = 0 \qquad (j = 1, 2, \ldots, s-1)$$

$$x_s \mu = 0 \qquad (\mu = 0, 1)$$

Let us now derive recurrence relations from (5.9.10), (5.9.11), and (5.9.12).
Consider the case of $s = 1$. We have that

$$g_1(\lambda_1, \mu) = \max_{R_1} \phi_1(x_1) \quad \text{and} \quad \lambda_s > 0$$

where R_1 is

$$x_1 \leq \lambda_1, \quad x_1 = 0, 1, \quad x_1 \mu = 0 \qquad (5.9.13)$$

If $\mu = x_2$ is 0, then

$$g_1(\lambda_1, 0) = \max[\phi_1(0), \ \phi_1(1)]$$

since if $\mu = 0$, x_1 can be either 0 or 1. However, if $\mu = x_2$ is 1, then

$$g_1(\lambda_1, 1) = \phi_1(0)$$

because x_1 must be zero. Summarizing then, we see that

$$\begin{aligned} g_1(\lambda_1, 0) &= \max[\phi_1(0), \ \phi_1(1)] \\ g_1(\lambda_1, 1) &= \phi_1(0) \end{aligned} \qquad \lambda_1 > 0 \qquad (5.9.14)$$

Let us also calculate another special case, i.e., $g_s(0)$. As in the previous problem we have

$$g_s(0, \mu) = \sum_{j=1}^{s} \phi_s(0) \qquad (5.9.15)$$

irrespective of the value of μ.

We can now state the general recurrence relationship, keeping in mind the function of the label μ. If the constraint $x_j x_{j+1} = 0$ was *not* present, the recurrence relation would be

$$g_s(\lambda_s) = \max_{x_s]} [\phi_s(x_s) + g_{s-1}(\lambda_s - x_s)]$$

[†] One could argue that μ is really a second state variable. If so, it is a rather special case of one. General multidimensional problems are treated in the next chapter.

However, we now have $g_s(\lambda_s, \mu)$ and μ is a label which determines whether or not a particular x_s can be zero or one, depending on what x_{s+1} is. Therefore, if we designate $\mu = x_s$ in $g_{s-1}(\lambda_s - x_s, \mu)$ our goal will be accomplished. We then have

$$g_s(\lambda_s, \mu) = \max_{x_s} [\phi_s(x_s) + g_{s-1}(\lambda_s - x_s, x_s)] \qquad (5.9.16)$$

where x_s is subject to

$$x_s = 0, 1, \quad x_s \leqslant \lambda_s, \quad x_s \mu = 0 \qquad (5.9.17)$$

In order to use (5.9.15), (5.9.14), (5.9.16), and (5.9.17) to solve the original problem, what we do is to compute two sequences

$$g_s(\lambda_s, 0) \quad \text{and} \quad g_s(\lambda_s, 1) \qquad (s = 1, 2, \ldots, n)$$

It is easy to see that (5.9.16) can be rewritten as

$$g_s(\lambda_s, 0) = \max[\phi_s(0) + g_{s-1}(\lambda_s, 0), \ \phi_s(1) + g_{s-1}(\lambda_s - 1, 1)] \quad (s > 1; \ \lambda_s > 0)$$
$$g_s(\lambda_s, 1) = \phi_s(0) + g_{s-1}(\lambda_s, 0) \qquad\qquad (5.9.18)$$

Hence we can use (5.9.15), (5.9.14), and (5.9.18) to compute the two sequences $g_s(\lambda_s, 0)$, $g_s(\lambda_s, 1)$ for $s = 1, 2, \ldots, n$.

Let us now solve (5.9.7) using the data in Table 5.9.1. From (5.9.15) we have

$$g_1(0, 0) = \phi_1(0) = 15, \quad x_1^*(0) = 0$$
$$g_1(0, 1) = \phi_1(0) = 15, \quad x_1^*(0) = 0$$

From (5.9.14) we have

$$g_1(\lambda_1, 0) = \max[\phi_1(0), \ \phi_1(1)]$$

Therefore

$$g_1(\lambda_1, 0) = \max(15, 20) = 20$$

for

$$\lambda_1 = 1, 2, 3 \quad \text{and} \quad x_1^*(\lambda_1) = 1 \quad \text{for} \quad \lambda_1 = 1, 2, 3.$$

Also $g_1(\lambda_1, 1) = \phi_1(0) = 15$ and $x_1^*(\lambda_1) = 0$ for $\lambda_1 = 1, 2, 3$. The results are summarized in Table 5.9.3.

TABLE 5.9.3. $g_1(\lambda_1, \mu)$

λ_1	$g_1(\lambda_1, 0)$	$x_1^*(\lambda_1)$	$g_1(\lambda_1, 1)$	$x_1^*(\lambda_1)$
0	15	0	15	0
1	20	1	15	0
2	20	1	15	0
3	20	1	15	0

Next we calculate $g_2(\lambda_2, 0)$ and $g_2(\lambda_2, 1)$. We have

$$g_2(0, 0) = g_2(0, 1) = 15 + 30 = 45$$

and $x_2^*(0) = 0$ for both. Next we compute

$$g_2(\lambda_2, 0) = \max[\phi_2(0) + g_1(\lambda_2, 0), \quad \phi_2(1) + g_1(\lambda_2 - 1, 1)]$$

Therefore

$$g_2(1, 0) = \max(30 + 20, 20 + 15) = 50, \quad x_2^*(1) = 0$$
$$g_2(2, 0) = \max(30 + 20, 20 + 15) = 50, \quad x_2^*(2) = 0$$
$$g_2(3, 0) = \max(30 + 20, 20 + 15) = 50, \quad x_2^*(3) = 0$$

For $g_2(\lambda_2, 1)$ we have

$$g_2(\lambda_2, 1) = \phi_2(0) + g_1(\lambda_2, 0)$$

Then

$$g_2(1, 1) = 30 + 20 = 50, \quad x_2^*(1) = 0$$
$$g_2(2, 1) = 30 + 20 = 50, \quad x_2^*(2) = 0$$
$$g_2(3, 1) = 30 + 20 = 50, \quad x_2^*(3) = 0$$

These results are summarized in Table 5.9.4.

TABLE 5.9.4. $g_2(\lambda_2, \mu)$

λ_2	$g_2(\lambda_2, 0)$	$x_2^*(\lambda_2)$	$g_2(\lambda_2, 1)$	$x_2^*(\lambda_2)$
0	45	0	45	0
1	50	0	50	0
2	50	0	50	0
3	50	0	50	0

The calculations for $g_3(\lambda_3, \mu)$ are

$$g_3(0, 0) = g_3(0, 1) = 15 + 30 + 30 = 75$$

and $x_3^*(0) = 0$ for both. Next we have

$$g_3(\lambda_3, 0) = \max[\phi_3(0) + g_2(\lambda_3, 0), \quad \phi_3(1) + g_2(\lambda_3 - 1, 1)]$$

Therefore

$$g_3(1, 0) = \max(30 + 50, 40 + 45) = 85, \quad x_3^*(1) = 1$$
$$g_3(2, 0) = \max(30 + 50, 40 + 50) = 90, \quad x_3^*(2) = 1$$
$$g_3(3, 0) = \max(30 + 50, 40 + 50) = 90, \quad x_3^*(3) = 1$$

Then we have

$$g_3(\lambda_3, 1) = \phi_3(0) + g_2(\lambda_3, 0)$$
$$g_3(1, 1) = 30 + 50 = 80, \quad x_3^*(1) = 0$$
$$g_3(2, 1) = 30 + 50 = 80, \quad x_3^*(2) = 0$$
$$g_3(3, 1) = 30 + 50 = 80, \quad x_3^*(3) = 0$$

These results are summarized in Table 5.9.5.

TABLE 5.9.5. $g_3(\lambda_3, \mu)$

λ_3	$g_3(\lambda_3, 0)$	$x_3^*(\lambda_3)$	$g_3(\lambda_3, 1)$	$x_3^*(\lambda_3)$
0	75	0	75	0
1	85	1	80	0
2	90	1	80	0
3	90	1	80	0

The calculations for $g_4(\lambda_4, \mu)$ are

$g_4(0, 0) = g_4(0, 1) = 15+30+30+10 = 85$ and $x_4^*(0) = 0$ for both

$g_4(\lambda_4, 0) = \max[\phi_4(0)+g_3(\lambda_4, 0),\ \phi_4(1)+g_3(\lambda_4-1, 1)]$

$g_4(1, 0) = \max(10+85, 40+75) = 115,\quad x_4^*(1) = 1$

$g_4(2, 0) = \max(10+90, 40+80) = 120,\quad x_4^*(2) = 1$

$g_4(3, 0) = \max(10+90, 40+80) = 120,\quad x_4^*(3) = 1$

$g_4(\lambda_4, 1) = \phi_4(0)+g_3(\lambda_4, 0)$

$g_4(1, 1) = 10+85 = \ \ 95,\quad x_4^*(1) = 0$

$g_4(2, 1) = 10+90 = 100,\quad x_4^*(2) = 0$

$g_4(3, 1) = 10+90 = 100,\quad x_4^*(3) = 0$

These results are summarized in Table 5.9.6.

TABLE 5.9.6. $g_4(\lambda_4, \mu)$

λ_4	$g_4(\lambda_4, 0)$	$x_4^*(\lambda_4)$	$g_4(\lambda_4, 1)$	$x_4^*(\lambda_4)$
0	85	0	85	0
1	115	1	95	0
2	120	1	100	0
3	120	1	100	0

The calculations for $g_5(\lambda_5, \mu)$ are:

$g_5(0, 0) = g_5(0, 1) = 15+30+30+10+25 = 110$ and $x_5^*(0) = 0$ for both

$g_5(\lambda_5, 0) = \max [\phi_5(0)+g_4(\lambda_5, 0),\ \phi_5(1)+g_4(\lambda_5-1, 1)]$

$g_5(1, 0) = \max(25+115, 20+\ \ 85) = 140,\quad x_5^*(1) = 0$

$g_5(2, 0) = \max(25+120, 20+\ \ 95) = 145,\quad x_5^*(2) = 0$

$g_5(3, 0) = \max(25+120, 20+100) = 145,\quad x_5^*(3) = 0$

$g_5(\lambda_5, 1) = \phi_5(0)+g_4(\lambda_5, 0)$

$g_5(1, 1) = 25+115 = 140,\quad x_5^*(1) = 0$

$g_5(2, 1) = 25+120 = 145,\quad x_5^*(2) = 0$

$g_5(3, 1) = 25+120 = 145,\quad x_5^*(3) = 0$

These results are summarized in Table 5.9.7.

TABLE 5.9.7. $g_5(\lambda_5, \mu)$

λ_5	$g_5(\lambda_5, 0)$	$x_5^*(\lambda_5)$	$g_5(\lambda_5, 1)$	$x_5^*(\lambda_5)$
0	110	0	110	0
1	140	0	140	0
2	145	0	145	0
3	145	0	145	0

Finally, we compute $g_6(3, 0)$ and $g_6(3, 1)$. There is no need to calculate g_6 for any value of λ_6 other than $\lambda_6 = b = 3$. We then have

$$g_6(3, 0) = \max[\phi_6(0)+g_5(3, 0), \quad \phi_6(1)+g_5(3-1, 1)]$$
$$= \max(10+145, 15+145) = 160, \quad x_6^*(3) = 1$$
$$g_6(3, 1) = \phi_6(0)+g_5(3, 0)$$
$$= 10+145 = 155, \quad x_6^*(3) = 0$$

We now trace our way back through the tables to determine the optimal solution. We see that the maximum of $g_6(3, 0)$ and $g_6(3, 1)$ is $g_6(3, 0) = 160$ with $x_6^* = 1$. Since $x_6^* = 1$, we know that x_5^* will have to be zero in order to satisfy the constraint $x_5 x_6 = 0$. We also see that

$$\lambda_5 = \lambda_6 - x_6 = 3-1 = 2$$

Therefore we enter Table 5.9.7 for $g_5(2, 0)$ and $x_5^* = 0$. Since $x_5^* = 0$, x_4^* can be either 0 or 1 since for either $x_4 x_5 = 0$. Hence we examine Table 5.9.6 for $\lambda_4 = 2$ and choose $x_4^* = 1$ which gives the larger g_4. Next we go to Table 5.9.5 with $\lambda_3 = 1$ and we know that x_3^* must be 0 in order that $x_3 x_4 = 0$. In Table 5.9.4 with $\lambda_2 = 1$ we choose $x_2^* = 0$ and, finally, in Table 5.9.3 with $\lambda_1 = 1$ we choose $x_1^* = 1$, again because $g_1(1, 0)$ is greater than $g_1(1, 1)$.

We have found the optimal solution to be $x_1^* = 1$, $x_2^* = 0$, $x_3^* = 0$, $x_4^* = 1$, $x_5^* = 0$, $x_6^* = 1$ and the value of the objective function is 160. To verify the solution, we see that

$$\phi_1(1)+\phi_2(0)+\phi_3(0)+\phi_4(1)+\phi_5(0)+\phi_6(1) = 20+30+30+40+25+15 = 160.$$

5.10. A Deterministic Inventory Problem—Forward and Backward Recursion

We shall consider a problem in inventory management which is interesting in its own right and, in addition, will serve as a vehicle to illustrate the differences between forward and backward recursion calculations.

Consider a company that manufactures some product and also makes a component that is required in this product. The company's marketing department supplies a forecast for the next 6–12 months of what the demand for the product will be by month. The manufacturing director has a number of general alternatives available to him. He could simply schedule for production each month the number that are to be used in or at the end of the month. For simplicity, we will ignore time lags. The disadvantage to this policy is, if the numbers required each month vary widely, then some months the required number may be too small to justify the cost of setting up the production machinery for the component. On the other hand, if the number was very great in other months, a considerable amount of overtime might be required to produce the required number of components. Hence it might be better to produce several months' requirements in one month. However, if this is done, an inventory cost is incurred because storage must be provided for the parts to be used in future months. We can see that the company may desire some guidance in formulating an optimal policy to follow.

We assume that production is to be scheduled for the next n months. A maximum of one production run per month is allowed but not required. We define the following:

$r_j =$ the number of units that are required in month j.
$x_j =$ the number of units to be produced in month j.
$v_j =$ the inventory at the beginning of month j (not including what is produced in month j).
$F_j =$ fixed charge or set-up cost for a production run in month j.
$P_j(x_j) =$ production cost for producing x_i units in month j.
$H_j(v_j+x_j) =$ inventory holding cost in month j.

We assume that $P_j(0) = 0$ and that all costs are discounted to the first month of the period with α_j the discount rate. Then if $\delta_j = 0$ when $x_j = 0$ and $\delta_j = 1$ when $x_j > 0$, the total cost of production and inventory in month j is $\phi_j(x_j, v_j)$ where

$$\phi_j(x_j, v_j) = \alpha_j[F_j\delta_j+P_j(x_j)+H_j(v_j+x_j)] \tag{5.10.1}$$

Using the above definitions and notation the total discounted cost over the planning period of n months is

$$C = \sum_{j=1}^{n} \phi_j(x_j, v_j) \tag{5.10.2}$$

We shall assume that v_1, the starting inventory, is known. We may or may not specify the ending inventory v_{n+1}. This will determine whether we use a forward or backward recursion. We also have material balance equations which relate the inventory at the end of month j to the starting inventory in month j, the production in month j, and the requirement in month j, i.e.,

$$v_{j+1} = v_j+x_j-r_j \quad (j = 1, 2, \ldots, n) \tag{5.10.3}$$

If we assume that all requirements r_j are to be met, then we wish to solve the following problem:

$$\min \quad C = \sum_{j=1}^{n} \phi_j(x_j, v_j)$$

subject to
$$v_j+x_j-r_j = v_{j+1} \quad (j = 1, 2, \ldots, n) \tag{5.10.4}$$
$$v_j \geqslant 0 \quad (j = 1, 2, \ldots, n)$$
$$x_j \geqslant 0 \quad (j = 1, 2, \ldots, n)$$

Although (5.10.4) has n constraints, by a judicious choice of state variable it can be solved as a one-state variable problem. It can be considered an n-stage problem in which, at each stage, an amount x_j is determined. Since v_j and r_j are known, v_{j+1} can be determined. The state variable λ_j will be either the initial inventory for month j, i.e., $\lambda_j = v_j$, or if ending inventory is specified $\lambda_j = v_{j+1}$. We shall now develop both methods of solution.

A brief explanation of the words "forward" and "backward" is in order. Usage varies from author to author on whether the words "forward" and "backward" refer to the order in which the optimal return functions are calculated or the order in which the stages are numbered. When g_{s+1} is calculated from g_s, the solution x_s is calculated from x_{s+1} in a backward pass since the stages are numbered in reverse order, i.e., $n, n-1, \ldots, 1$. We might speak in this case of a forward recursion or backward solution. Unfortunately, some authors use the term backward recursion for calculations that are in a direction opposite to the flow direction. Hence, usage is not at all consistent. By always using the word "recursion" in connection with the words "forward" and "backward" we shall mean, unambiguously, the order in which the recursion takes place. Therefore if g_{s+1} is calculated from g_s then this is a forward recursion. If g_s is calculated from g_{s+1} this is a backward recursion. We shall illustrate both procedures for this problem by first generating both sets of dynamic programming solution equations for our problem.

Let us first consider the case where both a starting inventory v_1 and a final inventory v_{n+1} are specified. For this case it is more convenient to use a forward recursion. We shall define the state variable λ_s as follows:

$$\lambda_s = v_{s+1}, \quad \text{the inventory at the end of month } s$$

Hence we can write for $j = s$ in (5.10.3)

$$\lambda_s = v_s + x_s - r_s \tag{5.10.5}$$

We see therefore that the state transformation equation is

$$\lambda_{s-1} = T_s(\lambda_s, x_s(\lambda_s)) = \lambda_s + r_s - x_s \tag{5.10.6}$$

Therefore if we define

$$g_s(\lambda_s) \equiv \min_{x_1, x_2, \ldots, x_s} \sum_{j=1}^{s} \phi_j(x_j, v_j) \quad (s = 1, 2, \ldots, n) \tag{5.10.7}$$

then from (5.10.6) and (5.10.7) the recurrence relations are

$$g_s(\lambda_s) = \min_{x_s} [\phi_s(x_s, \lambda_s + r_s - x_s) + g_{s-1}(\lambda_s + r_s - x_s)] \quad (s = 2, 3, \ldots, n) \tag{5.10.8}$$

and
$$g_1(\lambda_1) = \min_{x_1} \phi_1(x_1, v_1)$$

where

$$v_1 + x_1 - r_1 = \lambda_1$$

Therefore $x_1 = \lambda_1 + r_1 - v_1$. Hence we have

$$g_1(\lambda_1) = \phi_1(\lambda_1 + r_1 - v_1, v_1) \tag{5.10.9}$$

We use (5.10.9) and (5.10.8) to compute $g_1(\lambda_1), g_2(\lambda_2), \ldots, g_{n-1}(\lambda_{n-1})$ and at the last stage we calculate $C^* = g_n(v_{n+1})$ and note the value of $x_n^*(v_{n+1})$ that led to the optimal return. Then using (5.10.6) and the tables we have created, we determine successively, $x_{n-1}^*, x_{n-2}^*, \ldots, x_1^*$.

Now let us suppose we only had an initial inventory v_1 specified and that the final inventory is not specified. For this case we define the state variables λ_s as

$$\lambda_s = v_s, \quad \text{the inventory at the beginning of month } j$$

Hence we can write

$$\lambda_{s+1} = T_s(\lambda_s, x_s(\lambda_s)) = \lambda_s + x_s - r_s \tag{5.10.10}$$

We now define

$$g_s(\lambda_s) = \min_{x_s, x_{s+1}, \ldots, x_n} \sum_{j=s}^{n} \phi_j(x_j, v_j) \quad (s = 1, 2, \ldots, n) \tag{5.10.11}$$

Then from (5.10.10) and (5.10.11), the recurrence relations can be seen to be

$$g_s(\lambda_s) = \min_{x_s} [\phi_s(x_s, \lambda_s) + g_{s+1}(\lambda_s + x_s - r_s)] \quad (s = 1, 2, \ldots, n-1) \tag{5.10.12}$$

and $\quad g_n(\lambda_n) = \min_{x_n} \phi_n(x_n, \lambda_n)$

We use (5.10.12) and (5.10.11) to compute $g_n(\lambda_n), g_{n-1}(\lambda_{n-1}), \ldots,$ and at the last stage we compute $C^* = g_1(v_1)$ and note the value of $x_1^*(v_1)$ that led to the optimal value C^*. We then use (5.10.10) and the optimal return tables; we determine, successively, $x_2^*, x_3^*, \ldots, x_n^*$.

It is possible to use either a forward or backward recursion to solve either of the problems we have stated, i.e., with both initial and final inventory specified or only initial inventory specified. However, it is not as convenient, for example, to use the forward recursion process if no final inventory is specified. In order to solve this problem with forward recursion, we would have to determine some final value and use the forward recursion to generate the $g_s(\lambda_s)$ and, after solving for all the x_j^*, see if in fact the initial inventory equalled v_1. If it did not, we would guess another value of v_{n+1} and repeat the process as many times as necessary. Since this involves a great deal more calculation than the backward recursion for this case, it would be foolish to employ such a method. We shall now illustrate, in detail, the forward recursion.

Consider the following problem. A manufacturer of precision pumps for carefully controlled flow has a subcontract to deliver the following number of pumps to the major contractor for the next six months:

Period	1	2	3	4	5	6
Required number	40	20	40	60	40	80

The set-up cost for this manufacturing process is $800, no matter which month they are produced. The process produces pumps in lots of 20. The production cost and inventory costs are as Table 5.10.1 shows:

TABLE 5.10.1

Number produced	Production cost ($)	Inventory cost ($)	Number produced	Production cost ($)	Inventory cost ($)
0	0	0	140	12,400	330
20	2,000	40	160	14,000	390
40	3,800	80	180	16,200	450
60	5,400	120	200	17,800	520
80	7,000	170	220	19,000	590
100	8,600	220	240	21,200	660
120	9,800	270	260	23,000	740

The starting inventory is 20 pumps and he wishes to end the six months with 20 on hand. We will use a discount factor of 1. What is the number of pumps to be produced each month so as to minimize total cost?

First we calculate $g_1(\lambda_1)$ from

$$g_1(\lambda_1) = \phi_1(\lambda_1 + r_1 - v_1, \, v_1)$$

$$\phi_1(0, 20) = P_1(0) + H_1(20 + 0) = 40$$

$$\phi_1(x_1, 20) = F_1 + P_1(x_1) + H_1(20 + x_1)$$

since $v_1 = 20$.

Some sample calculations are

$$\phi_1(20, 20) = 800 + 2000 + \ 80 = 2880$$

$$\phi_1(40, 20) = 800 + 3800 + 120 = 4720$$

A complete tabulation of $\phi_1(x_1, 20)$ is given in Table 5.10.2.

TABLE 5.10.2. $\phi_1(x_1, v_1)$

x_1	$\phi_1(x_1, 20)$ ($)	x_1	$\phi_1(x_1, 20)$ ($)
0	0	140	13,560
20	2,880	160	15,220
40	4,720	180	17,490
60	6,370	200	19,160
80	8,020	220	20,430
100	9,670	240	22,710
120	10,930	260	24,590

From $\phi_1(x_1, 20)$ we can compute $g_1(\lambda_1)$. For example,

$$g_1(20) = \phi_1(20+40-20, 20) = \phi_1(40, 20) = 4720, \quad x_1^*(20) = 40$$
$$g_1(40) = \phi_1(40+40-20, 20) = \phi_1(60, 20) = 6370, \quad x_1^*(40) = 60$$

A complete tabulation of $g_1(\lambda_1)$ is given in Table 5.10.3.

TABLE 5.10.3. $g_1(\lambda_1)$

λ_1	$g_1(\lambda_1)$ ($)	$x_1^*(\lambda_1)$	λ_1	$g_1(\lambda_1)$ ($)	$x_1^*(\lambda_1)$
0	2,880	20	140	15,220	160
20	4,720	40	160	17,490	180
40	6,370	60	180	19,160	200
60	8,020	80	200	20,430	220
80	9,670	100	220	22,710	240
100	10,930	120	240	24,590	260
120	13,560	140			

In order to calculate $g_2(\lambda_2)$ we need to first calculate $\phi_2(x_2, \lambda_2+r_2-x_2) = \phi_2(x_2, \lambda_2+20-x_2)$. We calculate

$$\phi_2(0, v_2) = P_2(0)+H_2(v_2) = H_2(v_2)$$
$$\phi_2(x_2, v_2) = F_2+P_2(x_2)+H_2(v_2+x_2)$$

Some sample calculations are:

$$\phi_2(0, 20) \; = H_2(20) = 40$$
$$\phi_2(20, 40) = 800+2000+120 = 2920$$
$$\phi_2(40, 40) = 800+3800+170 = 4770$$

A complete tabulation of $\phi_2(x_2, \lambda_2+r_2-x_2)$ is given in Table 5.10.3. Since F_j, P_j, H_j do not depend upon j, it can be seen $\phi_j(x_j, v_j)$ will be the same for $j = 2, 3, \ldots, 6$. Hence Table 5.10.4 will be used to calculate all $\phi_j(x_j, v_j)$. We calculate $g_2(\lambda_2)$ from

$$g_2(\lambda_2) = \min_{x_2} [\phi_2(x_2, \lambda_2+20-x_2)+g_1(\lambda_2+20-x_2)]$$

Therefore we have

$$g_2(0) = \min_{x_2} [\phi_2(x_2, 20-x_2)+g_1(20-x_2)]$$
$$= \min(40+4720, 2840+2880) = 4760, \quad x_2^*(0) = 0$$

$$g_2(20) = \min[\phi_2(x_2, 40-x_2)+g_1(40-x_2)]$$
$$= \min(80+6370, 2880+4720, 4680+2880)$$
$$= 6450, \quad x_2^*(20) = 0$$

9

TABLE 5.10.4. $\phi_1(x_j, v_j)$

x_j \ v_j	0	20	40	60	80	100	120	140	160	180	200	220	240	260
0	0	40	80	120	170	220	270	330	390	450	520	590	660	740
20	2,840	2,880	2,920	2,970	3,020	3,070	3,130	3,190	3,250	3,320	3,390	3,460	3,540	
40	4,680	4,720	4,770	4,820	4,870	4,930	4,990	5,050	5,120	5,190	5,260	5,340		
60	6,320	6,370	6,420	6,470	6,530	6,590	6,650	6,720	6,790	6,860	6,940			
80	7,970	8,020	8,070	8,130	8,190	8,250	8,320	8,390	8,460	8,540				
100	9,620	9,670	9,730	9,790	9,850	9,920	9,990	10,060	10,140					
120	10,870	10,930	10,990	11,050	11,120	11,190	11,260	11,340						
140	13,530	13,590	13,650	13,720	13,790	13,860	13,940							
160	15,190	15,250	15,320	15,390	15,460	15,540								
180	17,450	17,520	17,590	17,660	17,740									
200	19,120	19,190	19,260	19,340										
220	20,390	20,460	20,540											
240	22,660	22,740												
260	24,540													

and so forth. A complete tabulation of $g_2(\lambda_2)$ is given in Table 5.10.5.

TABLE 5.10.5. $g_2(\lambda_2)$

λ_2	$g_2(\lambda_2)$ ($)	$x_2^*(\lambda_2)$	λ_2	$g_2(\lambda_2)$ ($)	$x_2^*(\lambda_2)$
0	4,760	0	120	15,550	0
20	6,450	0	140	17,360	120
40	8,140	0	160	19,070	120
60	9,840	0	180	20,790	120
80	11,150	0	200	22,120	120
100	13,750	120	220	24,790	140

The remaining calculations are carried out in the same fashion as $g_2(\lambda_2)$ using

$$g_s(\lambda_s) = \min_{x_s} [\phi_s(x_s, \lambda_s + r_s - x_s) + g_{s-1}(\lambda_s + r_s - x_s)] \qquad (s = 3, 4, 5)$$

The tabulations are given in Tables 5.10.6, 5.10.7 and 5.10.8.

TABLE 5.10.6. $g_3(\lambda_3)$

λ_3	$g_3(\lambda_3)$	$x_3^*(\lambda_3)$
0	8,220	0
20	9,960	0
40	11,320	0
60	13,970	0
80	15,630	120
100	17,380	120
120	19,130	120
140	20,890	140
160	22,270	120
180	24,940	120, 140

TABLE 5.10.7. $g_4(\lambda_4)$

λ_4	$g_4(\lambda_4)$	$x_4^*(\lambda_4)$
0	14,090	0
20	15,800	0
40	17,600	0
60	19,090	120
80	20,890	120
100	22,310	120
120	24,940	140

TABLE 5.10.8. $g_5(\lambda_5)$

λ_5	$g_5(\lambda_5)$	$x_6^*(\lambda_5)$
0	17,680	0
20	19,210	0
40	21,060	0
60	22,530	0
80	24,960	120

At the last stage we wish to find $C^* = g_6(v_7) = g_6(20)$. Therefore we have

$$g_6(20) = \min_{x_6} [\phi_6(x_6, 20+80-x_6)+g_5(20+80-x_6)]$$

$$= \min(3020+24\,960, 4820+22\,530, 6420+21\,060, 8020+19\,210, 9620+17\,680)$$

$$= 27\,230, \quad x_6^*(20) = 80$$

Therefore
$$\lambda_6 = 20, \quad x_6^* = 80$$
$$\lambda_5 = \lambda_6+r_6-x_6 = 20+80-80 = 20$$
$$x_5^*(20) = 0$$
$$\lambda_4 = \lambda_5+r_5-x_5 = 20+40-0 = 60$$
$$x_4^*(60) = 120$$
$$\lambda_3 = \lambda_4+r_4-x_4 = 60+60-120 = 0$$
$$x_3^*(0) = 0$$
$$\lambda_2 = \lambda_3+r_3-x_3 = 0+40-0 = 40$$
$$x_2^*(40) = 0$$
$$\lambda_1 = \lambda_2+r_2-x_2 = 40+20-0 = 60$$
$$x_1^*(60) = 80$$

The optimal policy is then to produce 80 units in the first month, to produce nothing in the second and third months, to produce 120 units in the fourth month, nothing in the fifth month, and 80 units in the sixth month. Since we started with and wish to end up with 20, we see that this optimal policy satisfies this requirement, i.e.,

$$\sum_{j=1}^{6} r_j = 40+20+40+60+40+80 = 280 = 80+120+80$$

and the cost is $27,230. Any other policy will incur a greater cost.

Exercises—Chapter 5

5.1. Solve by dynamic programming

$$\max \quad z = 2x_1+x_2+x_3+3x_4^2$$

subject to
$$x_1+2x_2+x_3+4x_4 \leqslant 10$$
$$x_1 \geqslant 2$$
$$x_2 \geqslant 3$$

$$x_1, x_2, x_3, x_4 \quad \text{non-negative integers}$$

5.2. Solve by dynamic programming

$$\min \quad z = 3x_1^2 - 4x_2 - 5x_3^2$$

subject to

$$3x_1 + 2x_2 + 6x_3 \geqslant 20$$
$$x_2 \leqslant 4$$
$$x_3 \leqslant 6$$
$$x_1, x_2, x_3 \geqslant 0$$

5.3. Solve by dynamic programming

$$\max \quad z = 3x_1^3 - 4x_1 + 2x_2^2 - 5x_2 + 2x_3$$

subject to

$$4x_1 + 2x_2 + 3x_3 \leqslant 18$$
$$x_1, x_2, x_3 \geqslant 0$$

5.4 Solve by dynamic programming

$$\min \quad z = 3x_1^2 - 5x_1 + 3x_2^2 - 3x_2 + 2x_3^2 - 7x_3$$

subject to

$$2x_1 + 3x_2 + 2x_3 \geqslant 16$$
$$x_1, x_2, x_3 \geqslant 0, \quad \text{integer}$$

5.5. Consider a truck whose maximum loading capacity is 50 tons. Suppose that there are four different items, various quantities of which are to make up a load to be carried to a remote geographical area. Suppose we wish to maximize the value of what the truck carries to the inhabitants, given the following weights and values of the four items.

	Weight (tons)	Value
1	3	5
2	4	7
3	5	8
4	6	10

Find the optimal solution by dynamic programming.

5.6. A fast food franchise has decided to add a total of 16 new franchises to four geographical areas, with at least two new franchises going to each area. The expected profit that the company will achieve from each area, depending on the number of franchises opened, is:

Number of franchises opened	Profit in area 1	Profit in area 2	Profit in area 3	Profit in area 4
0	100	200	150	175
1	200	300	250	275
2	300	400	350	375
3	390	480	440	475
4	470	540	520	550
5	530	580	590	610
6	580	600	650	645
7	620	615	700	670
8	650	625	740	685
9	670	630	770	695
10	680	635	790	700

How should the new franchises be distributed so as to maximize total profit?

5.7. We are given the following map of distances between 7 cities with the distances between them as indicated:

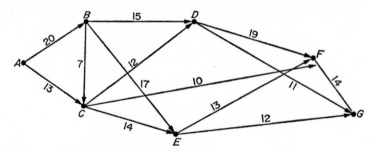

We wish to find the route from *A* to *G* with the shortest sum of distances. Formulate this problem and solve by dynamic programming.

5.8. The development of large computers has enabled some reasonable prediction to be made for the next 10 years. The following tables give costs of income, operating costs and replacement costs for the next 10 years, assuming improvements in technology.

Machine made in year 1

Age of machine	0	1	2	3	4	5	6	7	8	9
Income	180	170	160	150	140	140	140	120	120	120
Operating cost	40	40	50	50	60	60	70	80	90	100
Replacement cost	400	440	480	500	510	520	530	540	540	540

Machine made in year 2

Age of machine	0	1	2	3	4	5	6	7	8
Income	200	180	160	150	140	130	130	130	130
Operating cost	30	40	40	50	50	60	60	70	70
Replacement cost	400	440	480	500	510	520	530	540	540

Machine made in year 3

Age of machine	0	1	2	3	4	5	6	7
Income	220	210	200	190	180	160	140	120
Operating cost	30	30	40	40	50	50	60	60
Replacement cost	400	440	480	500	510	520	530	540

Machine made in year 4

Age of machine	0	1	2	3	4	5	6
Income	230	220	200	180	160	140	120
Operating cost	30	30	40	40	50	50	60
Replacement cost	410	430	440	450	460	470	480

Machine made in year 5

Age of machine	0	1	2	3	4	5
Income	240	230	230	220	210	200
Operating cost	20	20	30	30	40	40
Replacement cost	420	430	440	450	460	470

Machine made in year 6

Age of machine	0	1	2	3	4
Income	250	240	220	210	200
Operating cost	20	20	20	30	30
Replacement cost	420	440	460	480	500

Machine made in year 7

Age of machine	0	1	2	3
Income	270	250	220	210
Operating cost	20	20	20	20
Replacement cost	420	440	460	480

Machine made in year 8

Age of machine	0	1	2
Income	280	270	250
Operating cost	10	20	20
Replacement cost	440	460	480

Machine made in year 9

Age of machine	0	1
Income	300	280
Operating cost	10	20
Replacement cost	440	450

Machine made in year 10

Age of machine	0
Income	310
Operating cost	10
Replacement cost	440

We assume that we own a machine that is three years old with the following characteristics:

Incumbent machine

Age	3	4	5	6	7	8	9	10	11	12
Income	120	120	100	100	100	80	80	80	60	60
Operating cost	110	110	110	120	120	120	120	130	130	140
Replacement cost	500	520	540	560	560	580	580	600	600	620

Find the optimal policy (keep incumbent or replace) for the 10-year period.

5.9. Find the solution to the following problem:

$$\max \quad z = \sum_{j=1}^{10} \phi_j(x_j)$$

subject to

$$\sum_{j=1}^{10} x_j \leqslant 7$$

$$x_j x_{j+1} = 0 \qquad (j = 1, 2, \ldots, 9)$$
$$x_j = 0, 1 \qquad (j = 1, 2, \ldots, 10)$$

where the $\phi_j(x_j)$ are as follows:

x_j	$\phi_1(x_1)$	$\phi_2(x_2)$	$\phi_3(x_3)$	$\phi_4(x_4)$	$\phi_5(x_5)$	$\phi_6(x_6)$	$\phi_7(x_7)$	$\phi_8(x_8)$	$\phi_9(x_9)$	$\phi_{10}(x_{10})$
0	15	40	30	20	50	10	30	40	20	30
1	30	20	40	50	40	20	10	20	30	20

Chapter 6

Multidimensional Problems

6.1. Introduction

In the previous chapters we considered a wide variety of problems which we were able to formulate as dynamic programming problems. All of these problems, which at first glance seemed to be quite different in structure, were such that a single state variable at each stage (λ_s) was sufficient to completely characterize the state of the system under study. In addition, at each stage only a single decision variable (x_s) had to be chosen in order to find $g_s(\lambda_s)$. When we speak of single dimensional dynamic programming processes we mean that a single-state variable suffices to represent the state of the system. The subject of multidimensional problems deals with situations where two or more state variables are required to formulate and obtain a dynamic programming solution. It may also be the case that the values of two or more decision variables are chosen at each stage.

As we shall see, problems with two or more state variables involve much greater amounts of numerical computation and storage. The rapid increase in these requirements is such that, for all practical purposes, problems with only three or four state variables are the maximum that can be considered, unless some special state reduction technique is employed. This is true even if only a single decision variable is determined at each stage. The reverse situation is equally difficult, i.e., problems with a single-state variable and two or more decision variables at each stage are also more difficult from the standpoint of numerical computation. We shall now examine the nature of the solutions and their attendant difficulties.

6.2. A Nonlinear Allocation Problem

Let us now consider a general nonlinear allocation (nonlinear programming) problem of the form

$$\max \quad z = \sum_{j=1}^{n} \phi_j(x_j)$$

subject to
$$\sum_{j=1}^{n} h_{1j}(x_j) \leqslant b_1 \qquad (6.2.1)$$

$$\sum_{j=1}^{n} h_{2j}(x_j) \leqslant b_2$$

$$x_j \geqslant 0, \quad \text{integer} \quad (j = 1, 2, \ldots, n)$$

This problem is similar to the problem given by (5.5.1) except that here we have two constraints on the x_j, in addition to the nonnegativity and integrality constraints. In the context of a nonlinear allocation problem, the values of b_1, b_2 can be considered to be the availabilities of two different resources. The functions $h_{1j}(\cdot)$ and $h_{2j}(\cdot)$ determine the amount of each of the resources that are used in order to produce x_j units of the jth product (or service) and are assumed to be increasing functions. The $\phi_j(\cdot)$ are unit profits that are obtained from the production of the jth product.

It is no more difficult to derive recurrence relations to solve (6.2.1) than it was to do the same for (5.5.1), once we see that we require *two* state variables, one for each of the resources that are to be allocated. Accordingly, we introduce state variables λ_{1s}, λ_{2s} for each of the stages. The state transformations are given by

$$\lambda_{1,s-1} = T_{1s}(\lambda_{1s}, x_s(\lambda_{1s}, \lambda_{2s})) = \lambda_{1s} - h_{1s}(x_s)$$
$$\lambda_{2,s-1} = T_{2s}(\lambda_{2s}, x_s(\lambda_{1s}, \lambda_{2s})) = \lambda_{2s} - h_{2s}(x_s)$$
(6.2.2)

Using (6.2.2) and the principle of optimality, we readily derive the following recurrence relations

$$g_1(\lambda_{11}, \lambda_{21}) = \max_{0 \le x_1 \le [\xi_1]} \phi_1(x_1)$$
$$g_s(\lambda_{1s}, \lambda_{2s}) = \max_{0 \le x_s \le [\xi_s]} [\phi_s(x_s) + g_{s-1}(\lambda_{1s} - h_{1s}(x_s), \lambda_{2s} - h_{2s}(x_s))]$$
(6.2.3)
$$(s = 2, 3, \ldots, n)$$

where ξ_s is determined from

$$\lambda_{1s} - h_{1s}(\xi_{1s}) = 0$$
(6.2.4)
$$\lambda_{2s} - h_{2s}(\xi_{2s}) = 0 \qquad (s = 1, 2, \ldots, n)$$
$$\xi_s = \min(\xi_{1s}, \xi_{2s})$$

In (6.2.4), for given values of λ_{1s} and λ_{2s}, ξ_{1s} and ξ_{2s} represent solutions to their respective nonlinear equations. It is possible that the nonlinear equations in (6.2.4) have multiple solutions. We shall assume that this situation can be dealt with in the context of any particular problem.

The formal solution process is completely analogous to that employed in Section 5.5. At each stage we determine $g_s(\lambda_{1s}, \lambda_{2s})$ and at the same time we determine $x_s^*(\lambda_{1s}, \lambda_{2s})$ which yielded the value of $g_s(\lambda_{1s}, \lambda_{2s})$. At the nth stage we determine $g_n(b_1, b_2)$ and the value $x_n^*(b_1, b_2) = x_n^*$. The optimal values of the remaining variables are determined from the g_s tables or functional representations from the equations

$$x_{n-k}^* = x_{n-k}^* \left[b_1 - \sum_{i=0}^{k-1} h_{1, n-i}(x_{n-i}^*), b_2 - \sum_{i=0}^{k-1} h_{2, n-i}(x_{n-i}^*) \right] \qquad (k = 1, 2, \ldots, n-1) \quad (6.2.5)$$

Observe that the state functions depend on two state variables, which is the general case we considered in Section 3.3. This means that $g_s(\lambda_{1s}, \lambda_{2s})$ represents the maximum return from the first s processes of our allocation problem, when λ_{1s} and λ_{2s} units of the two resources are available for allocation to these stages.

The nature of the difficulty that we face in dealing with the recurrence relations (6.2.3) and (6.2.4) to solve the original problem is not hard to find. Consider how we might construct a table of optimal values for $g_s(\lambda_{1s}, \lambda_{2s})$, which is analogous to what we did in constructing a table of optimal values of $g_s(\lambda_s)$. We shall now have to let λ_{1s} range over the values $0, 1, 2, \ldots, b_1$ and λ_{2s} range over the values $0, 1, 2, \ldots, b_2$. Hence, in general, we shall have to construct a two-dimensional table with $(b_1+1)(b_2+1)$ entries. This contrasts with a table of $b+1$ entries for $g_s(\lambda_s)$. We shall also have had to do a great deal more computation to find each of the entries of the $g_s(\lambda_{1s}, \lambda_{2s})$ table. We shall now present an example of the use of the recurrence relations we have derived.

Consider the following problem:

$$\max \quad z = 3x_1^2 + 3x_2 + x_2^2 + x_3 + x_3^2$$

subject to
$$3x_1 + 2x_2 + x_3 \leqslant 12 \tag{6.2.6}$$
$$4x_1 + 3x_2 + 2x_3 \leqslant 17$$
$$x_1, x_2, x_3 \geqslant 0, \quad \text{integer}$$

Applying (6.2.3) and (6.2.4) we obtain

$$\lambda_{11} - 3\xi_{11} = 0, \quad \lambda_{21} - 4\xi_{21} = 0$$

Therefore
$$\xi_{11} = \frac{\lambda_{11}}{3}, \quad \xi_{21} = \frac{\lambda_{21}}{4}$$

and
$$\xi_1 = \min\left(\frac{\lambda_{11}}{3}, \frac{\lambda_{21}}{4}\right) \tag{6.2.7}$$

and
$$g_1(\lambda_{11}, \lambda_{21}) = \max_{0 \leqslant x_1 \leqslant [\xi_1]} 3x_1^2 = 3[\xi_1]^2 \tag{6.2.8}$$

Some sample calculations using (6.2.7) and (6.2.8) are:

$$g_1(0, 2) = \max_{0 \leqslant x_1 \leqslant 0} 3(0) = 0 \quad \text{and} \quad x_1^*(0, 2) = 0$$

$$g_1(2, 6) = \max_{0 \leqslant x_1 \leqslant 0} 3(0) = 0 \quad \text{and} \quad x_1^*(2, 6) = 0$$

$$g_1(3, 5) = \max_{0 \leqslant x_1 \leqslant 1} 3[\xi_1]^2 = \max(0, 3) = 3 \quad \text{and} \quad x_1^*(3, 5) = 1$$

$$g_1(7, 10) = \max_{0 \leqslant x_1 \leqslant 2} 3[\xi_1]^2 = \max(0, 3, 12) = 12 \quad \text{and} \quad x_1^*(7, 10) = 2$$

A complete tabulation of $g_1(\lambda_{11}, \lambda_{21})$ is given in Table 6.2.1.

Next we compute $g_2(\lambda_{12}, \lambda_{22})$ and ξ_2 from

$$\xi_2 = \min\left(\frac{\lambda_{12}}{2}, \frac{\lambda_{22}}{3}\right)$$

and
$$g_2(\lambda_{12}, \lambda_{22}) = \max_{0 \leqslant x_2 \leqslant [\xi_2]} [3x_2 + x_2^2 + g_1(\lambda_{12} - 2x_2, \lambda_{22} - 3x_2)]$$

TABLE 6.2.1. $g_1(\lambda_{11}, \lambda_{21})$

λ_{11} \ λ_{21}	0	1	2	3	4	5	6	7	8	9	10	11	12	13	14	15	16	17
0	0	0	0	0	0	0	0	0	0	0	0	0	0	0	0	0	0	0
1	0	0	0	0	0	0	0	0	0	0	0	0	0	0	0	0	0	0
2	0	0	0	0	0	0	0	0	0	0	0	0	0	0	0	0	0	0
3	0	0	0	0	3	3	3	3	3	3	3	3	3	3	3	3	3	3
4	0	0	0	0	3	3	3	3	3	3	3	3	3	3	3	3	3	3
5	0	0	0	0	3	3	3	3	3	3	3	3	3	3	3	3	3	3
6	0	0	0	0	3	3	3	3	12	12	12	12	12	12	12	12	12	12
7	0	0	0	0	3	3	3	3	12	12	12	12	12	12	12	12	12	12
8	0	0	0	0	3	3	3	3	12	12	12	12	12	12	12	12	12	12
9	0	0	0	0	3	3	3	3	12	12	12	12	27	27	27	27	27	27
10	0	0	0	0	3	3	3	3	12	12	12	12	27	27	27	27	27	27
11	0	0	0	0	3	3	3	3	12	12	12	12	27	27	27	27	27	27
12	0	0	0	0	3	3	3	3	12	12	12	12	27	27	27	27	48	48

Note: For entries of 0, $x_1^*(\lambda_{11}, \lambda_{21}) = 0$.   For entries of 27, $x_1^*(\lambda_{11}, \lambda_{21}) = 3$.

For entries of 3, $x_1^*(\lambda_{11}, \lambda_{21}) = 1$.   For entries of 48, $x_1^*(\lambda_{11}, \lambda_{21}) = 4$.

For entries of 12, $x_1^*(\lambda_{11}, \lambda_{21}) = 2$.

Some sample calculations are

$$g_2(2, 3) = \max_{0 \leqslant x_2 \leqslant 1} [3x_2 + x_2^2 + g_1(2 - 2x_2, 3 - 3x_2)]$$

$$= \max[0 + g_1(2, 3), \; 3 + 1 + g_1(0, 0)]$$

$$= \max(0, 4) = 4 \quad \text{and} \quad x_2^*(2, 3) = 1$$

$$g_2(5, 7) = \max_{0 \leqslant x_2 \leqslant 2} [3x_2 + x_2^2 + g_1(5 - 2x_2, 7 - 3x_2)]$$

$$= \max[0 + g_1(5, 7), \; 3 + 1 + g_1(3, 4), \; 6 + 4 + g_1(1, 1)]$$

$$= \max(0 + 3, \; 4 + 3, \; 10 + 0) = 10 \quad \text{and} \quad x_2^*(5, 7) = 2$$

A complete tabulation of $g_2(\lambda_{12}, \lambda_{22})$ is given in Table 6.2.2.

Finally we calculate

$$\xi_3 = \min(12, \tfrac{17}{2}) = 8.5$$

$$g_3(12, 17) = \max_{0 \leqslant x_3 \leqslant 8} [x_3 + x_3^2 + g_2(12 - x_3, 17 - 2x_3)]$$

$$= \max[0 + g_2(12, 17), \; 2 + g_2(11, 15), \; 6 + g_2(10, 13),$$

$$12 + g_2(9, 11), \; 20 + g_2(8, 9), \; 30 + g_2 (7, 7),$$

$$40 + g_2(6, 5), \; 56 + g_2(5, 3), \; 72 + g_2(4, 1)]$$

$$= \max(40, 42, 34, 30, 38, 40, 46, 60, 72)$$

$$= 72 \quad \text{and} \quad x_3^* = 8$$

Therefore $\lambda_{12} = \lambda_{13} - x_3 = 12 - 8 = 4$

$$\lambda_{22} = \lambda_{23} - 2x_3 = 17 - 16 = 1$$

and $x_2^*(4, 1) = 0$

TABLE 6.2.2. $g_2(\lambda_{12}, \lambda_{22})$

λ_{12} \ λ_{22}	0	1	2	3	4	5	6	7	8	9	10	11	12	13	14	15	16	17
0	0	0	0	0	0	0	0	0	0	0	0	0	0	0	0	0	0	0
1	0	0	0	0	0	0	0	0	0	0	0	0	0	0	0	0	0	0
2	0	0	0	4	4	4	4	4	4	4	4	4	4	4	4	4	4	4
3	0	0	0	4	4	4	4	4	4	4	4	4	4	4	4	4	4	4
4	0	0	0	4	4	4	4	4	4	4	4	4	4	4	4	4	4	4
5	0	0	0	4	4	4	10	10	10	10	10	10	10	10	10	10	10	10
6	0	0	0	4	4	4	10	10	12	18	18	18	18	18	18	18	18	18
7	0	0	0	4	4	4	10	10	12	18	18	18	18	18	18	18	18	18
8	0	0	0	4	4	4	10	10	12	18	18	18	28	28	28	28	28	28
9	0	0	0	4	4	4	10	10	12	18	18	18	28	28	28	28	28	28
10	0	0	0	4	4	4	10	10	12	18	18	18	28	28	28	40	40	40
11	0	0	0	4	4	4	10	10	12	18	18	18	28	28	28	40	40	40
12	0	0	0	4	4	4	10	10	12	18	18	18	28	28	28	40	40	40

Note: For entries of 0, $x_2^*(\lambda_{12}, \lambda_{22}) = 0$. For entries of 12, $x_2^*(\lambda_{12}, \lambda_{22}) = 0$.
For entries of 4, $x_2^*(\lambda_{12}, \lambda_{22}) = 1$. For entries of 18, $x_2^*(\lambda_{12}, \lambda_{22}) = 3$.
For entries of 10, $x_2^*(\lambda_{12}, \lambda_{22}) = 2$. For entries of 28, $x_2^*(\lambda_{12}, \lambda_{22}) = 4$.
For entries of 40, $x_2^*(\lambda_{12}, \lambda_{22}) = 5$.

Then
$$\lambda_{11} = \lambda_{12} - 3x_2 = 4 - 0 = 4$$
$$\lambda_{21} = \lambda_{22} - 4x_2 = 1 - 0 = 1$$

and
$$x_1^*(4, 1) = 0$$

Therefore the optimal solution is

$$x_1^* = 0, \quad x_2^* = 0, \quad x_3^* = 8, \quad \text{and} \quad z^* = 72$$

It is fairly obvious that the problem given by (6.2.1) can be generalized to any number of constraints without affecting the theoretical capability of dynamic programming to determine a solution. The computational utility of this generalization is severely limited, however.

Consider the generalization of (6.2.1) to any finite number of constraints:

$$\max \quad z = \sum_{j=1}^{n} \phi_j(x_j)$$

subject to
$$\sum_{j=1}^{n} h_{ij}(x_j) \leqslant b_i \qquad (i = 1, 2, \ldots, m)$$

$$x_j \geqslant 0, \quad \text{integer} \quad (j = 1, 2, \ldots, n)$$

(6.2.9)

We define state variables λ_{is} where at each stage s the vector $\boldsymbol{\lambda}_s$ contains the state variables corresponding to each of the constraints of (6.2.9). The state transformations are given by

$$\boldsymbol{\lambda}_{s-1} = T_s(\boldsymbol{\lambda}_s, x_s(\boldsymbol{\lambda}_s)) = \boldsymbol{\lambda}_s - \mathbf{h}_s(x_s) \qquad (6.2.10)$$

where
$$\boldsymbol{\lambda}_s = (\lambda_{1s}, \lambda_{2s}, \ldots, \lambda_{ms})$$
$$\mathbf{h}_s(x_s) = (h_{1s}(x_s), h_{2s}(x_s), \ldots, h_{ms}(x_s)) \qquad (6.2.11)$$

Using (6.2.10) and the principle of optimality, we obtain the following recurrence relations

$$g_1(\lambda_1) = \max_{0 \leqslant x_1 \leqslant [\xi_1]} \phi_1(x_1)$$

$$g_s(\lambda_s) = \max_{0 \leqslant x_s \leqslant [\xi_s]} [\phi_s(x_s) + g_{s-1}(\lambda_s - \mathbf{h}_s(x_s))] \qquad (s = 2, 3, \ldots, n) \qquad (6.2.12)$$

where ξ_s is determined from

$$\lambda_{is} - h_{is}(\xi_{is}) = 0 \qquad (i = 1, 2, \ldots, m) \qquad (6.2.13)$$

$$\xi_s = \min_i \xi_{is}$$

In the above, for given values of λ_{is}, ξ_{is} is the solution to the ith equation of (6.2.13). One should recognize that in component form, the general recurrence relation of (6.2.12) is

$$g_s(\lambda_{1s}, \lambda_{2s}, \ldots, \lambda_{ms}) = \max_{0 \leqslant x_s \leqslant [\xi_s]} [\phi_s(x_s) + g_{s-1}(\lambda_{1s} - h_{1s}(x_s),$$

$$\lambda_{2s} - h_{2s}(x_s), \ldots, \lambda_{ms} - h_{ms}(x_s))]$$

This, or the equivalent vector form (6.2.12), indicates that each optimal return function depends upon m state variables. We still have a one-dimensional search for the optimal x_s, but the dimensionality of the state space is now m.

Let us consider the computational implications of (6.2.12). We have already considered the cases of $m = 1$ and $m = 2$. We saw that for $m = 1$, calculation and storage of $g_s(\lambda_s)$ required us to provide a one-dimensional table of $g_s(\lambda_s)$ for each value of λ_s and a similar tabulation of $x_s^*(\lambda_s)$. For $m = 2$, the storage requirement grew significantly as we saw in the previous numerical example. We had to compute and store a table of $g_s(\lambda_{1s}, \lambda_{2s})$ at each state and a similar tabulation of $x_s^*(\lambda_{1s}, \lambda_{2s})$. We see that if we consider all the b_i equal to b (for simplicity) then for $m = 1$, the tables have $2(b+1)$ entries (for the g_s and x_s). For $m = 2$, the tables have $2(b+1)^2$ entries. For the general case, the tables will have $2(b+1)^m$ entries. A problem with 10 constraints, $b = 99$ and $n = 50$ (a relatively small size optimization problem) would require the calculation and storage of

$$(50)(2)(100)^{10} = 10^{22}$$

numbers, which is a number not to be taken lightly, even with computers available. Hence this approach for solving (6.2.9) is not practical for $m > 5$ in the general case. However, we should not leave this topic without once more emphasizing that when dynamic programming can solve (6.2.9) it can find a global maximum, no matter what the form of $h_{ij}(\cdot)$ and $\phi_j(\cdot)$. No other technique is available with this property.

6.3. A Nonlinear Allocation Problem with Several Decision Variables

The allocation problem we studied in Section 6.2 required m state variables to describe the system at each stage. However, only one decision variable x_j was selected at the jth stage. We would like to consider now a problem similar to (6.2.1) in that two state variables are required. It will differ from (6.2.1) in that two decision variables x_j and y_j are selected at each stage. The problem is

$$\max \quad z = \sum_{j=1}^{n} \phi_j(x_j, y_j)$$

subject to
$$\sum_{j=1}^{n} h_{1j}(x_j) \leq b_1 \tag{6.3.1}$$

$$\sum_{j=1}^{n} h_{2j}(y_j) \leq b_2$$

$$x_j, y_j \geq 0, \quad \text{integer} \quad (j = 1, 2, \ldots, n)$$

In (6.3.1), $h_{1j}(\cdot)$ and $h_{2j}(\cdot)$ are increasing functions. (6.3.1) can be treated in the same way as (6.2.1) as long as we keep in mind that $\mathbf{x}_s$ is now a vector, i.e., $\mathbf{x}_s = (x_s, y_s)$. The analysis of functional equations in Section 3.3 was in terms of a vector of decision variables. Hence we may introduce state variables

$$\boldsymbol{\lambda}_s = (\lambda_{1s}, \lambda_{2s}) \quad (s = 1, 2, \ldots, n)$$

as well as decision variables

$$\mathbf{x}_s = (x_s, y_s) \quad (s = 1, 2, \ldots, n)$$

The state transformations are given by

$$\lambda_{1, s-1} = T_{1s}(\lambda_{1s}, x_s(\lambda_{1s}, \lambda_{2s})) = \lambda_{1s} - h_{1s}(x_s)$$
$$\lambda_{2, s-1} = T_{2s}(\lambda_{2s}, y_s(\lambda_{1s}, \lambda_{2s})) = \lambda_{2s} - h_{2s}(y_s) \qquad (s = 1, 2, \ldots, n) \tag{6.3.2}$$

The use of (6.3.2) and the principle of optimality results in the following recurrence relations:

$$g_1(\lambda_{11}, \lambda_{21}) = \max_{\substack{0 \leq x_1 \leq [\xi_{11}] \\ 0 \leq y_1 \leq [\xi_{21}]}} \phi_1(x_1, y_1)$$

$$g_s(\lambda_{1s}, \lambda_{2s}) = \max_{\substack{0 \leq x_s \leq [\xi_{1s}] \\ 0 \leq y_s \leq [\xi_{2s}]}} [\phi_s(x_s, y_s) + g_{s-1}(\lambda_{1s} - h_{1s}(x_s), \tag{6.3.3}$$

$$\lambda_{2s} - h_{2s}(y_s))] \qquad (s = 2, \ldots, n)$$

where ξ_{1s}, ξ_{2s} are the solutions of

$$\lambda_{1s} - h_{1s}(\xi_{1s}) = 0$$
$$\lambda_{2s} - h_{2s}(\xi_{2s}) = 0 \qquad (s = 1, 2, \ldots, n) \tag{6.3.4}$$

The solution process that we use is, as usual, to determine $g_s(\lambda_{1s}, \lambda_{2s})$ for each s and at the same time we determine the values $x_s^*(\lambda_{1s}, \lambda_{2s})$ and $y_s^*(\lambda_{1s}, \lambda_{2s})$ which yielded the particular value of $g_s(\lambda_{1s}, \lambda_{2s})$. Note, however, that in order to do this, the amount of computation required has grown enormously. In solving (6.2.1), at each stage it was necessary to evaluate, for fixed values of λ_{1s} and λ_{2s},

$$G_s(\lambda_{1s}, \lambda_{2s}, x_s) \equiv \phi_s(x_s) + g_{s-1}(\lambda_{1s} - h_{1s}(x_s), \lambda_{2s} - h_{2s}(x_{2s}))$$

for $x_s = 0, 1, \ldots, [\xi_s]$.

However, for (6.3.1) we must evaluate, for fixed values of λ_{1s} and λ_{2s},

$$G_s(\lambda_{1s}, \lambda_{2s}, x_s, y_s) \equiv \phi_s(x_s, y_s) + g_{s-1}(\lambda_{1s} - h_{1s}(x_s), \lambda_{2s} - h_{2s}(y_s))$$

for every combination of $x_s = 0, 1, \ldots, [\xi_{1s}]$ and $y_s = 0, 1, \ldots, [\xi_{2s}]$.

We can see that now a very great amount of calculation is required just to determine the absolute maximum of G_s in order to find $g_s(\lambda_{1s}, \lambda_{2s})$. Whereas for problem (6.2.1) the computation varied linearly with the number of values of x_s, it now varies as the product of the number of values of x_s and y_s, which if $[\xi_{1s}] = [\xi_{2s}]$, means that it varies as the square of the number of values of x_s or y_s.

We can also generalize (6.3.1) to any number of constraints. The problem we consider is

$$\max \quad z = \sum_{j=1}^{n} \phi_j(x_{1j}, x_{2j}, \ldots, x_{mj})$$

subject to

$$\sum_{j=1}^{n} h_{1j}(x_{1j}) \leqslant b_1 \qquad\qquad (6.3.5)$$

$$\sum_{j=1}^{n} h_{2j}(x_{2j}) \leqslant b_2$$

$$\cdot$$
$$\cdot$$
$$\cdot$$

$$\sum_{j=1}^{n} h_{mj}(x_{mj}) \leqslant b_m$$

$$x_{ij} \geqslant 0, \quad \text{integer} \quad (i = 1, 2, \ldots, m)$$
$$(j = 1, 2, \ldots, n)$$

We introduce state variables

$$\boldsymbol{\lambda}_s = (\lambda_{1s}, \lambda_{2s}, \ldots, \lambda_{ms}) \qquad (s = 1, 2, \ldots, n)$$

and designate the vector of decision variables

$$\mathbf{x}_s = (x_{1s}, x_{2s}, \ldots, x_{ms}) \qquad (s = 1, 2, \ldots, n)$$

The state transformation equations are then

$$\lambda_{1, s-1} = T_{1s}(\lambda_{1s}, x_{1s}(\boldsymbol{\lambda}_s)) = \lambda_{1s} - h_{1s}(x_{1s})$$
$$\lambda_{2, s-1} = T_{2s}(\lambda_{2s}, x_{2s}(\boldsymbol{\lambda}_s)) = \lambda_{2s} - h_{2s}(x_{2s}) \qquad (6.3.6)$$
$$\cdot$$
$$\cdot$$
$$\cdot$$
$$\lambda_{m, s-1} = T_{ms}(\lambda_{ms}, x_{ms}(\boldsymbol{\lambda}_s)) = \lambda_{ms} - h_{ms}(x_{ms}) \qquad (s = 1, 2, \ldots, n)$$

We shall apply the principle of optimality and (6.3.6) to (6.3.5) in order to obtain the recurrence relations. Before doing so we shall require some additional notation. Let

$$\boldsymbol{\xi}_s = (\xi_{1s}, \xi_{2s}, \ldots, \xi_{ms})$$
$$\mathbf{h}_s(\mathbf{x}_s) = (h_{1s}(x_{1s}), h_{2s}(x_{2s}), \ldots, h_{ms}(x_{ms}))$$

then the recurrence relations are

$$g_1(\lambda_1) = \max_{0 \leqslant x_1 \leqslant [\xi_1]} \phi_1(x_1)$$

$$g_s(\lambda_s) = \max_{0 \leqslant x_s \leqslant [\xi_s]} [\phi_s(x_s) + g_{s-1}(\lambda_s - \mathbf{h}_s(x_s))] \qquad (s = 2, 3, \ldots, n)$$

(6.3.7)

where ξ_s is the solution of

$$\lambda_s - \mathbf{h}_s(\xi_s) = 0 \qquad (s = 1, 2, \ldots, n)$$

(6.3.8)

The solution process is the obvious extension of the two decision variable case. However, the amount of computation has now increased quite alarmingly. In order to employ (6.3.7) we must evaluate, for each combination of fixed values of λ_s,

$$G_s(\lambda_s; \mathbf{x}_s) \equiv \phi_s(x_s) + g_{s-1}(\lambda_s - \mathbf{h}_s(x_s))$$

for every combination of allowable values for each component of $\mathbf{x}_s$. If we assume, for simplicity, that $\xi_{1s} = \xi_{2s} = \ldots = \xi_{ms} = \xi$, then in order to evaluate each value of $g_s(\lambda_s)$ we have to perform ξ^m calculations. If the tables have, as in Section 6.2, $2(b+1)^m$ entries and n stages, the total amount of calculation involved is

$$2n(b+1)^m \xi^m$$

Suppose $n = 50$, $m = 10$, $b = 99$, and $\xi = 40$, which are relatively modest assumptions. Then the calculation involved is

$$2(50)(100)^{10}(40)^{10} \approx 10^{38}$$

individual calculations. Hence this approach for solving (6.3.5) is limited to relatively small values of m and n. In the next chapter we shall consider methods for reducing dimensionality and the use of approximate methods for handling larger dimensioned problems.

6.4. An Equipment Replacement Problem

In Section 5.8 we considered an equipment replacement problem in which at each time period a decision was made to keep the current machine or replace it with a new machine. We also took into account the fact that technological change may be an important factor. Hence the costs and income involved were a function of the age of the machine. Let us now consider problems where a third alternative to keeping or replacing the machine is present, viz., overhauling the current machine.

In order to consider machine overhaul as an alternative, the costs and income will have to depend not only on the age of the machine and the year in which it was purchased but also on the time since the last overhaul. This will necessitate the use of two state parameters to describe the state of the system. One will relate to the age of the machine currently in use and the other will keep track of the time periods since the last overhaul. First we define the notation we shall use:

$I_j(t_1, t_2)$ = income in period j from a machine of age t_1 that was last overhauled at age t_2.

$O_j(t_1, t_2) =$ operating cost in period j for a machine of age t_1 that was last overhauled at age t_2.

$C_j(t_1, t_2) =$ replacement cost at the start of period j for a machine of age t_1 that was last overhauled at age t_2.

$M_j(t_1, t_2) =$ overhaul cost in period j of a machine of age t_1 last overhauled at age t_2.

$T_1 =$ age of the incumbent machine at the beginning of the first period.

$T_2 =$ age of incumbent machine when last overhauled.

$\alpha =$ discount factor $(0 \leqslant \alpha \leqslant 1)$.

$N =$ total number of periods in the plan.

$g_j(t_1, t_2) =$ optimal return for periods $j, j+1, \ldots, N$ when the jth period is started with a machine of age t_1 last overhauled at age t_2.

$x_j(t_1, t_2) =$ decision (K, R, O) at the beginning of period j that will yield $g_j(t_1, t_2)$.

$K =$ keep (no overhaul).

$R =$ replace with new machine.

$O =$ overhaul.

In order to derive the optimal decision rule, we make the following analysis. If a new machine is purchased at the beginning of period j, the total return from periods $j, j+1, \ldots, N$ will be the income from a new machine in period j ($I_j(0, 0)$) minus the operating cost of the new machine in period j ($O_j(0, 0)$) minus the cost of replacing a machine that is t_1 years old and was last overhauled at age t_2 ($C_j(t_1, t_2)$) plus the *optimal* return from periods $j+1, j+2, \ldots, N$ starting with a machine that is one year old, discounted to the beginning of period j, ($\alpha g_{j+1}(1, 0)$). If a machine that is t_1 years old is kept (not overhauled or replaced) during the jth period, the total return from periods $j, j+1, \ldots, N$ will be the income from a machine that is t_1 years old and was last overhauled at age t_2 ($I_j(t_1, t_2)$) minus the operating expense of the machine that is t_1 years old in period j and was last overhauled at age t_2 ($O_j(t_1, t_2)$) plus the *optimal* return from periods $j+1, j+2, \ldots, N$ starting with a machine that is t_1+1 years old and was last overhauled at age t_2 and discounted to the beginning of period j, ($\alpha g_{j+1}(t_1+1, t_2)$). Finally, if a machine that is t_1 years old is overhauled at the beginning of the jth period, the total return from periods $j, j+1, \ldots, N$ will be the income from the overhauled machine in period j ($I_j(t_1, t_1)$) minus the operating expense of the overhauled machine in period j ($O_j(t_1, t_1)$) minus the cost of overhauling a machine that is t_1 years old and was last overhauled at age t_2 ($M_j(t_1, t_2)$) plus the *optimal* return from periods $j+1, j+2, \ldots, N$ starting with a machine that is t_1+1 years old and was last overhauled at age t_2, discounted to the beginning of period j ($\alpha g_{j+1}(t_1+1, t_1)$).

A mathematical transliteration of the preceding paragraph, with the addition of choosing whichever total return is the greatest, will provide us with a set of recurrence relations for solving the problem of maximizing the total return provided by the machine over a total time of N periods. These recurrence relations are

$$g_j(t_1, t_2) = \begin{bmatrix} (R): & I_j(0, 0) - O_j(0, 0) - C_j(t_1, t_2) + \alpha g_{j+1}(1, 0) \\ (K): & I_j(t_1, t_2) - O_j(t_1, t_2) + \alpha g_{j+1}(t_1+1, t_2) \\ (O): & I_j(t_1, t_1) - O_j(t_1, t_1) - M_j(t_1, t_2) + \alpha g_{j+1}(t_1+1, t_1) \end{bmatrix} \quad (6.4.1)$$

$$(j = 1, 2, \ldots, N)$$

We also require that

$$g_{N+1}(t_1, t_2) = 0 \quad (j = 1, 2, \ldots, N) \tag{6.4.2}$$

as well as the fact that for $g_1(t_1, t_2)$ the only allowable value t_1 is T_1 since we enter the planning process with a machine of age T_1. Similarly the only allowable value of t_2 is T_2.

We shall not present a numerical example because of the large volume of cost and income data that we would have to record. This is so because each of the tables of cost data given in Section 5.8 would become a matrix of data for each of income, operating cost, replacement cost, and overhaul cost. For example, for the row of income data in the table for a machine made in year 1, we would require a column of entries for each age that would correspond to various years of overhaul. It can therefore be seen that the input data requirements are quite large. Although the computational requirements have greatly increased, they are well within the capabilities of a computer for any realistic set of time periods.

6.5. Some Investment Problems

The following problem is stated as an exercise in [3]. We consider two corporations with an interlocking directorate such that they are enjoined by anti-monopoly statutes from investing in the same enterprise. The first corporation has capital C_1 to invest and the second corporation has capital C_2 to invest. If a quantity of capital w is invested in the ith investment opportunity, then a return $h_i(w)$ is realized. There are n investment opportunities. Let us consider how the two corporations can maximize the return from all the investments that are made.

Let x_i = the amount invested by the first corporation in the ith investment.

y_i = the amount invested by the second corporation in the ith investment.

The objective function is simply the sum of the investments of both of the corporations, i.e.,

$$z = \sum_{i=1}^{n} h_i(x_i) + \sum_{i=1}^{n} h_i(y_i) \tag{6.5.1}$$

The amounts of capital invested by each of the two corporations cannot exceed the total amounts of capital available, C_1 and C_2, respectively. Hence we have the constraints

$$\sum_{i=1}^{n} x_i = C_1$$

$$\sum_{i=1}^{n} y_i = C_2 \tag{6.5.2}$$

$$x_i, y_i \geqslant 0 \quad (i = 1, 2, \ldots, n)$$

Lastly we must add a constraint which prevents both corporations from investing in the same investment opportunity. This is accomplished with

$$x_i y_i = 0 \quad (i = 1, 2, \ldots, n) \tag{6.5.3}$$

In summary, the problem we wish to solve is

$$\max \quad z = \sum_{i=1}^{n} h_i(x_i) + \sum_{i=1}^{n} h_i(y_i)$$

subject to

$$\sum_{i=1}^{n} x_i = C_1 \tag{6.5.4}$$

$$\sum_{i=1}^{n} y_i = C_2$$

$$x_i y_i = 0 \qquad (i = 1, 2, \ldots, n)$$
$$x_i, y_i \geqslant 0 \qquad (i = 1, 2, \ldots, n)$$

The approach to solving (6.5.4) is relatively simple and is based on the following observation. Suppose we only had one investment opportunity. Then the optimal policy would be to choose either $h_1(C_1)$ or $h_1(C_2)$, whichever is greater. Now if we define

$g_s(\lambda_{1s}, \lambda_{2s}) \equiv$ optimal return at the sth stage when amounts $\lambda_{1s}, \lambda_{2s}$ of capital are available for investment by each corporation

then it is clear that

$$g_1(\lambda_{11}, \lambda_{21}) = \max_{\substack{x_1 = \lambda_{11} \\ y_1 = \lambda_{21}}} [h_1(x_1), h_1(y_1)]$$

$$= \max[h_1(\lambda_{11}), h_1(\lambda_{21})] \tag{6.5.5}$$

Now suppose at stage s we wish to determine $g_s(\lambda_{1s}, \lambda_{2s})$. We, of course, have available to us a tabulation or other representation of $g_{s-1}(\lambda_{1, s-1}, \lambda_{2, s-1})$. Suppose we only had the first corporation to be concerned with. Then we need not concern ourselves with $\lambda_{2, s-1}$ and so by the usual argument we would have that

$$g_{1s}(\lambda_{1s}, \lambda_{2s}) = \max_{0 \leqslant x_s \leqslant \lambda_{1s}} [h_s(x_s) + g_{s-1}(\lambda_{1s} - x_s, \lambda_{2s})] \tag{6.5.6}$$

where $g_{1s}(\ldots)$ represents a maximization with respect to x_s alone. It is clear that we have two decision variables, x_s and y_s, so that in (6.5.6) we are ignoring y_s. On the other hand, since we cannot, at stage s, have both corporations invest in opportunity s, (6.5.6) is correct as long as the investment by the second corporation does not yield a greater return. However, using the same argument that led to (6.5.6) but reversing the roles of x_s and y_s as well as λ_{1s} and λ_{2s}, we obtain the partial maximization

$$g_{2s}(\lambda_{1s}, \lambda_{2s}) = \max_{0 \leqslant y_s \leqslant \lambda_{2s}} [h_s(y_s) + g_{s-1}(\lambda_{1s}, \lambda_{2s} - y_s)] \tag{6.5.7}$$

It is now obvious that what we should do at each stage is choose whichever of $g_{1s}(\lambda_{1s}, \lambda_{2s})$ and $g_{2s}(\lambda_{1s}, \lambda_{2s})$ is largest, i.e.,

$$g_s(\lambda_{1s}, \lambda_{2s}) = \max[g_{1s}(\lambda_{1s}, \lambda_{2s}), g_{2s}(\lambda_{1s}, \lambda_{2s})] \tag{6.5.8}$$

From (6.5.5) to (6.5.8) we see that the recurrence relations for the solution of (6.5.4) are then given by

$$g_1(\lambda_{11}, \lambda_{21}) = \max[h_1(\lambda_{11}), h_1(\lambda_{21})] \tag{6.5.9}$$

$$g_s(\lambda_{1s}, \lambda_{2s}) = \max \begin{bmatrix} \max_{0 \leqslant x_s \leqslant \lambda_{1s}} [h_s(x_s) + g_{s-1}(\lambda_{1s} - x_s, \lambda_{2s})] \\ \max_{0 \leqslant y_s \leqslant \lambda_{2s}} [h_s(y_s) + g_{s-1}(\lambda_{1s}, \lambda_{2s} - y_s)] \end{bmatrix} \quad (s = 2, 3, \ldots, n) \tag{6.5.10}$$

It is useful to state explicitly the state transformations that are used in (6.5.10). These are

$$\lambda_{1, s-1} = \begin{cases} \lambda_{1s} - x_s, & g_{1s} \geqslant g_{2s} \\ \lambda_{1s}, & g_{1s} < g_{2s} \end{cases} \tag{6.5.11}$$

$$\lambda_{2, s-1} = \begin{cases} \lambda_{2s} - y_s, & g_{2s} \geqslant g_{1s} \\ \lambda_{2s}, & g_{2s} < g_{1s} \end{cases} \tag{6.5.12}$$

(6.5.11) and (6.5.12) are used in the usual way to calculate the state variables. The decision variable x_n^* is determined from $g_n(C_1, C_2)$. The values of the remaining variables $x_{n-1}^* \ldots x_1^*$ are then calculated using (6.5.11) and (6.5.12) in conjunction with the tabulations of $g_s(\lambda_{1s}, \lambda_{2s})$.

The case where the two corporations derive different returns from investing in the same enterprise or investment opportunity can be analyzed similarly. We define:

$h_{i1}(w)$ = return on the investment of w dollars in the ith investment opportunity by the first corporation.

$h_{i2}(w)$ = return on the investment of w dollars in the ith investment opportunity by the second corporation.

The problem we wish to solve now is

$$\max \quad z = \sum_{i=1}^{n} h_{i1}(x_i) + \sum_{i=1}^{n} h_{i2}(y_i)$$

subject to

$$\sum_{i=1}^{n} x_i = C_1 \tag{6.5.13}$$

$$\sum_{i=1}^{n} y_i = C_2$$

$$x_i y_i = 0 \quad (i = 1, 2, \ldots, n)$$

$$x_i, y_i \geqslant 0 \quad (i = 1, 2, \ldots, n)$$

Using the same argument as before we have

$$g_{1s}(\lambda_{1s}, \lambda_{2s}) = \max_{0 \leqslant x_s \leqslant \lambda_{1s}} [h_{1s}(x_s) + g_{s-1}(\lambda_{1s} - x_s, \lambda_{2s})] \tag{6.5.14}$$

$$g_{2s}(\lambda_{1s}, \lambda_{2s}) = \max_{0 \leqslant y_s \leqslant \lambda_{2s}} [h_{2s}(y_s) g_{s-1} + (\lambda_{1s}, \lambda_{2s} - y_s)] \tag{6.5.15}$$

We then have

$$g_s(\lambda_{1s}, \lambda_{2s}) = \max[g_{1s}(\lambda_{1s}, \lambda_{2s}), g_{2s}(\lambda_{1s}, \lambda_{2s})] \tag{6.5.16}$$

which yields

$$g_1(\lambda_{11}, \lambda_{21}) = \max[h_{11}(\lambda_{11}), \ h_{21}(\lambda_{21})] \qquad (6.5.17)$$

$$g_s(\lambda_{1s}, \lambda_{2s}) = \max \begin{bmatrix} \max_{0 \leq x_s \leq \lambda_{1s}} [h_{1s}(x_s) + g_{s-1}(\lambda_{1s} - x_s, \ \lambda_{2s})] \\ \max_{0 \leq y_s \leq \lambda_{2s}} [h_{2s}(y_s) + g_{s-1}(\lambda_{1s}, \ \lambda_{2s} - y_s)] \end{bmatrix} \quad (s = 2, 3, \ldots, n) \quad (6.5.18)$$

and the calculation of the optimal solution is the same as in the previous case.

6.6. A Stochastic Decision Problem

Suppose we own two gold mines which we will number 1 and 2. Each of the mines contains an amount of gold a_1 and a_2, respectively. We also have a valuable gold-mining machine with the peculiar property that if we use it to mine gold in the first mine there is a probability p_1 that it will mine a fraction r_1 of gold and remain in working order and a probability $(1-p_1)$ that it will mine no gold and be damaged beyond repair. Similarly, the second mine has associated with it the probabilities p_2 and $(1-p_2)$ and fraction r_2.[†] We can begin mining in either mine. If the machine is undamaged, we can again make a choice of either mine and continue in this way. Clearly, if the machine is damaged we must stop. What we would like to determine is what sequence of choices will maximize the total amount of gold we remove from both mines before the machine is damaged.

We define an optimal expected return as follows.

Let $g_s(\lambda_{1s}, \lambda_{2s})$ = expected amount of gold mined before the machine is damaged when the first mine has λ_{1s} left, the second mine has λ_{2s} and an optimal policy is employed which can last at most s stages.

First we consider the case when $s = 1$. It is obvious that the expected amount of gold from the first mine is $p_1 r_1 \lambda_{11}$ and from the second mine is $p_2 r_2 \lambda_{21}$. Therefore

$$g_1(\lambda_{11}, \lambda_{21}) = \max(p_1 r_1 \lambda_{11}, \ p_2 r_2 \lambda_{21}) \qquad (6.6.1)$$

We can analyze the general s stage process as follows. According to the principle of optimality, whatever our first decision is, the remaining decisions (which mine we use) must be optimal if we wish to have an optimal policy overall. If at stage s we choose the first mine, then λ_{11} will be affected but not λ_{21} since it refers to the second mine. If we define g_{1s} as the return from a choice of mine 1 and g_{2s} as the return from a choice of mine 2, then we have

$$g_{1s}(\lambda_{1s}, \lambda_{2s}) = p_1[r_1\lambda_{1s} + g_{s-1}((1-r_1)\lambda_{1s}, \lambda_{2s})] \qquad (6.6.2)$$

and

$$g_{2s}(\lambda_{1s}, \lambda_{2s}) = p_2[r_2\lambda_{2s} + g_{s-1}(\lambda_{1s}, (1-r_2)\lambda_{2s})] \qquad (6.6.3)$$

---

† This problem is due to Bellman [3]. One suspects that the original problem did not deal with gold mines and a mythical gold-mining machine, but rather with military objectives (gold mines), and weapons or missiles (gold-mining machine).

Since we wish to maximize the total amount of gold recovered from s stages we then have the following result:

$$g_s(\lambda_{1s}, \lambda_{2s}) = \max[g_{1s}(\lambda_{1s}, \lambda_{2s}), \ g_{2s}(\lambda_{1s}, \lambda_{2s})] \qquad (s = 2, 3, \ldots, n) \qquad (6.6.4)$$

From (6.6.1) to (6.6.4) we then have the recurrence relations

$$g_1(\lambda_{11}, \lambda_{21}) = \max(p_1 r_1 \lambda_{11}, \ p_2 r_2 \lambda_{21}) \qquad (6.6.5)$$

$$g_s(\lambda_{1s}, \lambda_{2s}) = \max\{p_1[r_1\lambda_{1s} + g_{s-1}((1-r_1)\lambda_{1s}, \lambda_{2s})],$$
$$p_2[r_2\lambda_{2s} + g_{s-1}(\lambda_{1s}, (1-r_2)\lambda_{2s})]\} \qquad (s = 2, 3, \ldots, n) \quad (6.6.6)$$

Suppose we wished to perform the calculation using (6.6.5) and (6.6.6) for a process consisting of n stages. The usual method of first calculating $g_s(\lambda_{1s}, \lambda_{2s})$ tables for $s = 1, 2, \ldots, n$ and the decision (mine 1 or mine 2) that led to the tabular value of g_s has an unfortunate complication. As we move backwards through the optimal decision tabulations, each successive $x_s^*, x_{s-1}^*, \ldots, x_1^*$ will require a finer and finer grid in the two-dimensional tables whose coordinates are λ_{1s} and λ_{2s}. Since $g_{1s}(\lambda_{1s}, \lambda_{2s})$ and $x_s^*(\lambda_{1s}, \lambda_{2s})$ is the first table calculated, an extremely fine grid size, which is difficult to predict in advance, is required. Since the decision variables are dichotomous (either the first mine or the second mine), interpolation is impossible. It is also not possible to use the computational strategy we employed for continuous variables in Section 5.6 because the $g_s(\lambda_{1s}, \lambda_{2s})$ are not continuous.

An alternative computational strategy can be employed which is awkward to describe but which can be programmed for a computer. We shall illustrate the procedure for $n = 3$. We have, from (6.6.5) and (6.6.6),

$$g_1(\lambda_{11}, \lambda_{21}) = \max(p_1 r_1 \lambda_{11}, \ p_2 r_2 \lambda_{21}) \qquad (6.6.7)$$

$$g_2(\lambda_{12}, \lambda_{22}) = \max\big[p_1\big(r_1\lambda_{12} + g_1((1-r_1)\lambda_{12}, \lambda_{22})\big),$$
$$p_2\big(r_2\lambda_{22} + g_1(\lambda_{12}, (1-r_2)\lambda_{22})\big)\big] \qquad (6.6.8)$$

$$g_3(a_1, a_2) = \max\big[p_1\big(r_1 a_1 + g_2((1-r_1)a_1, a_2)\big),$$
$$p_2 r_2 a_2 + a_1, \ (1-r_2)a_2\big) \big](\bar{z}_8) \qquad (6.6.9)$$

First we substitute (6.6.7) into (6.6.8) to obtain:

$$g_2(\lambda_{12}, \lambda_{22}) = \max\big[p_1\big(r_1\lambda_{12} + \max(p_1 r_1(1-r_1)\lambda_{12}, \ p_2 r_2\lambda_{22})\big),$$
$$p_2\big(r_2\lambda_{22} + \max(p_1 r_1\lambda_{12}, \ p_2 r_2(1-r_2)\lambda_{22})\big)\big] \qquad (6.6.10)$$

Then we substitute (6.6.10) into (6.6.9) to obtain

$$g_3(a_1, a_2) = \max\big\{p_1\big(r_1 a_1 + \max\big[p_1\big(r_1(1-r_1)a_1 + \max(p_1 r_1(1-r_1)^2 a_1, \ p_2 r_2 a_2)\big),$$
$$p_2\big(r_2 a_2 + \max(p_1 r_1(1-r_1)a_1, \ p_2 r_2(1-r_2)a_2)\big)\big]\big),$$
$$p_2\big(r_2 a_2 + \max\big[p_1\big(r_1 a_1 + \max(p_1 r_1(1-r_1)a_1, \ p_2 r_2(1-r_2)a_2)\big),$$
$$p_2\big(r_2(1-r_2)a_2 + \max(p_1 r_1 a_1, \ p_2 r_2(1-r_2)^2 a_2)\big)\big]\big)\big\} \qquad (6.6.11)$$

The first term in the curly brackets represents mine 1 and the second term mine 2. Depending upon which is larger, we then know whether $x_3^*(a_1, a_2) = 1$ or 2. Suppose $x_3^* = 1$. Then

$$\lambda_{12} = (1-r_1)\lambda_{13} = (1-r_1)a_1$$
$$\lambda_{22} = \lambda_{23} = a_2$$

(6.6.12)

If $x_3^* = 2$, then $\lambda_{12} = a_1$ and $\lambda_{22} = (1-r_2)a_2$.

From (6.6.12) and (6.6.10) we now have

$$g_2((1-r_1)a_1, a_2) = \max\left[p_1\left(r_1(1-r_1)a_1 + \max(p_1r_1(1-r_1)^2\,a_1,\ p_2r_2a_2)\right),\right.$$
$$\left.p_2\left(r_2a_2 + \max(p_1r_1(1-r_1)a_1,\ p_2r_2(1-r_2)a_2)\right)\right]$$

(6.6.13)

Again depending upon which term in the square bracket is larger, we find $x_2^* = 1$ or 2. Suppose $x_2^* = 2$. Then we have

$$\lambda_{11} = \lambda_{12} = (1-r_1)a_1$$
$$\lambda_{21} = (1-r_2)\lambda_{22} = (1-r_2)a_2$$

(6.6.14)

Substituting (6.6.14) into (6.6.7) we have

$$g_1((1-r_1)a_1, ((1-r_2)a_2)) = \max(p_1r_1(1-r_1)a_1,\ p_2r_2(1-r_2)a_2)$$

(6.6.15)

Depending upon which term is larger in (6.6.15) we have found $x_1^* = 1$ or 2. It should be noted that in (6.6.12) and (6.6.14) we made use of the general state transformations

$$\left.\begin{array}{l} \lambda_{1,\,s-1} = (1-r_1)\lambda_{1s} \\ \lambda_{2,\,s-1} = \lambda_{2s} \end{array}\right\} \quad \text{if mine 1 is selected}$$

$$\left.\begin{array}{l} \lambda_{1,\,s-1} = \lambda_{1s} \\ \lambda_{2,\,s-1} = (1-r_2)\lambda_{2s} \end{array}\right\} \quad \text{if mine 2 is selected}$$

$$(s = 2, 3, \ldots, n)$$

6.7. The Traveling Salesman Problem

The traveling salesman problem exemplifies a whole class of optimal scheduling problems which are difficult to solve. A statement of the problem is as follows. A salesman is required to visit, once and only once, each of n different cities starting from a base city and returning to this city. What path minimizes the total distance traveled by the salesman?

The obvious way to "solve" this problem is to calculate every possible permutation of the n cities and calculate the sum of the distances for each permutation or traveling salesman tour, as it is often called. It is clear that for n cities there are $n!$ permutations. Since this number grows large very rapidly, total enumeration of the tours is hardly a feasible computational method. While dynamic programming helps, it too suffers from severe problems of storage and computation beyond ~ 17 cities.

We fix the origin of the traveling salesman's tour at city 0. Now suppose that at a certain stage of an *optimal tour* starting at 0 one has reached a city i and there remain k

cities $j_1, j_2, \ldots, j_k$ to be visited before returning to 0. It is clear that since the tour is optimal, the path from i through $j_1, j_2, \ldots, j_k$ in some order and back to 0 must be of minimum length; if not the entire tour could not be optimal since a shorter path from i through $j_1, j_2, \ldots, j_k$ to 0 could be chosen. The reader will recognize that this argument is merely an application of the principle of optimality of dynamic programming.

We then define

$g_k(i; j_1, j_2, \ldots, j_k) \equiv$ length of a path of minimum length from i to 0 which passes, once and only once, through each of the remaining k cities $j_1, j_2, \ldots, j_k$.

Then by the above definition, if we obtain $g_n(0; j_1, j_2, \ldots, j_n)$ we shall have solved the traveling salesman problem. We also define

$$d_{ij} \equiv \text{distance between city } i \text{ and city } j.$$

Using the notation we have introduced and the principle of optimality, i.e., the argument of the preceding paragraph, we obtain the following recurrence relations:

$$g_k(i; j_1, j_2, \ldots, j_k) = \min_{1 \le m \le k} [d_{ij_m} + g_{k-1}(j_m; j_1, j_2, \ldots, j_{m-1}, j_{m+1}, \ldots, j_k)] \quad (6.7.1)$$
$$(i = 1, 2, \ldots, n)$$

We start the computation with

$$g_1(i; j_1) = d_{ij_1} + d_{j_10} \quad (i = 1, 2, \ldots, n) \quad (6.7.2)$$
$$(j_1 \neq i)$$

The computational procedure is just as we would expect. First we calculate $g_1(i; j_1)$, $i = 1, 2, \ldots, n$ from (6.7.2). Next we calculate $g_2(i; j_1, j_2)$ from (6.7.1) and so forth until at the last stage we compute $g_n(0; j_1, j_2, \ldots, j_n)$. In the calculation of g_n functions we also note which g_{n-1} led to the minimum or minima. We then go to the tabulation for g_{n-1} and note from which city (j_m) the return to city 0 takes place, as well as which g_{n-1} led to the minimum. We now continue this process until we have found the city to which the salesman went from city 0. We then have the optimal tour.

To illustrate the computational method we shall solve a four-city problem with the following distance matrix:

i \ j	0	1	2	3	4
0	0	10	8	18	14
1	10	0	7	11	4
2	8	7	0	6	5
3	18	11	6	0	9
4	14	4	5	9	0

First we calculate

$$g_1(i; j_1) = d_{ij_1} + d_{j_10}$$

Some sample calculations are:

$$g_1(1; 2) = d_{12} + d_{20} = 7 + 8 = 15$$
$$g_1(1; 4) = d_{14} + d_{40} = 4 + 14 = 18$$
$$g_1(2; 3) = d_{23} + d_{30} = 6 + 18 = 24$$

The complete tabulation of $g_1(i; j_1)$ is given in Table 6.7.1.

TABLE 6.7.1. $g_1(i; j_1)$

$g_1(1; 2) = 15$	$g_1(3; 1) = 21$
$g_1(1; 3) = 29$	$g_1(3; 2) = 14$
$g_1(1; 4) = 18$	$g_1(3; 4) = 23$
$g_1(2; 1) = 17$	$g_1(4; 1) = 14$
$g_1(2; 3) = 24$	$g_1(4; 2) = 13$
$g_1(2; 4) = 19$	$g_1(4; 3) = 27$

Next we calculate

$$g_2(i; j_1, j_2) = \min[d_{ij_1} + g_1(j_1; j_2), \ d_{ij_2} + g_1(j_2; j_1)]$$

For example:

$$g_2(1; 2, 3) = \min[d_{12} + g_1(2; 3), \ d_{13} + g_1(3; 2)]$$
$$= \min(7 + 24, \ 11 + 14) = 25 \ [g_1(3; 2)]$$
$$g_2(1; 3, 4) = \min[d_{13} + g_1(3; 4), \ d_{14} + g_1(4; 3)]$$
$$= \min(11 + 23, \ 4 + 27) = 31 \ [g_1(4; 3)]$$
$$g_2(2; 3, 4) = \min[d_{23} + g_1(3; 4), \ d_{24} + g_1(4; 3)]$$
$$= \min(6 + 23, \ 5 + 27) = 29 \ [g_1(3; 4)]$$

A complete listing of $g_2(i; j_1, j_2)$ is given in Table 6.7.2. In addition to the value of $g_2(i; j_1, j_2)$, the value of $g_1(i; j_1)$ that led to the optimal g_2 is also listed for use when we trace the optimal tour.

TABLE 6.7.2. $g_2(i; j_1, j_2)$

$g_2(1; 2, 3) = 25$	$[g_1(3; 2)]$	$g_2(3; 1, 2) = 23$	$[g_1(2; 1)]$
$g_2(1; 2, 4) = 17$	$[g_1(4; 2)]$	$g_2(3; 1, 4) = 23$	$[g_1(4; 1)]$
$g_2(1; 3, 4) = 31$	$[g_1(4; 3)]$	$g_2(3; 2, 4) = 22$	$[g_1(4; 2)]$
$g_2(2; 1, 3) = 27$	$[g_1(3; 1)]$	$g_2(4; 1, 2) = 19$	$[g_1(1; 2)]$
$g_2(2; 1, 4) = 19$	$[g_1(4; 1)]$	$g_2(4; 1, 3) = 30$	$[g_1(3; 1)]$
$g_2(2; 3, 4) = 29$	$[g_1(3; 4)]$	$g_2(4; 2, 3) = 23$	$[g_1(3; 2)]$

Next we calculate $g_3(i; j_1, j_2, j_3)$ from

$$g_3(i; j_1, j_2, j_3) = \min[d_{ij_1} + g_2(j_1; j_2, j_3), \ d_{ij_2} + g_2(j_2; j_1, j_3), \ d_{ij_3} + g_2(j_3; j_1, j_2)]$$

Some sample calculations are

$$g_3(1; 2, 3, 4) = \min[d_{12}+g_2(2; 3, 4), \ d_{13}+g_2(3; 2, 4), \ d_{14}+g_2(4; 2, 3)]$$
$$= \min(7+29, \ 11+22, \ 4+23) = 27 \ [g_2(4; 2, 3)]$$
$$g_3(3; 1, 2, 4) = \min[d_{31}+g_2(1; 2, 4), \ d_{32}+g_2(2; 1, 4), \ d_{34}+g_2(4; 1, 2)]$$
$$= \min(11+17, \ 6+19, \ 9+19) = 25 \ [g_2(2; 1, 4)]$$

A complete listing of $g_3(i; j_1, j_2, j_3)$ is given in Table 6.7.3.

TABLE 6.7.3. $g_3(i; j_1, j_2, j_3)$

$$g_3(1; 2, 3, 4) = 27 \quad [g_2(4; 2, 3)]$$
$$g_3(2; 1, 3, 4) = 29 \quad [g_2(3; 1, 4)]$$
$$g_3(3; 1, 2, 4) = 25 \quad [g_2(2; 1, 4)]$$
$$g_3(4; 1, 2, 3) = 29 \quad [g_2(1; 2, 3)]$$

At the last stage we calculate

$$g_4(0; 1, 2, 3, 4) = \min[d_{01}+g_3(1; 2, 3, 4), \ d_{02}+g_3(2; 1, 3, 4),$$
$$d_{03}+g_3(3; 1, 2, 4), \ d_{04}+g_3(4; 1, 2, 3)]$$

$$= \min(10+27, \ 8+29, \ 18+25, \ 14+29) = 37 \quad \begin{array}{l} [g_3(1; 2, 3, 4)] \\ [g_3(2; 1, 3, 4)] \end{array}$$

It should be noted that 37, the minimal cost tour, corresponds to both $10+27$ and $8+29$, i.e., there are two tours that lead to the minimum sum of distances. This comes about because the table of distances is symmetric, i.e., $d_{ij} = d_{ji}$. As we shall see, the two tours that we trace out will be the same sequence of cities but traversed in opposite directions.

Let us consider the first minimum tour. Since $g_3(1; 2, 3, 4)$ led to the minimum we know that we return to city 0 from city 1. Next we go to Table 6.7.3 and look at $g_3(1; 2, 3, 4)$. We see that $g_2(4; 2, 3)$ led to the minimum. Therefore we go to city 1 from city 4. Next we examine $g_2(4; 2, 3)$ in Table 6.7.2 and we find that $g_1(3; 2)$ led to this value and so we see that we go to city 4 from city 3 and to city 3 from city 2 and from 0 to city 2. Hence the optimal tour of the cities is

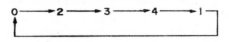

If we trace the solution corresponding to $g_3(2; 1, 3, 4)$ in the same way as we traced $g_3(1; 2, 3, 4)$, we obtain the tour

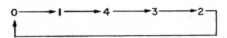

which is the reverse of the first tour. They both give the minimum sum of distances which is 37.

6.8. A Multicomponent Reliability Problem

A problem addressed and solved by Bellman [18] is one that arises in the design of complex systems such as switching networks, electronic systems, digital computers, etc. The problem is concerned with how to achieve a relatively high degree of reliability from components each of whose reliabilities may not be very high. An approach to dealing with this matter is to provide duplicate or, in general, a multiple number of one or more of the most unreliable components, so as to minimize the possibility of failure.

For conceptual purposes, the system will be regarded as a sequence of stages. Thus

The reliability of the system will be considered to be the probability that it operates successfully. This in turn will be taken to be the product of the reliabilities of each of the *n* stages. If the overall reliability of the system is too low, we can introduce one or more identical components at each stage, e.g.,

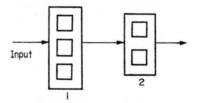

We must assume, of course, that the automatic sensing and switching apparatus that introduces a duplicate component, in place of a faulty one, is itself completely reliable.

The process of using multiple components at each stage can, in principle, enable one to approach any arbitrary degree of reliability, if sufficient replication is employed at each stage. What usually limits this process in a practical sense are considerations of such matters as cost, weight, size, etc., depending on the environment and function of the system. The general optimization problem we wish to solve is to determine how much duplication we need to employ at each of the *n* stages so as to maximize the overall reliability of the system and stay within constraints that we have imposed. We shall now formulate the problem.

We assume that at least one component must be used at each stage. Therefore we define:

$p_j(x_j)$ = probability of successful performance at the jth stage if $1+x_j$ components are used at the jth stage.

$\quad c_j$ = cost of the component at stage j.

$\quad w_j$ = weight of the component at stage j.

$\quad C$ = maximum allowable cost.

$\quad W$ = maximum allowable weight.

The problem we wish to solve is to

$$\max \quad z = \prod_{j=1}^{n} p_j(x_j) \qquad (6.8.1)$$

subject to

$$\sum_{j=1}^{n} c_j x_j \leq C \qquad (6.8.2)$$

$$\sum_{j=1}^{n} w_j x_j \leq W \qquad (6.8.3)$$

$$x_j \geq 0, \quad \text{integer} \qquad (6.8.4)$$

The problem given by (6.8.1)–(6.8.4) is similar to that of (6.2.1) except that the objective function involves a product of separable functions rather than a sum. We considered one-dimensional examples of such problems in Section 4.7. It should be clear that the recurrence relations for the solution of (6.8.1)–(6.8.4) are

$$g_1(\lambda_{11}, \lambda_{21}) = \max_{0 \leq x_1 \leq \xi_1} p_1(x_1) \qquad (6.8.5)$$

$$g_s(\lambda_{1s}, \lambda_{2s}) = \max_{0 \leq x_s \leq \xi_s} [p_s(x_s)g_{s-1}(\lambda_{1s}-c_s x_s, \lambda_{2s}-w_s x_s)] \qquad (s = 2, 3, \ldots, n)$$

where

$$\xi_s = \min\left(\left[\frac{\lambda_{1s}}{c_s}\right], \left[\frac{\lambda_{2s}}{w_s}\right]\right)$$

The state transformations are

$$\begin{aligned} \lambda_{1, s-1} &= \lambda_{1s} - c_s x_s \\ \lambda_{2, s-1} &= \lambda_{2s} - w_s x_s \end{aligned} \qquad (6.8.6)$$

The determination of $x_s^*(\lambda_{1s}, \lambda_{2s})$ is as described in Section 6.2.

We shall now consider a variation of our original problem. Suppose that at each stage we have a choice of two types of components, which we shall designate as component type A and component type B. We define

$p_{jA}(x_j), p_{jB}(x_j) =$ probability of successful performance at the jth state if $1+x_j$ of component type A or $1+x_j$ of type B, respectively, are used at stage j.

$c_{jA}, c_{jB} =$ cost of component type A and component type B, respectively, at stage j.

$w_{jA}, w_{jB} =$ weight of component type A and component type B, respectively, at stage j.

Given the same restrictions on total cost and total weight as in (6.8.2) and (6.8.3), we wish to determine at each stage which component (A or B) and the quantities which will maximize the overall reliability of the system. We shall assume for simplicity that it is not allowed, at any stage, to combine components of type A and components of type B. (In principle, it is no more difficult to solve this problem.)

Using the same guiding principles as in the previous case we obtain the following recurrence relations:

$$g_1(\lambda_{11}, \lambda_{21}) = \max \begin{bmatrix} \max_{0 \le x_1 \le \xi_{1A}} p_{1A}(x_1) \\ \max_{0 \le x_1 \le \xi_{1B}} p_{1B}(x_1) \end{bmatrix} \tag{6.8.7}$$

$$g_s(\lambda_{1s}, \lambda_{2s}) = \max \begin{bmatrix} \left[\max_{0 \le x_s \le \xi_{sA}} p_{sA}(x_s)g_{s-1}(\lambda_{1s} - c_{sA}x_s, \ \lambda_{2s} - w_{sA}x_s) \right] \\ \left[\max_{0 \le x_s \le \xi_{sB}} p_{sB}(x_s)g_{s-1}(\lambda_{1s} - c_{sB}x_s, \ \lambda_{2s} - w_{sB}x_s) \right] \end{bmatrix} \tag{6.8.8}$$

where

$$\xi_{sA} = \min\left(\left[\frac{\lambda_{1s}}{c_{sA}} \right], \ \left[\frac{\lambda_{2s}}{w_{sA}} \right] \right)$$

$$\xi_{sB} = \min\left(\left[\frac{\lambda_{1s}}{c_{sB}} \right], \ \left[\frac{\lambda_{2s}}{w_{sB}} \right] \right) \tag{6.8.9}$$

The state transformations are

$$\left. \begin{array}{l} \lambda_{1,s-1} = \lambda_{1s} - c_{sA}x_s \\ \lambda_{2,s-1} = \lambda_{2s} - w_{sA}x_s \end{array} \right\} \quad \text{if component type } A \text{ is chosen}$$

$$\left. \begin{array}{l} \lambda_{1,s-1} = \lambda_{1s} - c_{sB}x_s \\ \lambda_{2,s-1} = \lambda_{2s} - w_{sB}x_s \end{array} \right\} \quad \text{if component type } B \text{ is chosen}$$

$$(s = 1, 2, \ldots, n)$$

6.9. A Problem in Product Development and Planning

Suppose we are engaged in developing a new product for a market in which there are also others interested. We do not know exactly when a substantial demand for the product will emerge and we are currently in the initial phases of developing a large-scale production capacity. Suppose, further, that we are producing the product in a small expensive interim production facility. We have available to us T dollars and a quantity P of the product, together with the prerogative of investing more money to increase production at specified times $t_1 < t_2 < \ldots$. At the jth time t_j, a quantity $c_j y$ may be produced for y dollars used to expand production capability, where c_j is a monotone increasing function. The condition that $c_j > c_{j-1}$ indicates that it will cost less to produce one unit of product at a later date because of improved production techniques. Hence the longer we can wait to go into full-scale production, the cheaper the cost of full-scale production becomes. Given the probability that large-scale demand for the product occurs between t_j and t_{j+1} and the assumption that we can only get a viable share of the market if the amount of product on hand is sufficient to meet some minimum demand, the problem is to determine how much to invest in production in each period so as to maximize the over-all probability of successful market penetration, if the probability of success with a given amount of product is known.

We define

x_j = number of dollars invested in production in period j.

n = total number of time periods under consideration.

p_j = probability of large-scale demand occurring between t_j and t_{j+1}, assuming that it has not occurred previously.

$\phi(y)$ = probability of success with a quantity y of product.

We shall also define the following optimal return functions:

$g_s(\lambda_{1s}, \lambda_{2s})$ = over-all probability of success using an optimal investment in production from t_s on, given λ_{1s} dollars and a quantity λ_{2s} of product on hand.

It is clear that in the last period, t_n to t_{n+1}, we have that

$$g_n(\lambda_{1n}, \lambda_{2n}) = \max_{0 \leqslant x_n \leqslant \lambda_{1n}} p_n \phi(\lambda_{2n} + c_n x_n) \tag{6.9.1}$$

Now suppose we are in period s. The over-all probability of success using an optimal investment policy is obtained by choosing x_s according to the principle of optimality, i.e., choosing x_s so that the probability of success in the current period plus the probability of success in all subsequent periods using an optimal policy is maximized. The probability of success in the current period t_s to t_{s+1} is

$$p_s \phi(\lambda_{2s} + c_s x_s) \tag{6.9.2}$$

The probability of success in all subsequent periods using an optimal policy is

$$(1 - p_s) g_{s+1}(\lambda_{1s} - x_s, \lambda_{2s} + c_s x_s) \tag{6.9.3}$$

We wish to choose x_s so that the sum of (6.9.2) and (6.9.3) is maximized. But this maximum sum is, by definition, the over-all probability of success using an optimal investment policy from t_s on, given λ_{1s} dollars and a quantity λ_{2s} of product on hand. We therefore have the recurrence relations

$$g_s(\lambda_{1s}, \lambda_{2s}) = \max_{0 \leqslant x_s \leqslant \lambda_{1s}} [p_s \phi(\lambda_{2s} + c_s x_s)$$
$$+ (1 - p_s) g_{s+1}(\lambda_{1s} - x_s, \lambda_{2s} + c_s x_s)] \quad (s = 1, 2, \ldots, n-1) \tag{6.9.4}$$

In making the computations, we would also tabulate the values of $x_s^*(\lambda_{1s}, \lambda_{2s})$ which yielded the optimal returns $g_s(\lambda_{1s}, \lambda_{2s})$. Observe that we proceed *backwards* through the optimal return functions. First we compute $g_n(\lambda_{1n}, \lambda_{2n})$ for all possible values of $\lambda_{1s}, \lambda_{2s}$. Then we calculate $g_{n-1}(\lambda_{1, n-1}, \lambda_{2, n-1})$ from (6.9.4) and the previously calculated values of $g_n(\lambda_{1n}, \lambda_{2n})$. We proceed this way until we get to the first stage. At this stage we calculate $g_1(T, P)$ from

$$g_1(T, P) = \max_{0 \leqslant x_1 \leqslant T} [p_1 \phi(P + c_1 x_1) + (1 - p_1) g_2(T - x_1, P + c_1 x_1)]$$

This also gives us x_1^*. Then we use the state transformation relationships

$$\lambda_{1,\,s+1} = \lambda_{1s} - x_s$$
$$\lambda_{2,\,s+1} = \lambda_{2s} + c_s x_s \qquad (s = 1, 2, \ldots, n-1) \qquad (6.9.5)$$

to calculate $x_2^*, x_3^*, \ldots, x_n^*$ as we move forward through the tables or other functional representation.

6.10. A Smoothing Problem

In Section 4.8 we discussed a one-dimensional smoothing problem. Let us now consider a more complex example of a smoothing process. This example of quadratic smoothing has numerous applications in control theory and data analysis.

Suppose we wish to minimize the function

$$z = \alpha_1(x_1 - r_1)^2 + \alpha_2(x_2 - 2x_1 + r_2)^2 + \sum_{j=3}^{n} \alpha_j(x_j - 2x_{j-1} + x_{j-2})^2 + \sum_{j=1}^{n} \beta_j x_j^2 \qquad (6.10.1)$$

It is a simple matter to develop two-dimensional recurrence relations by applying the principle of optimality if one utilizes the appropriate definition of state variables. Otherwise, solving (6.10.1) by dynamic programming does not look promising.

We define the optimal return functions as follows:

$$g_s(\lambda_{1s}, \lambda_{2s}) \equiv \min_{x_s} \left[\alpha_s(x_s - \lambda_{1s})^2 + \alpha_{s+1}(x_{s+1} - 2x_s + \lambda_{2s})^2 \right.$$
$$\left. + \sum_{j=s+2}^{n} \alpha_j(x_j - 2x_{j-1} + x_{j-2})^2 + \sum_{j=s}^{n} \beta_j x_j^2 \right] \qquad (s = 1, 2, \ldots, n-2) \qquad (6.10.2)$$

The only complication we must deal with in using the definitions (6.10.2) to derive recurrence relations is that the last *two* stages must be treated simultaneously, i.e., we simultaneously determine x_n and x_{n-1} when we calculate $g_{n-1}(\lambda_{1,\,n-1}, \lambda_{2,\,n-1})$. Hence we calculate at this terminal stage (which we compute first)

$$g_{n-1}(\lambda_{1,\,n-1}, \lambda_{2,\,n-1}) = \min_{x_n,\,x_{n-1}} [\alpha_{n-1}(x_{n-1} - \lambda_{1,\,n-1})$$
$$+ \alpha_n(x_n - 2x_{n-1} + \lambda_{2,\,n-1})^2 + b_{n-1}x_{n-1}^2 + b_n x_n^2] \qquad (6.10.3)$$

Now suppose we are at stage $n-2$. We can see from (6.10.2) that

$$g_{n-2}(\lambda_{1,\,n-2}, \lambda_{2,\,n-2}) = \min_{x_{n-2}} \left[\alpha_{n-2}(x_{n-2} - \lambda_{1,\,n-2})^2 + \alpha_{n-1}(x_{n-1} - 2x_{n-2} + \lambda_{2,\,n-2})^2 \right.$$
$$\left. + \alpha_n(x_n - 2x_{n-1} + x_{n-2})^2 + \beta_{n-2}x_{n-2}^2 + {}_{n-2}^{2} + \sum_{j=n-1}^{n} \beta_j x_j^2 \right]$$
$$= \min_{x_{n-2}} \left\{ \alpha_{n-2}(x_{n-2} - \lambda_{1,\,n-2})^2 + \beta_{n-2}x_{n-2}^2 + \left[\alpha_{n-1}(x_{n-1} - 2x_{n-2} \right. \right.$$
$$\left. \left. + \lambda_{2,\,n-2})^2 + \alpha_n(x_n - 2x_{n-1} + x_{n-2})^2 + \sum_{j=n-1}^{n} \beta_j x_j^2 \right] \right\} \qquad (6.10.4)$$

It can be seen that the term in the square brackets [ ] in (6.10.4) is $g_{n-1}(2x_{n-2}-\lambda_{2,n-2}, x_{-2})$. This can be directly verified by using (6.10.3), i.e.,

$$g_{n-1}(2x_{n-2}-\lambda_{2,n-2}, x_{n-2})\} = \min_{x_n,\, x_{n-1}} [[\alpha_{n-1}(x_{n-1}-2x_{n-2}-\lambda_{2,n-2})$$

$$+\alpha_n(x_n-2x_{n-1}+x_{n-2})^2+b_{n-1}x_{n-1}^2+b_nx_n^2] \qquad (6.10.5)$$

Therefore, we have from (6.10.4) and (6.10.5) that

$$g_{n-2}(\lambda_{1,n-2}, \lambda_{2,n-2}) = \min_{x_{n-2}} [\alpha_{n-2}(x_{n-2}-\lambda_{1,n-2})^2+b_{n-2}x_{n-2}^2$$

$$+g_{n-1}(2x_{n-2}-\lambda_{2,n-2}, x_{n-2})] \qquad (6.10.6)$$

A repetition of the above argument for all subsequent stages gives us the recurrence relations

$$g_s(\lambda_{1s}, \lambda_{2s}) = \min_{x_s} [\alpha_s(x_s-\lambda_{1s})^2+b_sx_s^2+g_{s+1}(2x_s-\lambda_{2s}, x_s)] \qquad (6.10.7)$$

$$(s = 1, 2, \ldots, n-2)$$

Hence (6.10.3) and (6.10.7) enable us to solve the original problem.

It is possible to determine analytically the optimal values of $x_n^*, x_{n-1}^*, \ldots, x_1^*$ by differentiating and setting equal to zero the arguments of the minimands in (6.10.3) and (6.10.7). We carried out an analogous analysis for the one-dimensional process in Section 4.8. However, the amount of algebra probably does not justify the effort. Any numerical problem is probably solved more easily by tabulation.

6.11. Operation of a Chemical Reactor

We wish to consider a chemical reactor which has a single feed stream which reacts inside the reactor over a catalyst to produce a product. We wish to distribute a fixed quantity of the feed material over various stages of time, i.e., introduce a certain fraction of the feed (or feed rate) in the first period, another fraction in the second period, etc., until the total feed rate desired is reached. We also wish to use a staged distribution of the feed (instead of all at once) because the activity of the catalyst, which determines the conversion of feed to product, as well as the purity of the product, depends both upon the feed rate as well as the cumulative feed rate.

Our only decision variables are x_j, the feed rates. The profit of the reactor depends upon the quantity of the product as well as its purity. The product purity depends upon the current feed rate as well as the cumulative throughput of feed material through the catalyst bed. The conversion also depends on current feed rate as well as cumulative throughput of feed through the catalyst bed. For example, conversion is usually a maximum at some current feed rate and it decreases with increasing cumulative feed rates X_j. A typical conversion plot would be

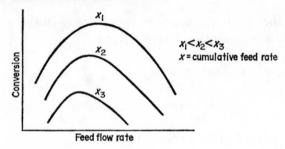

Similarly, the product purity plot might be

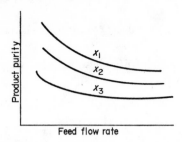

We now define some quantities of interest. Let

x_j = feed flow rate in period j.

$$X_j = \sum_{k=1}^{j-1} x_k \qquad = \text{cumulative feed flow rate at the beginning of period } j.$$

$C_j = C_j(x_j, X_j) = $ conversion of feed, i.e., the fraction of x_j converted to product in period j.

$P_j = P_j(x_j, X_j) = $ product purity per unit of x_j during period j.

$R_j = R_j(P_j) \qquad = $ market value of product purity per unit of P_j.

$V_j(x_j, X_j) = x_j C_j P_j R_j \qquad = $ product value in period j.

$T = $ total feed flow rate.

We wish to maximize the total product value over n periods, i.e.,

$$\max \quad z = \sum_{j=1}^{n} V_j(x_j, X_j)$$

subject to

$$\sum_{j=1}^{n} x_j = T \qquad\qquad (6.11.1)$$

$$x_j \geqslant 0 \qquad (j = 1, 2, \ldots, n)$$

In order to solve (6.11.1) we shall require two state variables. The first state variable, λ_{1s}, will limit the range over which x_s may vary, i.e., it will relate to the current feed rate. The second state variable, λ_{2s}, will specify the cumulative throughput of fresh feed rate. If we then define

$g_s(\lambda_{1s}, \lambda_{2s}) \equiv$ maximum profit over n periods if the feed rates are selected optimally.

The state variables are

$$\lambda_{1s} = \sum_{j=1}^{s} x_j, \quad \lambda_{2s} = X_s = \sum_{j=1}^{s-1} x_j \qquad (6.11.2)$$

The state transformations are given by

$$\lambda_{1, s-1} = \lambda_{1s} - x_s, \quad \lambda_{2, s-1} = \lambda_{2s} + x_s \qquad (6.11.3)$$

which indicates the stages are numbered in reverse order to the direction of time.

The recurrence relations for the optimal returns, $g_s(\lambda_{1s}, \lambda_{2s})$, are obtained in the usual way by applying the principle of optimality to (6.11.1) with the state transformations given by (6.11.2). They are

$$g_1(\lambda_{11}, \lambda_{21}) = \max_{0 \leqslant x_1 \leqslant \lambda_{11}} V_1(x_1, \lambda_{21}) = V_1(\lambda_{11}, \lambda_{21}) \qquad (6.11.4)$$

for the first stage and the general recurrence relation is given by

$$g_s(\lambda_{1s}, \lambda_{2s}) = \max_{0 \leqslant x_s \leqslant \lambda_{1s}} [V_s(x_s, \lambda_{2s}) + g_{s-1}(\lambda_{1s} - x_s, \lambda_{2s} + x_s)] \quad (s = 2, 3, \ldots, n) \quad (6.11.5)$$

The values of $x_s^*(\lambda_{1s}, \lambda_{2s})$ are noted as usual in the calculations using (6.11.4) and (6.11.5).

The technique employed in using a second state variable to keep track of a cumulative variable such as the sum of the decision variables can be applied to other problems where some measure of performance depends upon a sum of decisions as well as the current decision.

Exercises—Chapter 6

6.1. Solve by dynamic programming

$$\max \quad z = 3x_1^2 + 20x_2 + x_2^2 + x_3 + 2x_3^2$$

subject to
$$2x_1 + 3x_2 + 4x_3 \leqslant 16$$
$$4x_1 + 2x_2 + 3x_3 \leqslant 18$$
$$x_1, x_2, x_3 \geqslant 0, \quad \text{integer}$$

6.2. Solve by dynamic programming

$$\max \quad z = 2e^{x_1} + 3x_2^2 + 9 \ln x_3$$

subject to
$$5x_1 + 2x_2 + x_3 \leqslant 20$$
$$7x_1 + 4x_2 + 2x_3 \leqslant 24$$
$$x_1, x_2, x_3 \geqslant 0, \quad \text{integer}$$

6.3. Solve by dynamic programming

$$\max \quad z = 2y_1 e^{x_1} + 3x_2 y_2 + x_3^2 y_3^2$$

subject to
$$8x_1^2 + 2x_2^2 + 6x_3^2 \leqslant 66$$
$$5y_1 + y_2 + 3y_3 \leqslant 42$$
$$x_1, x_2, x_3, y_1, y_2, y_3 \geqslant 0, \quad \text{integer}$$

6.4. Solve by dynamic programming

$$\min \quad z = x_1^2 x_2^3 x_3$$

subject to
$$5x_1 + 10x_2 + x_3 \geqslant 24$$
$$x_1 x_2 x_3 \geqslant 3$$
$$x_1, x_2, x_3 \geqslant 0$$

11*

6.5. Solve the following six-city traveling salesman pro blem with the cost matrix

i \ j	0	1	2	3	4	5	6
0	0	10	20	30	21	40	27
1	10	0	15	20	25	30	40
2	20	15	0	20	18	15	10
3	30	20	20	0	6	12	18
4	21	25	18	6	0	14	28
5	40	30	15	12	14	0	11
6	27	40	10	18	28	11	0

6.6. Solve the following five-city traveling salesman problem with the cost matrix

i \ j	0	1	2	3	4	5
0	0	10	20	30	40	50
1	12	0	18	30	25	21
2	23	19	0	5	10	15
3	34	32	4	0	8	16
4	45	27	11	10	0	18
5	56	22	16	20	12	0

6.7. The wandering applied mathematician, referred to and discussed in Section 2.3, finds that his problem is somewhat more complicated than he first thought. In addition to total weight, he remembers that his airline also has a stipulation of total volume on his baggage. Hence, he finds that his total volume cannot exceed 8 cubic feet. A summary of the relevant data is:

Item	Weight (lb)	Volume (ft^3)	Estimated profit
1	2	3	110
2	3	1	160
3	5	2	260
4	4	1	210

Find the solution which maximizes his estimated profit.

6.8. Suppose you wish to buy stock in one or all of three different corporations. Stock A is presently worth $60 per share and your broker says that one month after its purchase it may be worth $56, $58, $60, or $62, each of these being equally likely. Stock B is worth $56 and after one month may be worth $58, or $60, each being equally likely. Stock C is worth $58 and it is predicted to remain constant after one month. Your purchases must be in blocks of 100 shares and the total purchase is not to exceed 1000 shares. What is the buying policy that will maximize the expected value of your holdings after one month?

Chapter 7

Reduction of State Dimensionality and Approximations

7.1. Introduction

In Chapter 6 we showed that problems for which there were more than one state variable and/or more than one decision variable at each stage became intractable in terms of both the storage and computation that were required. In general, we saw that for high dimensionality in the state variables and in the decision variables, the standard dynamic programming approach resulted in multidimensional tables or grids of points in the state variables and decision variables. Hence the direct application of the principle of optimality to multidimensional problems is probably limited to problems of dimensionality less than 6; otherwise the computational and storage requirements exceed those of even the largest and most rapid computer that can be imagined.

This limitation of the applicability of dynamic programming to problems of relatively low dimensionality is clearly its most significant drawback. A certain amount of work has been done to find ways to circumvent the dimensionality problem. The techniques that have been suggested, though widely different in outlook and methodology, all have the property that while the useful range of dimensionality is widened, it is by no means as great as we might like for all possible applications. Hence these techniques for extending the feasible range of the dimensionality of the state variables, while useful, do not generally go as far as we would like. The most fruitful area of research in dynamic programming is to find more effective means to deal with the vexing problem of high dimensionality. At this point in time it appears that there remains a great deal yet to do.

In the succeeding sections of this chapter we shall discuss several techniques for dealing with the dimensionality problem, using both exact and approximate methods.

7.2. Lagrange Multipliers and Reduction of State Variables

The use of Lagrange multipliers originated in efforts to solve problems in the calculus of variations which were also constrained by an equality relationship involving the unknown function. A more familiar use is probably in solving constrained optimization problems of the form

$$\max \quad z = \phi(\mathbf{x})$$

subject to
$$h_i(\mathbf{x}) = b_i \quad (i = 1, 2, \ldots, m) \tag{7.2.1}$$

where $\mathbf{x} = (x_1, x_2, \ldots, x_n)$. It is well known [1] that the problem given by (7.2.1) can be converted into the *unconstrained* optimization problem (providing certain conditions given below are met)

$$\max \quad Z(\mathbf{x}, \mu) = \phi(\mathbf{x}) + \sum_{i=1}^{m} \mu_i[b_i - h_i(\mathbf{x})] \qquad (7.2.2)$$

where $\mu = (\mu_1, \mu_2, \ldots, \mu_m)$ are called *Lagrange multipliers* and $Z(x, \mu)$ is called the *Lagrangian function*. Providing that the rank of the $m \times n$ matrix $\left\| \dfrac{\partial h_i}{\partial x_j} \right\|$ (the Jacobian matrix) is equal to m at the optimal point $\mathbf{x}^0$, then a necessary condition that $\phi(\mathbf{x})$ have a relative maximum at $\mathbf{x}^0$, subject to the constraints $h_i(\mathbf{x}) = b_i$, $i = 1, 2, \ldots, m$, is that the first partial derivatives of $Z(\mathbf{x}, \mu)$ with respect to each of the arguments x_j and μ_i vanish. In other words, $Z(\mathbf{x}, \mu)$ may be treated as an unconstrained function for purposes of optimization. In what follows we shall make use of this idea and (7.2.2) to reduce the dimensionality of a dynamic programming problem.

To illustrate how we utilize Lagrange multipliers, consider the following general problem:

$$\max \quad z = \sum_{j=1}^{n} \phi_j(x_j) \qquad (7.2.3)$$

subject to

$$\sum_{j=1}^{n} h_{1j}(x_j) \leq b_1 \qquad (7.2.4)$$

$$\sum_{j=1}^{n} h_{2j}(x_j) \leq b_2 \qquad (7.2.5)$$

$$x_j \geq 0 \quad (j = 1, 2, \ldots, n) \qquad (7.2.6)$$

where we assume that $\phi_j(x_j)$ are nondecreasing functions of x_j and for one of the constraints, say, $\sum_{j=1}^{n} h_{1j}(x_j) \leq \sum_{j=1}^{n} h_{1j}(x_j^*)$, where x_j^* are the components of the optimal solution. In Chapter 6 we discussed how (7.2.3)–(7.2.6) could be solved by the use of optimal return functions that depend upon two state variables. We shall now consider how we might solve (7.2.3)–(7.2.6) using one state variable. Since we assumed that the $\phi_j(x_j)$ were nondecreasing functions of x_j, the x_j are continuous variables, and the condition given above on the first constraint, then it is clear that at least one of the constraints (7.2.4) or (7.2.5) must hold as a strict equality for an optimal solution. Suppose we assume that the first constraint holds as an equality for an optimal solution. We now consider the following problem:

$$\max \quad Z = \sum_{j=1}^{n} \phi_j(x_j) - \mu \sum_{j=1}^{n} h_{1j}(x_j)$$

$$\qquad (7.2.7)$$

subject to

$$\sum_{j=1}^{n} h_{2j}(x_j) \leq b_2$$

$$x_j \geq 0 \quad (j = 1, 2, \ldots, n)$$

The problem (7.2.7) can be solved, for a fixed value of μ, using only one state variable since there is only one constraint. Hence we can solve (7.2.7) as we solved (5.5.1), using the following recurrence equations:

$$g_1(\lambda_1) = \max_{x_1 = \lambda_1} [\phi_1(x_1) - \mu h_{11}(x_1)] \tag{7.2.8}$$

$$g_s(\lambda_s) = \max_{0 \leqslant x_s \leqslant \xi_s} [\phi_s(x_s) - \mu h_{1s}(x_s) + g_{s-1}(\lambda_s - h_{2s}(x_s))] \quad (s = 2 \ldots n) \tag{7.2.9}$$

where ξ_s is a root of

$$\lambda_s - h_{2s}(\xi_s) = 0 \tag{7.2.10}$$

Hence, using (7.2.8)–(7.2.10) we obtain an optimal solution $\mathbf{x}^* = (x_1^*, x_2^*, \ldots, x_n^*)$ to (7.2.7) for some fixed value of μ. Obviously, we can do this for various values of μ. We shall now show that if a solution $\mathbf{x}^*(\mu)$ to (7.2.7) is obtained such that

$$\sum_{j=1}^{n} h_{1j}(x_j^*) = b_1 \tag{7.2.11}$$

then this particular solution $\mathbf{x}^*$ is an optimal solution to (7.2.3)–(7.2.6). We have written $\mathbf{x}^*$ as $\mathbf{x}^*(\mu)$ to emphasize that a different set of values $\mathbf{x}^*$ is obtained for every assumed value of μ. First, we may note that $\mathbf{x}^*(\mu)$ is clearly a feasible solution to (7.2.3)–(7.2.6) since (7.2.8)–(7.2.10) guarantees such a solution providing that (7.2.4) is satisfied, which (7.2.11) provides. Suppose we assume the contrary of what we wish to show, viz., an optimal solution $\mathbf{x}^0$ to (7.2.3)–(7.2.6) exists such that

$$z(\mathbf{x}^0) = \sum_{j=1}^{n} \phi_j(x_j^0) > \sum_{j=1}^{n} \phi_j(x_j^*) = z(\mathbf{x}^*) \tag{7.2.12}$$

However, since $\mathbf{x}^*$ is an optimal solution to (7.2.7) we know that

$$Z(\mathbf{x}^*) = \sum_{j=1}^{n} \phi_j(x_j^*) - \mu \sum_{j=1}^{n} h_{1j}(x_j^*) \geqslant \sum_{j=1}^{n} \phi_j(x_j^0) - \mu \sum_{j=1}^{n} h_{1j}(x_j^0) = Z(\mathbf{x}^0) \tag{7.2.13}$$

Noting that

$$z(\mathbf{x}^*) = \sum_{j=1}^{n} \phi_j(x_j^*)$$

and

$$z(\mathbf{x}^0) = \sum_{j=1}^{n} \phi_j(x_j^0)$$

we can rewrite (7.2.13) as

$$Z(\mathbf{x}^*) = z(\mathbf{x}^*) - \mu \sum_{j=1}^{n} h_{1j}(x_j^*) \geqslant z(\mathbf{x}^0) - \mu \sum_{j=1}^{n} h_{1j}(x_j^0) = Z(\mathbf{x}^0) \tag{7.2.14}$$

However, since both $\mathbf{x}^0$ and $\mathbf{x}^*$ satisfy (7.2.11),

$$\sum_{j=1}^{n} h_{1j}(\mathbf{x}^*) = b_1, \quad \sum_{j=1}^{n} h_{1j}(\mathbf{x}^0) = b_1 \tag{7.2.15}$$

then from (7.2.14) and (7.2.15) we have that

$$z(\mathbf{x}^*) \geqslant z(\mathbf{x}^0)$$

which contradicts our assumption in (7.2.12). Therefore $\mathbf{x}^*$ is a solution to (7.2.3)–(7.2.6) when (7.2.11) is satisfied.

Before we can use this result to put together a complete computational algorithm, we need to know how $\sum_{j=1}^{n} h_{1j}(\mathbf{x}_j^*)$ varies with μ since we must clearly solve (7.2.7) with various values of μ, until (7.2.11) is satisfied. We shall now show that as μ increases from 0 to ∞, the quantity $\sum_{j=1}^{n} h_{1j}(\mathbf{x}_j^*(\mu))$ decreases monotonically. First we define

$$\sum_{j=1}^{n} \phi_j(x_j^*(\mu)) = z_\mu, \quad \sum_{j=1}^{n} h_{1j}(x_j^*(\mu)) = h_\mu \tag{7.2.16}$$

From (7.2.16) and (7.2.7) we note that

$$Z(\mathbf{x}^*(\mu), \mu) = z_\mu - \mu h_\mu \tag{7.2.17}$$

We also note that

$$Z(\mathbf{x}^*(\mu), \mu') = z_\mu - \mu' h_\mu \tag{7.2.18}$$

Let us assume that $0 < \mu < \mu'$. Since the functions defined in (7.2.17) and (7.2.18) give the maximum values of Z, we see that

$$\begin{aligned} Z(\mathbf{x}^*(\mu), \mu) &\geqslant Z(\mathbf{x}^*(\mu'), \mu) \\ Z(\mathbf{x}^*(\mu'), \mu') &\geqslant Z(\mathbf{x}^*(\mu), \mu') \end{aligned} \tag{7.2.19}$$

Using (7.2.17) and (7.2.18) with (7.2.19) we obtain

$$\begin{aligned} z_\mu - \mu h_\mu &\geqslant z_{\mu'} - \mu h_{\mu'} \\ z_{\mu'} - \mu' h_{\mu'} &\geqslant z_\mu - \mu' h_\mu \end{aligned} \tag{7.2.20}$$

Combining the two inequalities of (7.2.20) we have

$$(\mu' - \mu)h_\mu \geqslant (\mu' - \mu)h_{\mu'} \tag{7.2.21}$$

Since $\mu' - \mu > 0$ we obtain from (7.2.21) that

$$h_\mu \geqslant h_{\mu'}$$

or

$$\sum_{j=1}^{n} h_{1j}(x_j^*(\mu)) \geqslant \sum_{j=1}^{n} h_{1j}(x_j^*(\mu'))$$

which is what we wished to prove.

We have shown that if (7.2.11) is satisfied, we have an optimal solution. We have also shown that the constraint function decreases monotonically with μ. However, it may not be possible by varying μ to ever satisfy (7.2.11). We shall return to this matter later.

First we shall describe how to use the Lagrange multiplier in practice and give some examples.

Based on what we have shown above, we can solve (7.2.3)–(7.2.6) as follows. Select an initial value of μ, say μ_1, and solve (7.2.7). If the solution $\mathbf{x}^*(\mu_1)$ satisfies (7.2.11) we are done. If not we select another value of μ, say μ_2, and repeat the calculation to obtain $\mathbf{x}^*(\mu_2)$. If this value of $\mathbf{x}^*$ does not satisfy (7.2.11) we can estimate a third value μ_3 to try by observing the difference between $\sum_{j=1}^{n} h_{1j}(x_j^*)$ and b_1 and using interpolation or extrapolation to continue the process. When this procedure works, it is a relatively simple matter to find the correct value of μ and the optimal solution $\mathbf{x}^*$ in five or six iterations of the process.

Most often we shall be concerned with problems for which the x_j are required to be integers. This may occur because the original constraints included such a stipulation or because we have made a discrete approximation to a continuous variable. In such a situation it is not necessarily true that either constraint (7.2.4) or (7.2.5) holds as a strict equality. Formally, one can proceed by varying μ so that $z(\mathbf{x}^*(\mu))$ is made as large as possible without violating either constraint. This procedure may fail, however, because no μ exists for an integer solution. The following examples serve to illustrate these ideas.

Consider the problem

$$\max \quad z = x_1 + 5x_2 + 7x_3 + 11x_4$$

subject to
$$8x_1 + 6x_2 + 5x_3 + 10x_4 \leqslant 30$$
$$x_1 + 3x_2 + 4x_3 + 6x_4 \leqslant 19 \qquad (7.2.22)$$
$$x_1, x_2, x_3, x_4 \geqslant 0, \quad \text{integer}$$

(7.2.22) is a linear programming problem, if we ignore the integrality constraint, and has the solution $z^* = 34.5$, $x_1^* = 0$, $x_2^* = 0$, $x_3^* = 1$, $x_4^* = 2.5$. For this solution both constraints hold as equalities. Let us now seek the solution to (7.2.22). We shall take the first constraint into the objective function. Hence we wish to solve

$$\max \quad Z = x_1 + 5x_2 + 7x_3 + 11x_4 - \mu(8x_1 + 6x_2 + 5x_3 + 10x_4)$$

subject to
$$x_1 + 3x_2 + 4x_3 + 6x_4 \leqslant 19 \qquad (7.2.23)$$
$$x_j \geqslant 0, \quad \text{integer} \quad (j = 1, 2, 3, 4)$$

It is usually wise to solve a problem such as (7.2.23) with an initial choice of $\mu = 0$. If the solution satisfied the first constraint it would automatically be optimal for (7.2.22). For $\mu = 0$, we obtain Table 7.2.1. Solving for the remaining variables, we obtain the solution: $x_1^* = 0$, $x_2^* = 1$, $x_3^* = 1$, $x_4^* = 2$. This solution yields a z value of 34. However, this solution does not satisfy the first constraint since

$$8(0) + 6(1) + 5(1) + 10(2) = 31 > 30$$

Hence we know that z^* can be no greater than 33.

TABLE 7.2.1. $\mu = 0$

	Stage 1			Stage 2			Stage 3	
λ_1	$g_1(\lambda_1)$	$x_1^*(\lambda_1)$	λ_2	$g_2(\lambda_2)$	$x_2^*(\lambda_2)$	λ_3	$g_3(\lambda_3)$	$x_3^*(\lambda_3)$
0	0	0	0	0	0	0	0	0
1	1	1	1	1	0	1	1	0
2	2	2	2	2	0	2	2	0
3	3	3	3	5	1	3	5	0
4	4	4	4	6	1	4	7	1
5	5	5	5	7	1	5	8	1
6	6	6	6	10	2	6	10	0
7	7	7	7	11	2	7	12	1
8	8	8	8	12	2	8	14	2
9	9	9	9	15	3	9	15	0
10	10	10	10	16	3	10	17	1
11	11	11	11	17	3	11	19	2
12	12	12	12	20	4	12	21	3
13	13	13	13	21	4	13	22	1
14	14	14	14	22	4	14	24	2
15	15	15	15	25	5	15	26	3
16	16	16	16	26	5	16	28	4
17	17	17	17	27	5	17	29	2
18	18	18	18	30	6	18	31	3
19	19	19	19	31	6	19	33	4

Stage 4.

$g_4(19) = 34, x_4^* = 2.$

TABLE 7.2.2. $\mu = 1$

	Stage 1			Stage 2			Stage 3	
λ_1	$g_1(\lambda_1)$	$x_1^*(\lambda_1)$	λ_2	$g_2(\lambda_2)$	$x_2^*(\lambda_2)$	λ_3	$g_3(\lambda_3)$	$x_3^*(\lambda_3)$
0	0	0	0	0	0	0	0	0
1	0	0	1	0	0	1	0	0
2	0	0	2	0	0	2	0	0
3	0	0	3	0	0	3	0	0
4	0	0	4	0	0	4	2	1
5	0	0	5	0	0	5	2	1
6	0	0	6	0	0	6	2	1
7	0	0	7	0	0	7	2	1
8	0	0	8	0	0	8	4	2
9	0	0	9	0	0	9	4	2
10	0	0	10	0	0	10	4	2
11	0	0	11	0	0	11	4	2
12	0	0	12	0	0	12	6	3
13	0	0	13	0	0	13	6	3
14	0	0	14	0	0	14	6	3
15	0	0	15	0	0	15	6	3
16	0	0	16	0	0	16	8	4
17	0	0	17	0	0	17	8	4
18	0	0	18	0	0	18	8	4
19	0	0	19	0	0	19	8	4

Stage 4.

$g_4(19) = 8, \ x_4^* = 0.$

Next we choose $\mu = 1$ and obtain Table 7.2.2. Solving for the remaining variables, we obtain the solution: $x_1^* = 0$, $x_2^* = 0$, $x_3^* = 4$, $x_4^* = 0$ with a corresponding z^* value of 28. A check on the first constraint shows that

$$8(0)+6(0)+5(4)+10(0) = 20 < 30$$

Hence, we know that if a μ can be found, it lies between 0 and 1.

Our next choice is $\mu = 0.5$ and we obtain Table 7.2.3. Calculating the remaining variables, we obtain the solution: $x_1^* = 0$, $x_2^* = 1$, $x_3^* = 4$, $x_4^* = 0$ with $z^* = 33$. Since we observed earlier that $z = 33$ was the largest possible value for z^* and that the first constraint is now satisfied since

$$8(0)+6(1)+5(4)+10(0) = 26 < 30$$

we have obtained the optimal solution.

TABLE 7.2.3. $\mu = 0.5$

	Stage 1			Stage 2			Stage 3	
λ_1	$g_1(\lambda_1)$	$x_1^*(\lambda_1)$	λ_2	$g_2(\lambda_2)$	$x_2^*(\lambda_2)$	λ_3	$g_3(\lambda_3)$	$x_3^*(\lambda_3)$
0	0	0	0	0	0	0	0	0
1	0	0	1	0	0	1	0	0
2	0	0	2	0	0	2	0	0
3	0	0	3	2	1	3	2	0
4	0	0	4	2	1	4	4	1
5	0	0	5	2	1	5	4	1
6	0	0	6	4	2	6	4	1
7	0	0	7	4	2	7	6	1
8	0	0	8	4	2	8	9	2
9	0	0	9	6	3	9	9	2
10	0	0	10	6	3	10	9	2
11	0	0	11	6	3	11	11	2
12	0	0	12	8	4	12	13	3
13	0	0	13	8	4	13	13	3
14	0	0	14	8	4	14	13	3
15	0	0	15	10	5	15	15	3
16	0	0	16	10	5	16	18	4
17	0	0	17	10	5	17	18	4
18	0	0	18	12	6	18	18	4
19	0	0	19	12	6	19	20	4

Stage 4.

$g_4(19) = 20$, $x_4^* = 0$.

We now consider the following example:

$$\max \quad z = 3x_1+4x_2$$

subject to

$$x_1-x_2 = 0$$
$$x_1+x_2 \leqslant 4 \tag{7.2.24}$$
$$x_1, x_2 \geqslant 0, \quad \text{integer}$$

It is relatively easy to see that the optimal solution is $x_1 = 2$, $x_2 = 2$, $z^* = 14$. If we try to solve this problem with a Lagrange multiplier, in the form

$$\max \quad Z = 3x_1 + 4x_2 - \mu(x_1 - x_2)$$

subject to
$$x_1 + x_2 \leqslant 4 \tag{7.2.25}$$

$$x_1, x_2 \geqslant 0, \quad \text{integer}$$

it is a simple matter to verify that for

$$\mu \geqslant -.5, \qquad x_1 = 0, \quad x_2 = 4$$
$$\mu < -.5, \qquad x_1 = 4, \quad x_2 = 0$$

are the only solutions obtained. Hence there does not exist a value of μ which will yield the optimal solution $(2, 2)$.

The use of Lagrange multipliers to reduce state dimensionality can readily be extended to the general case of a problem with m constraints. We can introduce k Lagrange multipliers μ_k and take k of the constraints into the objective function, leaving a problem with $m-k$ constraints. If the original problem was of the form

$$\max \quad z = \sum_{j=1}^{n} \phi_j(x_j)$$

subject to
$$\sum_{j=1}^{n} h_{ij}(x_j) \leqslant b_i \qquad (i = 1, 2, \ldots, m) \tag{7.2.26}$$

$$x_j \geqslant 0 \qquad (j = 1, 2, \ldots, n)$$

we could try to solve, instead of (7.2.26) which requires m state variables, the following:

$$\max \quad Z = \sum_{j=1}^{n} \phi_j(x_j) - \sum_{i=1}^{k} \mu_i \sum_{j=1}^{n} h_{ij}(x_j)$$

subject to
$$\sum_{j=1}^{n} h_{ij}(x_j) \leqslant b_i \qquad (i = k+1, \ldots, m) \tag{7.2.27}$$

More computation is required to solve (7.2.27) than the case of a single Lagrange multiplier. In order to solve (7.2.27) one has to fix the values of k Lagrange multipliers. Hence a more involved search over the possible values of μ_i will be required. Nevertheless, this search process, for $k = 2$ or 3, is probably more efficient than dealing with six or seven state variables without the use of Lagrange multipliers.

7.3. Method of Successive Approximations

We consider now an approach for reducing state dimensionality which is quite different than the use of Lagrange multipliers. It has its antecedents in techniques of univariate search which are widely used in unconstrained optimization (see [11]). The basic notion is quite simple. It involves holding a subset of the variables constant and performing the maximization with respect to the remaining variables and then reversing the process in an iterative fashion until some sort of convergence is obtained.

Consider the problem

$$\max \quad z = \sum_{j=1}^{n} \phi_j(x_j, y_j) \tag{7.3.1}$$

subject to

$$\sum_{j=1}^{n} h_{ij}(x_j) \leqslant b_1 \tag{7.3.2}$$

$$\sum_{j=1}^{n} h_{2j}(y_j) \leqslant b_2 \tag{7.3.3}$$

$$x_j, y_j \geqslant 0 \qquad (j = 1, 2, \ldots, n) \tag{7.3.4}$$

We choose an initial guess for the variables x_j, which we designate $\mathbf{x}^0 = (x_1^0, x_2^0, \ldots, x_n^0)$. We choose $\mathbf{x}^0$ so that (7.3.2) is satisfied. Using $\mathbf{x}^0$ we then solve

$$\max \quad Z = \sum_{j=1}^{n} \phi_j(x_j^0, y_j)$$

subject to

$$\sum_{j=1}^{n} h_{2j}(y_j) \leqslant b_2 \tag{7.3.5}$$

$$y_j \geqslant 0$$

Equation (7.3.5) can be solved by dynamic programming and requires only one state variable. Suppose we solve (7.3.5) and obtain a solution $\mathbf{y}^0$ and a corresponding value of the objective function Z_0.

Next we fix the y_j in (7.3.1)–(7.3.4) at $\mathbf{y}^0$ and solve the problem

$$\max \quad Z = \sum_{j=1}^{n} \phi_j(x_j, y_j^0)$$

subject to

$$\sum_{j=1}^{n} h_{ij}(x_j) \leqslant b_1 \tag{7.3.6}$$

$$x_j \geqslant 0$$

This again is a one state variable problem and can be solved to produce a set of x_j which we can designate $\mathbf{x}^1$ and a value of the objective function Z_1.

The pattern is now clear for this procedure. We alternately solve problems of the form given by (7.3.5) and (7.3.6), which means we alternately fix either $\mathbf{x}^k$ or $\mathbf{y}^k$, using the solution of the previous problem for this purpose. At each iteration of this process we have a problem in one state variable and so the calculation is relatively easy. Hence we produce two sequences from this procedure:

$$\mathbf{x}^0, \mathbf{x}^1, \mathbf{x}^2, \ldots$$
$$\mathbf{y}^0, \mathbf{y}^1, \mathbf{y}^2, \ldots \tag{7.3.7}$$

Corresponding to these sequences we produce a sequence of objective function values:

$$Z_{2k} = \max \sum_{j=1}^{n} \phi_j(x_j^k, y_j) \qquad (k = 0, 1, \ldots)$$

$$Z_{2k+1} = \max \sum_{j=1}^{n} \phi_j(x_j, y_j^k) \qquad (k = 1, 2, \ldots) \tag{7.3.8}$$

From the manner of generation of the sequence $\{Z_k\}$ it is clear that

$$Z_1 \leqslant Z_2 \leqslant Z_3 \leqslant \ldots \qquad (7.3.9)$$

Hence, the sequence (7.3.9) converges monotonically. However, it is not necessarily true that it converges to a solution of (7.3.1)–(7.3.4). In many instances it can be shown that this process will converge to the true solution. However, this method is also employed when no such assurance is known. In such cases, it may converge to a local optimum or a point that is not an optimum at all.

Consider the problem

$$\max \quad z = \phi_1(x_1, y_1) + \phi_2(x_2, y_2) + \phi_3(x_3, y_3)$$

subject to
$$2x_1 + 4x_2 + 3x_3 \leqslant 16 \qquad (7.3.10)$$

$$4y_1 + 3y_2 + 3y_3 \leqslant 10$$

$$x_j, y_j \geqslant 0, \quad \text{integer} \quad (j = 1, 2, 3)$$

where
$$\phi_1(x_1, y_1) = x_1^2 + 5x_1y_1 + 2y_1^2$$
$$\phi_2(x_2, y_2) = 2x_2^2 + x_2y_2 + y_2^2 \qquad (7.3.11)$$
$$\phi_3(x_3, y_3) = 3x_3^2 + 4x_3y_3 + 2y_3^2$$

Let us choose $\mathbf{x}^0 = (2, 2, 1)$ which clearly satisfies the constraint of (7.3.10) involving the x_j. Then the problem we need to solve at the first iteration is

$$\max \quad Z_0 = 2y_1^2 + 10y_1 + y_2^2 + 2y_2 + 2y_3^2 + 4y_3 + 15$$

subject to
$$4y_1 + 3y_2 + 3y_3 \leqslant 10 \qquad (7.3.12)$$

$$y_1, y_2, y_3 \geqslant 0, \quad \text{integer}$$

Using the usual approach we have the following recursion relations to solve (7.3.12):

$$g_1(\lambda_1) = \max_{y_1 = [\lambda_1/4]} (2y_1^2 + 10y_1)$$

$$g_2(\lambda_2) = \max_{0 \leqslant y_2 \leqslant [\lambda_2/3]} [y_2^2 + 2y_2 + g_1(\lambda_2 - 3y_2)] \qquad (7.3.13)$$

$$g_3(10) = \max_{0 \leqslant y_3 \leqslant [\frac{10}{3}]} [2y_3^2 + 4y_3 + g_2(10 - 3y_3)]$$

Table 7.3.1 gives the tabulations of $g_1(\lambda_1)$ and $g_2(\lambda_2)$. Calculation of $g_3(10)$ yields

$$g_3(10) = \max_{0 \leqslant y_3 \leqslant 3} [2y_3^2 + 4y_3 + g_2(10 - 3y_3)]$$

$$= \max[0 + g_2(10), \ 6 + g_2(7), \ 16 + g_2(4), \ 30 + g_2(1)]$$

$$= \max(28, 21, 28, 30) = 30, \quad y_3^* = 3$$

If $y_3^* = 3$, $\lambda_2 = 10 - 3(3) = 1$. Then $y_2^* = 0$ and $y_1^* = 0$. Hence we have $\mathbf{y}^0 = (0, 0, 3)$ and $Z_0 = 45$.

TABLE 7.3.1. Optimal return functions

λ_1	$g_1(\lambda_1)$	$y_1^*(\lambda_1)$	λ_2	$g_2(\lambda_2)$	$y_2^*(\lambda_2)$
0	0	0	0	0	0
1	0	0	1	0	0
2	0	0	2	0	0
3	0	0	3	3	1
4	12	1	4	12	0
5	12	1	5	12	0
6	12	1	6	12	0
7	12	1	7	15	1
8	28	2	8	28	0
9	28	2	9	28	0
10	28	2	10	28	0

Next we solve

$$\max \quad Z_1 = x_1^2 + 2x_2^2 + 3x_3^2 + 12x_3 + 18$$

subject to

$$2x_1 + 4x_2 + 3x_3 \leq 16 \qquad (7.3.14)$$

$$x_1, x_2, x_3 \geq 0, \quad \text{integer}$$

The recursion relations for solving (7.3.14) are:

$$g_1(\lambda_1) = \max_{x_1 = [\lambda_1/2]} x_1^2$$

$$g_2(\lambda_2) = \max_{0 \leq x_2 \leq [\lambda_2/4]} [2x_2^2 + g_1(\lambda_2 - 4x_2)] \qquad (7.3.15)$$

$$g_3(\lambda_3) = \max_{0 \leq x_3 \leq 5} [3x_3^2 + 12x_3 + g_2(16 - 3x_3)]$$

Table 7.3.2 gives the tabulations of $g_1(\lambda_1)$ and $g_2(\lambda_2)$.

TABLE 7.3.2. Optimal return functions

λ_1	$g_1(\lambda_1)$	$x_1^*(\lambda_1)$	λ_2	$g_2(\lambda_2)$	$x_2^*(\lambda_2)$
0	0	0	0	0	0
1	0	0	1	0	0
2	1	1	2	1	0
3	1	1	3	1	0
4	4	2	4	4	0
5	4	2	5	4	0
6	9	3	6	9	0
7	9	3	7	9	0
8	16	4	8	16	0
9	16	4	9	16	0
10	25	5	10	25	0
11	25	5	11	25	0
12	36	6	12	36	0
13	36	6	13	36	0
14	49	7	14	49	0
15	49	7	15	49	0
16	64	8	16	64	0

Calculating $g_3(16)$ we have

$$g_3(16) = \max_{0 \le x_3 \le 5} [3x_3^2 + 12x_3 + g_2(16 - 3x_3)]$$

$$= \max[0 + g_2(16), 15 + g_2(13), 36 + g_2(10), 63 + g_2(7), 96 + g_2(4), 135 + g_2(1)]$$

$$= \max(64, 51, 61, 72, 100, 135) = 135, \quad x_3^* = 5$$

If $x_3^* = 5$, $\lambda_2 = 16 - 3(5) = 1$. Then $x_2^* = 0$, $x_1^* = 0$. Hence we have $\mathbf{x}^1 = (0, 0, 5)$ and $Z_1 = 153$.

Next we solve

$$\max \quad Z_2 = 2y_1^2 + y_2^2 + 2y_3^2 + 20y_3 + 75$$

subject to
$$4y_1 + 3y_2 + 3y_3 \le 10 \tag{7.3.16}$$

$$y_1, y_2, y_3 \ge 0, \quad \text{integer}$$

It is clear from an inspection of (7.3.16) that the optimal solution is

$$\mathbf{y}^1 = (0, 0, 3)$$

which is the same as $\mathbf{y}^0$. We can see that we have converged to the optimal solution since

$$Z_2 = 2(9) + 20(3) + 75 = 153 = Z_1$$

7.4. Approximation in Policy and Function Space

Other approaches that are related to the successive approximation idea discussed in Section 7.3 are what has been called approximation in policy space and approximation in function space.

Consider a general form of the recursive functional equation

$$g_s(\lambda_s) = \max_{0 \le x_s \le \xi_s \le (\lambda_s)} [\phi_s(x_s) + g_{s-1}(\lambda_s - h_s(x_s))] \tag{7.4.1}$$

which is used to solve a problem by dynamic programming. When we employ approximation in function space, we guess an initial approximation to the form of $g_s(\lambda_s)$, the optimal return function. Then we determine the value(s) of x_s that maximize(s) the right-hand side of (7.4.1). Using this value of x_s we derive an improved approximation of $g_s(\lambda_s)$. Continuing this process, the approximations in function space hopefully converge in the limit to the actual solution of the original problem.

When we employ approximation in policy space we guess an initial approximation to the form of x_s, the optimal policy or decision which maximizes (7.4.1). This gives us an initial approximation to $g_s(\lambda_s)$. From this we derive an improved approximation to x_s. Again, we continue this process until convergence is achieved.

Let us now use both approaches, approximation in policy space and approximation in function space, to derive the solution to the following problem which is due to Bellman [3]. Suppose we have a resource w which is divided into two parts, x and $w - x$. The yields or profits from each of the parts are $f(x)$ and $h(w - x)$ in some operation or process. During this operation, the quantity x is reduced to αx, $\alpha > 0$ and the quantity

$w-x$ is reduced to $\beta(w-x)$, $0 < \beta < 1$. We wish to find the value of x which results in the maximum overall yield from the process. This process may be considered as one with an infinite number of stages. We have not considered such processes before, so an explanation is in order. If this process was repeated over n states we would obtain the recurrence relations

$$g_1(\lambda_1) = \max_{0 \leq x_1 \leq \lambda_1} [f(x_1) + h(\lambda_1 - x_1)]$$

$$g_s(\lambda_s) = \max_{0 \leq x_s \leq \lambda_s} [f(x_s) + h(\lambda_s - x_s) + g_{s-1}(\alpha x_s + \beta(\lambda_s - x_s))] \qquad (7.4.2)$$

$$(s = 2, 3, \ldots, n)$$

If n is very large, or if the process is actually continuing indefinitely, it may be convenient to consider an infinite stage process as a reasonable approximation to the requirement that the process continues indefinitely. We shall consider processes of this kind in more detail in Chapter 8. However, for our present purposes, we can see if we regard this process as an infinite stage process, the sequence of equations (7.4.2) can be replaced by the single equation

$$g(w) = \max_{0 \leq x \leq w} [f(x) + h(w-x) + g(\alpha x + \beta(w-x))] \qquad (7.4.3)$$

where the optimal return $g(w)$ is now determined by a single allocation, $x = x(w)$. Bellman [3] has shown that under certain fairly mild conditions on the continuity and boundedness of $f(\cdot)$ and $h(\cdot)$, the existence of a solution can be assured. Equation (7.4.3) cannot be solved in the way we have employed previously, since it is not a recurrence relationship. It is a single equation called a functional equation which has the unknown optimal return function on both sides of the equation. We need to find this function as well as the allocation $x(w)$ which yields the optimal return.

First we shall consider approximation in policy space to solve (7.4.3). What we shall do is assume a policy or decision $x(w)$ and calculate the return. We shall then use this calculated return to find the next approximation to the policy. We continue to repeat this process until the policies from successive iterations yield successive returns which differ from each other by some negligible amount.

As an example, we shall solve (7.4.3) for

$$f(x) = x^{1/2}$$

$$h(w-x) = w - x \qquad (7.4.4)$$

We choose, for our initial approximations,

$$x^{(0)}(w) = 0 \qquad (7.4.5)$$

Substitution of (7.4.5) in (7.4.3) yields

$$g^{(0)}(w) = w + g^{(0)}(\beta w) \qquad (7.4.6)$$

Now we use (7.4.6) to evaluate $g^{(0)}(\beta w)$. This yields

$$g^{(0)}(\beta w) = \beta w + g^{(0)}(\beta^2 w) \qquad (7.4.7)$$

12

If we repeatedly use (7.4.6) to evaluate successive values of $g^{(0)}(\cdot)$, we obtain the infinite series

$$g^{(0)}(w) = w + \beta w + \beta^2 w + \ldots + \beta^{k-1} w + \ldots \tag{7.4.8}$$

which, since $\beta < 1$, is a convergent series and we have

$$g^{(0)}(w) = \frac{w}{1-\beta} \tag{7.4.9}$$

Equation (7.4.9) gives the first approximation to $g(w)$ with an assumed policy of $x^{(0)}(w) = 0$.

We now use (7.4.9) with (7.4.3) in order to find an improved value of $x(w)$. From (7.4.3) and (7.4.4), we have

$$g^{(1)}(w) = \max_{0 \leqslant x \leqslant w} [x^{1/2} + (w-x) + g^{(0)}(\alpha x + \beta(w-x))] \tag{7.4.10}$$

Substituting (7.4.9) into (7.4.10) we obtain

$$g^{(1)}(w) = \max_{0 \leqslant x \leqslant w} \left[x^{1/2} + (w-x) + \frac{\alpha x + \beta(w-x)}{1-\beta} \right] \tag{7.4.11}$$

If we call the maximand in (7.4.11), $G_1(w, x)$, then

$$\frac{dG_1}{dx} = \frac{1}{2} x^{-1/2} - 1 + \frac{\alpha - \beta}{1-\beta} = 0 \tag{7.4.12}$$

Solving (7.4.12) for x yields $x^{(1)}(w)$. We can see that (7.4.12) yields a maximum since

$$\frac{d^2 G_1}{dx^2} = -\frac{1}{4} x^{-3/2} < 0 \quad \text{if} \quad 0 < x \leqslant w$$

Hence, solving (7.4.12) yields

$$x^{(1)}(w) = \frac{1}{4} \left(\frac{1-\beta}{1-\alpha} \right)^2 \tag{7.4.13}$$

From (7.4.13) and (7.4.11) we find $g^{(1)}(w)$ as

$$g^{(1)}(w) = \left[\frac{1}{4} \left(\frac{1-\beta}{1-\alpha} \right)^2 \right]^{1/2} + w - \frac{1}{4} \left(\frac{1-\beta}{1-\alpha} \right)^2 + \frac{1}{4} \left(\frac{\alpha-\beta}{1-\beta} \right) \left(\frac{1-\beta}{1-\alpha} \right)^2 + \frac{\beta w}{1-\beta}$$

which after simplification yields

$$g^{(1)}(w) = \frac{w}{1-\beta} + \frac{1}{4} \left(\frac{1-\beta}{1-\alpha} \right) \tag{7.4.14}$$

We can now repeat the above process to find $g^{(2)}(w)$ from $g^{(1)}(w)$ and then find $x^{(2)}(w)$. To do so, we use

$$g^{(2)}(w) = \max_{0 \leqslant x \leqslant w} [x^{1/2} + (w-x) + g^{(1)}(\alpha x + \beta(w-x))] \tag{7.4.15}$$

From (7.4.14) and (7.4.15) we obtain

$$g^{(2)}(w) = \max_{0 \leqslant x \leqslant w} \left[x^{1/2} + (w-x) + \frac{\alpha x + \beta(w-x)}{1-\beta} + \frac{1}{4}\left(\frac{1-\beta}{1-\alpha}\right) \right].$$
$$= \max_{0 \leqslant x \leqslant w} G_2(w, x) \tag{7.4.16}$$

In order to find the maximum in (7.4.16), we proceed as before:

$$\frac{dG_2}{dx} = \frac{1}{2} x^{-1/2} - 1 + \frac{\alpha - \beta}{1-\beta} = 0 \tag{7.4.17}$$

We see that (7.4.17) is the same as (7.4.12). Hence

$$x^{(2)}(w) = \frac{1}{4}\left(\frac{1-\beta}{1-\alpha}\right)^2 \tag{7.4.18}$$

as long as $0 < x \leqslant w$. Substituting (7.4.18) into (7.4.16) we obtain, after simplication,

$$g^{(2)}(w) = \frac{w}{1-\beta} + \frac{1}{2}\left(\frac{1-\beta}{1-\alpha}\right) \tag{7.4.19}$$

We shall now show that the pth order approximation is given by

$$x^{(p)}(w) = \frac{1}{4}\left(\frac{1-\beta}{1-\alpha}\right)^2 \tag{7.4.20}$$

$$g^{(p)}(w) = \frac{w}{1-\beta} + \frac{p}{4}\left(\frac{1-\beta}{1-\alpha}\right) \tag{7.4.21}$$

We proceed by induction. Equations (7.4.20) and (7.4.21) hold for $j = 1, 2$. Suppose they hold for $j = p$, as given by (7.4.20) and (7.4.21). We now show that (7.4.20) and (7.4.21) will also hold for $j = p+1$. The $(p+1)$st order approximation is found from

$$g^{(p+1)}(w) = \max_{0 \leqslant x \leqslant w} \left[x^{1/2} + (w-x) + g^{(p)}(\alpha x + \beta(w-x)) \right] \tag{7.4.22}$$

Substitution of (7.4.21) into (7.4.22) for the argument $\alpha x + \beta(w-x)$ yields

$$g^{(p+1)}(w) = \max_{0 \leqslant x \leqslant w} \left[x^{1/2} + (w-x) + \frac{\alpha x + \beta(w-x)}{1-\beta} + \frac{p}{4}\left(\frac{1-\beta}{1-\alpha}\right) \right]$$
$$= \max_{0 \leqslant x \leqslant w} G_{p+1}(w, x) \tag{7.4.23}$$

In order to find the maximum we differentiate G_{p+1}:

$$\frac{dG_{p+1}}{dx} = \frac{1}{2} x^{1/2} - 1 + \left(\frac{\alpha - \beta}{1-\beta}\right) = 0 \tag{7.4.24}$$

The solution to (7.4.24) is

$$x^{(p+1)}(w) = \frac{1}{4}\left(\frac{1-\beta}{1-\alpha}\right)^2 \tag{7.4.25}$$

Substituting (7.4.25) into (7.4.23) results in

$$g^{(p+1)}(w) = \left[\frac{1}{4}\left(\frac{1-\beta}{1-\alpha}\right)^2\right]^{1/2} + w - \frac{1}{4}\left(\frac{1-\beta}{1-\alpha}\right)^2 + \left(\frac{\alpha-\beta}{1-\beta}\right)\left[\frac{1}{4}\left(\frac{1-\beta}{1-\alpha}\right)^2\right]$$

$$+ \frac{\beta w}{1-\beta} + \frac{p}{4}\left(\frac{1-\beta}{1-\alpha}\right)$$

which simplifies to

$$g^{(p+1)}(w) = \frac{w}{1-\beta} + \frac{p+1}{4}\left(\frac{1-\beta}{1-\alpha}\right) \tag{7.4.26}$$

Hence, by (7.4.25) and (7.4.26) we have shown that the induction is complete.

In order to show that the approximations given by (7.4.25) and (7.4.26) are valid, we shall consider solving (7.4.3) by means of (7.4.2) in the usual stagewise fashion and then let s, the number of stages, become large. In this way we should be able to tell what the infinite stage solution is as a limiting case.

Using (7.4.4) and (7.4.2) we have

$$g_1(w) = \max_{0 \le x_1 \le w} [x_1^{1/2} + w - x_1] \tag{7.4.27}$$

We can evaluate (7.4.27) by setting the derivative of $G_1 = x_1^{1/2} + w - x_1$ equal to zero, etc., and find that

$$x_1^*(w) = \begin{cases} \frac{1}{4}, & w > \frac{1}{4} \\ w, & 0 \le w \le \frac{1}{4} \end{cases} \tag{7.4.28}$$

Substituting (7.4.28) into (7.4.27) yields

$$g_1(w) = \begin{cases} w + \frac{1}{4}, & w > \frac{1}{4} \\ w^{1/2}, & 0 \le w \le \frac{1}{4} \end{cases} \tag{7.4.29}$$

Next we consider the two-stage process and solve

$$g_2(w) = \max_{0 \le x_2 \le w} [x_2^{1/2} + (w - x_2) + g_1(\alpha x_2 + \beta(w - x_2))] \tag{7.4.30}$$

Using $g_1(w) = w + \frac{1}{4}$ from (7.4.29) and substituting into (7.4.30) we obtain

$$g_2(w) = \max_{0 \le x_2 \le w} [x_2^{1/2} + (w - x_2) + \alpha x_2 + \beta(w - x_2) + \frac{1}{4}] \tag{7.4.31}$$

Differentiating the right-hand side of (7.4.31) and solving for x_2 yields

$$x_2^*(w) = \begin{cases} \dfrac{1}{4[1-(\alpha-\beta)]^2}, & w > \dfrac{1}{4[1-(\alpha-\beta)]^2} \\ \\ w, & 0 \le w \le \dfrac{1}{4[1-(\alpha-\beta)]^2} \end{cases} \tag{7.4.32}$$

and substitution of (7.4.32) in (7.4.31) results in

$$
g_2(w) = \begin{cases} (1+\beta)w + \dfrac{1}{4[1-(\alpha-\beta)]} + \dfrac{1}{4}, & w > \dfrac{1}{4[1-(\alpha-\beta)]^2} \\[3mm] w^{1/2} + \alpha w + \dfrac{1}{4}, & 0 \leqslant w \leqslant \dfrac{1}{4[1-(\alpha-\beta)]^2} \end{cases}
\tag{7.4.33}
$$

In a similar fashion to the derivation of $x_2^*(w)$ and $g_2(w)$ we can use the recurrence relation to derive $x_3^*(w)$ and $g_3(w)$ to be

$$
x_3^*(w) = \begin{cases} \dfrac{1}{4[1-(1+\beta)(\alpha-\beta)]^2}, & w > \dfrac{1}{4[1-(1+\beta)(\alpha-\beta)]^2} \\[3mm] w, & 0 \leqslant w \leqslant \dfrac{1}{4[1-(1+\beta)(\alpha-\beta)]^2} \end{cases}
\tag{7.4.34}
$$

$$
g_3(w) = \begin{cases} [1+(1+\beta)\beta]w + \dfrac{1}{4[1-(1+\beta)(\alpha-\beta)]} + \dfrac{1}{4[1-(\alpha-\beta)]} + \dfrac{1}{4}, \\[3mm] \qquad\qquad\qquad\qquad\qquad w > \dfrac{1}{4[1-(1+\beta)(\alpha-\beta)]^2} \\[3mm] w^{1/2} + (1+\beta)\alpha w + \dfrac{1}{4[1-(\alpha-\beta)]} + \dfrac{1}{4}, \\[3mm] \qquad\qquad\qquad\qquad\qquad 0 \leqslant w \leqslant \dfrac{1}{4[1-(1+\beta)(\alpha-\beta)]^2} \end{cases}
\tag{7.4.35}
$$

It can be shown by mathematical induction that the sth stage expressions for the optimal allocation and return are

$$
x_s^*(w) = 1 \bigg/ \left\{ 4 \left[1 - \left(\sum_{j=0}^{s-2} \beta^j \right)(\alpha-\beta) \right]^2 \right\}
\tag{7.4.36}
$$

$$
g_s(w) = \left[\sum_{j=0}^{s-1} \beta^j \right] w + \sum_{j=0}^{s-1} 1 \bigg/ \left\{ 4 \left[1 - \left(\sum_{k=0}^{j-1} \beta^k \right)(\alpha-\beta) \right] \right\}, \quad w > x_s^*(w)
\tag{7.4.37}
$$

Since we wish to evaluate (7.4.36) and (7.4.37) as $s \to \infty$, we consider

$$
\lim_{s \to \infty} x_s^*(w) = \lim_{s \to \infty} 1 \bigg/ \left\{ 4 \left[1 - \left(\sum_{j=0}^{s-2} \beta^j \right)(\alpha-\beta) \right]^2 \right\}
\tag{7.4.38}
$$

We note that for $|\beta| < 1$, which we have assumed,

$$
\lim_{s \to \infty} \sum_{j=0}^{s-1} \beta^j = \lim_{s \to \infty} \frac{\beta^s - 1}{\beta - 1} = \frac{1}{1-\beta}
\tag{7.4.39}
$$

Using (7.4.39) and (7.4.38) we see that as $s \to \infty$

$$
x_s^*(w) \approx \frac{1}{4} \left(\frac{1-\beta}{1-\alpha} \right)^2
\tag{7.4.40}
$$

which agrees in the limit with the result, (7.4.20), which we obtained by approximation in the policy space. Similarly, if we apply (7.4.39) to (7.4.37) we obtain

$$g_s(w) \approx \frac{w}{1-\beta} + \frac{s}{4}\left(\frac{1-\beta}{1-\alpha}\right) \qquad (7.4.41)$$

which agrees in the limit with the result, (7.4.21), which was obtained by approximation in the policy space.

As we have noted previously, still another approximation technique is what is known as approximation in function space. We begin with an initial assumption of an approximation to $g(w)$ which we shall call $g^{(0)}(w)$. Then using the solution of the functional equation (7.4.3) we obtain $g^{(1)}(w)$ and the solution $x^{(1)}(w)$. Continuing this process of substitution of $g^{(k)}(w)$ into (7.4.3) to obtain $g^{(k+1)}(w)$, we can obtain as accurate an approximation as we desire, providing the method converges.

Let us solve the same problem as before. Therefore we wish to solve

$$g(w) = \max_{0 \leqslant x \leqslant w} \left[x^{1/2} + (w-x) + g(\alpha x + \beta(w-x))\right] \qquad (7.4.42)$$

Let us choose as an initial guess for the form of the optimal return function a linear approximation, i.e.,

$$g^{(0)}(w) = \alpha w \qquad (7.4.43)$$

Then using (7.4.42) in the form

$$g^{(1)}(w) = \max_{0 \leqslant x \leqslant w} \left[x^{1/2} + (w-x) + g^{(0)}(\alpha x + \beta(w-x))\right] \qquad (7.4.44)$$

we substitute (7.4.43) into (7.4.44) to obtain

$$g^{(1)}(w) = \max_{0 \leqslant x \leqslant w} \left[x^{1/2} + (w-x) + \alpha(\alpha x + \beta(w-x))\right]$$
$$= \max_{0 \leqslant x \leqslant w} G_1(w, x) \qquad (7.4.45)$$

Differentiating G_1 and solving for x we have

$$\frac{dG_1}{dx} = \frac{1}{2}x^{-1/2} - 1 + \alpha(\alpha - \beta) = 0 \qquad (7.4.46)$$

Solving (7.4.46) for $x^{(1)}(w)$ yields

$$x^{(1)}(w) = \frac{1}{4[1 - \alpha(\alpha - \beta)]^2} \qquad (7.4.47)$$

Substitution of (7.4.47) into (7.4.45) yields the next approximation to the optimal return function, $g^{(1)}(w)$, as

$$g^{(1)}(w) = (1 + \alpha\beta)w + \frac{1}{4[1 - \alpha(\alpha - \beta)]} \qquad (7.4.48)$$

Next we approximate $g^{(2)}(w)$ as

$$g^{(2)}(w) = \max_{0 \leqslant x \leqslant w} \left[x^{1/2} + (w-x) + g^{(1)}(\alpha x + \beta(w-x))\right] \qquad (7.4.49)$$

We substitute (7.4.48) into (7.4.49), differentiate, and solve for $x^{(2)}(w)$, which is

$$x^{(2)}(w) = \frac{1}{4[1-(1+\alpha\beta)(\alpha-\beta)]^2} \qquad (7.4.50)$$

Substitution of (7.4.50) into (7.4.49) yields

$$g^{(2)}(w) = [1+\beta(1+\alpha\beta)]w + \frac{1}{4[1-(1+\alpha\beta)(\alpha-\beta)]} + \frac{|1}{4[1-\alpha(\alpha-\beta)]} \qquad (7.4.51)$$

Clearly we can continue the process described in the foregoing paragraph. It can be shown by mathematical induction that the sth order approximations for the optimal allocation and return are

$$x^{(s)}(w) = 1 \Big/ \Big\{ 4\Big[1-\Big(\sum_{j=0}^{s-2}\beta^j+\alpha\beta^{s-1}\Big)(\alpha-\beta)\Big]^2 \Big\} \qquad (7.4.52)$$

$$g^{(s)}(w) = \Big[\sum_{j=0}^{s-1}\beta^j+\alpha\beta^s\Big]w + \sum_{j=0}^{s-1}1 \Big/ \Big\{ 4\Big[1-\Big(\sum_{k=0}^{j-1}\beta^k+\alpha\beta^j\Big)(\alpha-\beta)\Big]\Big\} \qquad (7.4.53)$$

Just as we did previously, in the case of the approximations in the policy space, we can show that the approximations (7.4.52) and (7.4.53) agree with (7.4.40) and (7.4.41) by making use of (7.4.39) in arriving at approximate values of (7.4.52) and (7.4.53).

In all of these approximations, the relative magnitudes of α and β will determine how many stages of approximation are required for an adequate approximation to $x(w)$ and $g(w)$.

7.5. Polynomial Approximation in Dynamic Programming

Typically, in obtaining the optimal return functions $g_s(\lambda_s)$ for a dynamic programming solution to some problem, we proceed as follows. We divide an interval $[0, b]$, over which $g_s(\lambda_s)$ is defined, into a grid of points and compute $g_s(k\Delta)$ where $N\Delta = b$, $k = 1, 2, \ldots, N$. λ_s takes on each of the values $k\Delta$. Similarly, a return function $g_s(\lambda_{1s}, \lambda_{2s})$ which depends upon two-state variables is evaluated as $g_s(k\Delta_1, l\Delta_2)$, where λ_{1s} varies over $[0, b_1]$, λ_{2s} varies over $[0, b_2]$, and $N_1\Delta_1 = b_1$, $N_2\Delta_2 = b_2$, $k = 0, 1, 2, \ldots, N_1$, $l = 0, 1, 2, \ldots, N_2$.

In general, an optimal return function which is a function of m state variables

$$g_s(\lambda_{1s}, \lambda_{2s}, \ldots, \lambda_{ms})$$

is evaluated as

$$g_s(k_1\Delta_1, k_2\Delta_2, \ldots, k_m\Delta_m)$$

where λ_{is} varies over $[0, b_i]$ for $i = 1, 2, \ldots, m$ and

$$\begin{aligned} N_i\Delta_i &= b_i & (i = 1, 2, \ldots, m) \\ k_i &= 1, 2, \ldots, N_i & (i = 1, 2, \ldots, m) \end{aligned}$$

We have noted previously that as we increase the number of grid points and/or as we increase the number of state variables, the increase in the number of points at which g is evaluated is disastrous. No computer memory is large enough to store the return functions nor is any computer fast enough to compute all the values to store.

In order to get around this "curse of dimensionality" we need, in effect, a way to describe $g_s(\lambda_s)$ in fewer than N_1 points or $g_s(\lambda_{1s}, \lambda_{2s})$ in fewer than $N_1 N_2$ points and in general $g_s(\lambda_{1s}, \lambda_{2s}, \ldots, \lambda_{ms})$ in fewer than $N_1 N_2 \ldots N_m$ points. Various methods have been proposed and used for finding more economical descriptions of functions. Indeed, this matter has a long and interesting history in mathematics and is the subject of the theory of approximation and the practice of a large area of numerical analysis. In the following discussion of the use of approximation methods, we shall use as a reference problem

$$\max \quad z = \sum_{j=1}^{n} \phi_j(x_j)$$

subject to

$$\sum_{j=1}^{n} x_j = b$$

$$x_j \geqslant 0$$

and the solution by dynamic programming,

$$g_1(\lambda_1) = \phi_1(\lambda_1)$$

$$g_s(\lambda_s) = \max_{0 \leqslant x_s \leqslant \lambda_s} [\phi_s(x_s) + g_{s-1}(\lambda_s - x_s)] \quad (s = 2, 3, \ldots, n)$$

One approach to finding, for example, a more compact representation of $g_s(\lambda_s)$ than a long tabulation would be to employ a power series representation of the form

$$g_s(\lambda_s) = \sum_{q=0}^{\infty} a_{qs} \lambda_s^q \tag{7.5.1}$$

which is assumed to be convergent for $0 \leqslant \lambda_s \leqslant b$. In practice one truncates the series of (7.5.1) and uses the polynomial approximation

$$g_s(\lambda_s) \approx \sum_{q=0}^{Q} a_{qs} \lambda_s^q \tag{7.5.2}$$

Note what (7.5.2) accomplishes for us, if it is, in fact, a good approximation. Instead of having a table of N_1 entries where $N_1 \varDelta_1 = b_1$, (7.5.2) is a representation of $g_s(\lambda_s)$ over $[0, b_1]$ and requires only the $Q+1$ coefficients a_{qs} to describe the representation. If $Q+1 \ll N_1$, then a significant savings is accomplished. Unfortunately, power series of the form given by (7.5.2) usually require that the function to be approximated be an analytic function and usually do not provide uniformly good approximations over an interval.

A more convenient choice is to represent $g_s(\lambda_s)$ in terms of some standard orthonormal expansion, i.e., a representation of $g_s(\lambda_s)$ in terms of a sum of weighted orthonormal polynomials. An orthonormal polynomial system is a set of polynomials in λ_s, say $f_i(\lambda_s)$, such that

$$\int_0^b w_i f_i(\lambda_s) f_j(\lambda_s) \, d\lambda_s = 0 \quad (i \neq j)$$

$$\int_0^b w_i [f_i(\lambda_s)]^2 \, d\lambda_s = 1 \tag{7.5.3}$$

A commonly used set of orthonormal polynomials for a finite interval are the Legendre polynomials $P(x)$ which are given by

$$P_0(x) = 1$$
$$P_1(x) = x$$
$$P_2(x) = \tfrac{1}{2}(3x^2 - 1) \tag{7.5.4}$$

$$\vdots$$

$$P_{r+1}(x) = \frac{2r+1}{r+1} x P_r(x) - \frac{r}{r+1} P_{r-1}(x)$$

A representation of $g_s(\lambda_s)$ in terms of the Legendre polynomials would be

$$g_s(\lambda_s) = \sum_{q=0}^{\infty} a_{qs} P_q(\lambda_s) \tag{7.5.5}$$

where the coefficients a_{qs} in (7.5.5) are given by

$$a_{qs} = \int_0^b g_s(\lambda_s) P_q(\lambda_s) \, d\lambda_s \tag{7.5.6}$$

Hence we can represent $g_s(\lambda_s)$ by

$$g_s(\lambda_s) \approx \sum_{q=0}^{Q} a_{qs} P_q(\lambda_s) \tag{7.5.7}$$

At this point the alert reader may well inquire as to what we have accomplished. Even if (7.5.7) is a good approximation with $Q \ll N$ terms, in general, in order to evaluate a_{qs} from (7.5.6), we must resort to numerical integration which results in something of the form

$$a_{qs} \approx \sum_{k=0}^{N} q_s(k\Delta) P_q(k\Delta) \tag{7.5.8}$$

where $N\Delta = b$. We see that to evaluate a_{qs} from (7.5.8) we must evaluate $g_s(k\Delta)$ for $k = 0, 1, \ldots, N$. This is just as much work as calculating and tabulating $g_s(k\Delta)$ in the first place and is what we have been attempting to avoid.

A way to avoid this problem is to not use (7.5.8) which is a simple Riemann sum used in the definition of an integral. Instead we use an integration formula of the form

$$\int_0^b h(x) \, dx \approx \sum_{i=1}^{m} w_i h(x_i) \tag{7.5.9}$$

where the x_i are fixed and known points in $[0, b]$ and are independent of $h(x)$ but do depend upon m. Similarly, the w_i are independent of $h(x)$ but are dependent on m. Such integration formulas are well known. A particularly useful set of formulas are the Gauss–Legendre quadrature formulas. Tabulations of the weights w_i and the points x_i (usually transformed to the interval $[-1, 1]$) are given in [19], with m ranging from 2 to 256. Actually, it is not often that one would require $m > 15$.

Assuming, then, that a formula of the type (7.5.9) is available we can now approximate (7.5.6) as

$$a_{qs} \approx \sum_{i=1}^{m} w_i g_s(\lambda_{si}) P_q(\lambda_{si}) \tag{7.5.10}$$

where the λ_{si} are the known points of the Gauss–Legendre formulas. Since the P_q are known Legendre (or other orthonormal) polynomials and the λ_{si} are fixed and known points, we can calculate the $P_q(\lambda_{si})$ once and for all. We can then write

$$a_{qs} \approx \sum_{i=1}^{m} \beta_{iq} g_s(\lambda_{si}) \tag{7.5.11}$$

where $\beta_{iq} \equiv w_i P_q(\lambda_{si})$. It will turn out that $\lambda_{1i} = \lambda_{2i} = \ldots = \lambda_{ni}$. Hence we will denote the λ_{si} as λ_i. Therefore we may write (7.5.11) as

$$a_{qs} \approx \sum_{i=1}^{m} \beta_{iq} g_s(\lambda_i) \tag{7.5.12}$$

and

$$\beta_{iq} \equiv w_i P_q(\lambda_i)$$

We now observe that the values of a_{qs} depend only on the values of $g_s(\lambda_i)$, i.e., $g_s(\lambda_s)$ at a fixed set of predetermined points λ_i. Hence this is also true for g_s.

Let us now consider how we utilize (7.5.7) and (7.5.11) in the calculation process. Assume we have the recurrence relation

$$g_s(\lambda_s) = \max_{0 \leqslant x_s \leqslant \lambda_s} [\phi_s(x_s) + g_{s-1}(\lambda_s - x_s)] \quad (s > 1) \tag{7.5.13}$$

and λ_s is restricted to $[0, b]$, and that

$$g_1(\lambda_1) = \max_{x_1 = \lambda_1} \phi(x_1) = \phi(\lambda_1) \tag{7.5.14}$$

Since $g_1(\lambda_1)$ can be expressed by (7.5.7) and (7.5.11) we can represent $g_1(\lambda_1)$ by the set of coefficients $[a_{01}, a_{11}, \ldots, a_{Q1}]$. Once we calculate these coefficients from (7.5.12), we can determine $g_1(\lambda_1)$ from (7.5.7) for any value of λ_1.

Now we observe that in order to determine $g_2(\lambda_2)$ we need only calculate $g_2(\lambda_i)$. We can see that this must be so by referring to (7.5.13) and consider how we calculate $g_2(\lambda_2)$ when $\lambda_2 = \lambda_i$:

$$g_2(\lambda_i) = \max_{0 \leqslant x_2 \leqslant \lambda_i} [\phi_2(x_2) + g_1(\lambda_i - x_2)] \quad (i = 1, 2, \ldots, m) \tag{7.5.15}$$

Since we can calculate $g_1(\lambda_i - x_2)$ for any value of $\lambda_i - x_2$ by using the set of coefficients $\{a_{q1}\}$ and (7.5.7) we can evaluate $g_2(\lambda_i)$ for the set of fixed values λ_i. Having computed all the values of $g_2(\lambda_i)$ we determine the new coefficients a_{q2} from (7.5.12) as

$$a_{q2} \approx \sum_{i=1}^{m} \beta_{iq} g_2(\lambda_i) \tag{7.5.16}$$

Therefore we now can represent the optimal return function $g_2(\lambda_2)$ in terms of the coefficients $[a_{02}, a_{12}, \ldots, a_{Q2}]$. This process can obviously be continued. Hence each of the return functions can be represented compactly by a small set of coefficients.

There are two numbers that must be fixed, depending upon the accuracy desired in the computation and the availability of computational aids. These are the value of m in (7.5.12) and the value of Q in (7.5.7). There are also other choices of polynomials that one could choose for (7.5.7) and other choices of quadrature formulas that one could use instead of the Gauss–Legendre formulas.

The technique described above is of even greater interest for optimal return functions with more than one state variable. We can apply the same general process to return functions $g_s(\lambda_{1s}, \lambda_{2s})$ defined on the region $0 \leqslant \lambda_{1s} \leqslant b_1$, $0 \leqslant \lambda_{2s} \leqslant b_2$. For this case, we might be solving the problem

$$\max \quad z = \sum_{j=1}^{n} \phi_j(x_j, y_j) \tag{7.5.17}$$

subject to

$$\sum_{j=1}^{n} x_j = b_1$$

$$\tag{7.5.17a}$$

$$\sum_{j=1}^{n} y_j = b_2$$

$$x_j, y_j \geqslant 0 \qquad (j = 1, 2, \ldots, n)$$

The general recurrence relations are

$$g_s(\lambda_{1s}, \lambda_{2s}) = \max_{\substack{0 \leqslant x_s \leqslant \lambda_{1s} \\ 0 \leqslant y_s \leqslant \lambda_{2s}}} [\phi_s(x_s, y_s) + g_{s-1}(\lambda_{1s} - x_s, \lambda_{2s} - y_s)] \qquad (s > 2) \tag{7.5.18}$$

and

$$g_1(\lambda_{11}, \lambda_{21}) = \phi_1(\lambda_{11}, \lambda_{21})$$

Instead of using (7.5.7) the analogous approximation for (7.5.18) is

$$g_s(\lambda_{1s}, \lambda_{2s}) \approx \sum_{q=0}^{Q} \sum_{t=0}^{Q} a_{qt}^s P_q(\lambda_{1s}) P_t(\lambda_{2s}) \tag{7.5.19}$$

where the coefficients a_{qt}^s are evaluated by a two-dimensional analog of (7.5.10) or (7.5.11).

A function of two variables such as (7.5.19) will require $[(Q+1)(Q+2)]/2$ coefficients (or approximately $Q^2/2$) a_{qt}^s to represent it. Similarly, a return function of three state variables will require $\sim N^3/6$ coefficients. These numbers are quite modest compared to the large multidimensional grids of points one would require for the usual continuous dynamic programming solutions.

In [20] numerical results, which make use of these approximation methods, are given for several test problems with very encouraging results reported.

7.6. Reduction of Dimensionality and Expanding Grids

We have noted in Section 5.6 as well as in Chapter 6 some of the computational problems encountered in dealing with the dynamic programming solution of problems with continuous variables and one or more state variables. Bellman [4] has suggested some methods for minimizing the computational chore of continuous variable problems as well as an associated problem encountered with expanding grids of points.

As an example, consider a two-constraint problem

$$\max \quad z = \sum_{j=1}^{n} c_j x_j$$

subject to

$$\sum_{j=1}^{n} a_{1j} x_j \leqslant b_1 \tag{7.6.1}$$

$$\sum_{j=1}^{n} a_{2j} x_j \leqslant b_2$$

$$x_j \geqslant 0 \quad (j = 1, 2, \ldots, n)$$

where $a_{1j}, a_{2j} \geqslant 0$, $c_j \geqslant 0$, $b_1, b_2 > 0$. The dynamic programming recurrence relations for the solution of (7.6.1) are

$$g_1(\lambda_{11}, \lambda_{21}) = \max_{0 \leqslant x_1 \leqslant \delta_1} c_1 x_1 \tag{7.6.2}$$

$$g_s(\lambda_{1s}, \lambda_{2s}) = \max_{0 \leqslant x_s \leqslant \delta_s} [c_s x_s + g_{s-1}(\lambda_{1s} - a_{1s} x_s, \lambda_{2s} - a_{2s} x_s)] \quad (s = 2, 3, \ldots, n) \tag{7.6.3}$$

where

$$\delta_s = \min\left(\frac{\lambda_{1s}}{a_{1s}}, \frac{\lambda_{2s}}{a_{2s}}\right) \quad (s = 1, 2, \ldots, n) \tag{7.6.4}$$

The functions $g_s(\lambda_{1s}, \lambda_{2s})$ given by (7.6.1) and (7.6.2) are easily seen to be homogeneous. (A function $f(x)$ is homogeneous if $f(\alpha x) = \alpha f(x)$.) In terms of $g_s(\lambda_{1s}, \lambda_{2s})$ it is readily shown that

$$g_s(\lambda_{1s}, \lambda_{2s}) = \lambda_{1s} g_s\left(1, \frac{\lambda_{2s}}{\lambda_{1s}}\right) = \lambda_{2s} g_s\left(\frac{\lambda_{1s}}{\lambda_{2s}}, 1\right) \tag{7.6.5}$$

Consider the definition of $g_1(\lambda_{11}, \lambda_{21})$:

$$g_1(\lambda_{11}, \lambda_{21}) = \max_{0 \leqslant x_1 \leqslant \delta_1} c_1 x_1 = \max_{0 \leqslant x_1 \leqslant \min\left(\frac{\lambda_{11}}{a_{11}}, \frac{\lambda_{21}}{a_{21}}\right)} c_1 x_1$$

$$= \min\left(\frac{c_1 \lambda_{11}}{a_{11}}, \frac{c_1 \lambda_{21}}{a_{21}}\right) \tag{7.6.6}$$

$$g_1\left(1, \frac{\lambda_{21}}{\lambda_{11}}\right) = \max_{0 \leqslant x_1 \leqslant \delta_1} c_1 x_1 = \max_{0 \leqslant x_1 \leqslant \min\left(\frac{1}{a_{11}}, \frac{\lambda_{21}}{a_{21}\lambda_{11}}\right)} c_1 x_1$$

$$= \min\left(\frac{c_1}{a_{11}}, \frac{c_1 \lambda_{21}}{a_{21}\lambda_{11}}\right)$$

Therefore
$$\lambda_{11}g_1\left(1, \frac{\lambda_{21}}{\lambda_{11}}\right) = \lambda_{11}\max\left(\frac{c_1}{a_{11}}, \frac{c_1\lambda_{21}}{a_{21}\lambda_{11}}\right)$$

$$= \min\left(\frac{c_1\lambda_{11}}{a_{11}}, \frac{c_1\lambda_{21}}{a_{21}}\right) \tag{7.6.7}$$

From (7.6.6) and (7.6.7) we see that

$$g_1(\lambda_{11}, \lambda_{21}) = \lambda_{11}g_1\left(1, \frac{\lambda_{21}}{\lambda_{11}}\right) \tag{7.6.8}$$

Using induction it is easily shown that (7.6.5) holds for all s.

We can now make use of (7.6.5) to rewrite (7.6.3) as follows:

$$g_s(\lambda_{1s}, \lambda_{2s}) = \lambda_{1s}g_s\left(1, \frac{\lambda_{2s}}{\lambda_{1s}}\right) = \max_{0 \leqslant x_s \leqslant \delta_s}\left[c_sx_s+(\lambda_{1s}-a_{1s}x_s)g_{s-1}\left(1, \frac{\lambda_{2s}-a_{2s}x_s}{\lambda_{1s}-a_{1s}x_s}\right)\right] \tag{7.6.9}$$

Rearranging (7.6.9) results in

$$g_s\left(1, \frac{\lambda_{2s}}{\lambda_{1s}}\right) = \max_{0 \leqslant x_s \leqslant \delta_s}\left[\frac{c_sx_s}{\lambda_{1s}}+\left(1-\frac{a_{1s}x_s}{\lambda_{1s}}\right)g_{s-1}\left(1, \frac{\dfrac{\lambda_{2s}}{\lambda_{1s}}-\dfrac{a_{2s}x_s}{\lambda_{1s}}}{1-\dfrac{a_{1s}x_s}{\lambda_{1s}}}\right)\right] \tag{7.6.10}$$

In a similar fashion we can use

$$g_s(\lambda_{1s}, \lambda_{2s}) = \lambda_{2s}g_s\left(\frac{\lambda_{1s}}{\lambda_{2s}}, 1\right)$$

to obtain

$$g_s\left(\frac{\lambda_{1s}}{\lambda_{2s}}, 1\right) = \max_{0 \leqslant x_s \leqslant \delta_s}\left[\frac{c_sx_s}{\lambda_{2s}}+\left(1-\frac{a_{2s}x_s}{\lambda_{2s}}\right)g_{s-1}\left(\frac{\dfrac{\lambda_{1s}}{\lambda_{2s}}-\dfrac{a_{1s}x_s}{\lambda_{2s}}}{1-\dfrac{a_{2s}x_s}{\lambda_{2s}}}, 1\right)\right] \tag{7.6.11}$$

If we compare the amount of calculation required in using (7.6.3) as compared with using (7.6.10) and (7.6.11) we can see the advantage of using the latter. In the normal calculation using (7.6.3) we have a calculation in two state variables $\lambda_{1s}, \lambda_{2s}$. By taking advantage of the homogeneity of the optimal return functions we can use (7.6.10) and (7.6.11), which involve only one state variable, the ratio $\lambda_{2s}/\lambda_{1s}$ in (7.6.10) and $\lambda_{1s}/\lambda_{2s}$ in (7.6.11).

The nature of the computational process will be clarified if we redefine the variables. We define

$$\mu_s = \frac{\lambda_{2s}}{\lambda_{1s}}, \qquad \nu_s = \frac{\lambda_{1s}}{\lambda_{2s}}$$

$$v_s = \frac{x_s}{\lambda_{1s}}, \qquad w_s = \frac{x_s}{\lambda_{2s}} \tag{7.6.12}$$

Using (7.6.12) we can rewrite (7.6.10) and (7.6.11) as

$$g_s(1, \mu_s) = \max_{0 \le v_s \le \delta_s'} \left[c_s v_s + (1 - a_{1s}v_s) g_{s-1}\left(1, \frac{v_s - a_{2s}v_s}{1 - a_{1s}v_s}\right) \right] \qquad (7.6.13)$$

$$g_s(v_s, 1) = \max_{0 \le w_s \le \delta_s''} \left[c_s w_s + (1 - a_{2s}w_s) g_{s-1}\left(\frac{v_s - a_{2s}w_s}{1 - a_{2s}w_s}, 1\right) \right] \qquad (7.6.14)$$

where $\qquad \delta_s' = \min\left(\dfrac{1}{a_{1s}}, \dfrac{\mu_s}{a_{2s}}\right) \qquad \delta_s'' = \min\left(\dfrac{v_s}{a_{1s}}, \dfrac{1}{a_{2s}}\right) \qquad (7.6.15)$

Since $0 \le \lambda_{1s} \le b_1$ and $0 \le \lambda_{2s} \le b_2$, it is clear that $0 \le \mu_s \le \infty$, $0 \le v_s \le \infty$. In order to keep μ_s, v_s bounded more conveniently, we use (7.6.13) and (7.6.14) to calculate $g_s(1, \mu_s)$ and $g_s(v_s, 1)$ for $0 \le \mu_s, v_s \le 1$. If $1 - a_{1s}v_s \ge \mu_s - a_{2s}v_s$ we use (7.6.13). If $1 - a_{1s}v_s < \mu_s - a_{2s}v_s$ we use (7.6.14). We see that this is correct since

$$\frac{v_s - a_{1s}w_s}{1 - a_{2s}w_s} = \frac{\dfrac{1}{\mu_s} - a_{1s}\dfrac{v_s}{\mu_s}}{1 - a_{2s}\dfrac{v_s}{\mu_s}} = \frac{1 - a_{1s}v_s}{\mu_s - a_{2s}v_s} < 1$$

if $1 - a_{1s}v_s < \mu_s - a_{2s}v_s$.

The utility of (7.6.13) and (7.6.14) is now clear. We have reduced a two-dimensional table to two one-dimensional tables, which is a drastic reduction in calculation and storage.

This technique is particularly useful for problems in which, at each stage, the number of entries in the tabulation of $g_s(\alpha_{1s}, \lambda_{2s})$ increases. This is true, e.g., in problems which have state transformations given by

$$\lambda_{1s} = \lambda_{1, s-1} + a_{1s}x_s \qquad (s = 2, 3, \ldots, n) \qquad (7.6.16)$$

instead of

$$\lambda_{1s} = \lambda_{1, s-1} - a_{1s}x_s$$

With (7.6.16) the calculation and storage increase as s increases. Hence, if we had a recurrence relation of the form

$$g_s(\lambda_{1s}, \lambda_{2s}) = \max_{0 \le x_s \le \delta_s} [c_s x_s + g_{s-1}(\lambda_{1s} + a_{1s}x_s, \lambda_{2s} + a_{2s}x_s)] \qquad (7.6.17)$$

we could replace (7.6.17) with expressions analogous to (7.6.13)–(7.6.15), namely,

$$g_s(1, \mu_s) = \max_{0 \le v_s \le \delta_s'} \left[c_s v_s + (1 + a_{1s}v_s) g_{s-1}\left(1, \frac{\mu_s + a_{2s}v_s}{1 + a_{2s}v_s}\right) \right] \qquad (7.6.18)$$

$$g_s(v_s, 1) = \max_{0 \le w_s \le \delta_s''} \left[c_s w_s + (1 + a_{2s}w_s) g_{s-1}\left(\frac{v_s + a_{1s}w_s}{1 + a_{2s}w_s}, 1\right) \right] \qquad (7.6.19)$$

when δ_s', δ_s'' are as in (7.6.15). Since μ_s and v_s are bounded, we no longer have a problem with an expanding grid of points.

7.7. A New Method for Reduction of Dimensionality

We have noted previously in Chapter 6 that problems with more than a few state variables are beyond the capability of the straightforward approach of dynamic programming. We shall consider now some recent work which uses dynamic programming in the context of an exact search process which greatly extends the utility of dynamic programming for an important class of problems.

Consider the discrete variable optimization problem

$$\max \quad z = \sum_{j=1}^{n} \phi_j(x_j) \tag{7.7.1}$$

subject to
$$h_i(\mathbf{x}) \leqslant 0 \qquad (i = 1, 2, \ldots, m) \tag{7.7.2}$$
$$x_j \geqslant 0, \quad \text{integer}, \qquad (j = 1, 2, \ldots, n) \tag{7.7.3}$$

where $\phi_j(x_j)$ are non-decreasing functions and the region defined by (7.7.2) and (7.7.3) is bounded and nonempty, and $\mathbf{x} = (x_1, x_2, \ldots, x_n)$.

The algorithm for solving (7.7.1)–(7.7.3) is based on using dynamic programming methodology for searching a series of hypersurfaces in E^n for a point which is feasible, i.e., which satisfies (7.7.2) and (7.7.3). Suppose that the optimal value of the objective function in (7.7.1) is z^*. We suppose further that by some means an upper bound z_0 on z^* is found, i.e., $z^* \leqslant z_0$. Then

$$z_0 = \sum_{j=1}^{n} \phi_j(x_j^0)$$
$$x_j^0 \geqslant 0, \quad \text{integer} \qquad (j = 1, 2, \ldots, n) \tag{7.7.4}$$

The basic notion behind the hypersurface search algorithm is to search the hypersurfaces

$$\sum_{j=1}^{n} \phi_j(x_j) = z_k \qquad (k = 0, 1, \ldots) \tag{7.7.5}$$

z_0 has already been defined. More will be said about the determination of the sequence z_k, $k \neq 0$, further on. The search is conducted using dynamic programming, but in such a way that the objective function is rapidly bounded by a feasible solution and can be terminated with the optimal solution as soon as a particular value of z_k is reached which is strictly less than the greatest feasible lower bound yet found. When this occurs, the bound is the optimal value of the objective function z^* and the corresponding optimal values of x_j^* are also known. This procedure is clearly finite (assuming that the sequence z_k is generated properly) since it was assumed that the region defined by (7.7.2) and (7.7.3) was bounded and nonempty.

We shall now describe this hypersurface search algorithm.

Hypersurface Search Algorithm

1. Determine upper bounds u_j for each variable. We then have

$$0 \leqslant x_j \leqslant u_j$$
$$x_j, \quad \text{integer} \quad (j = 1, 2, \ldots, n)$$

Let $X = \{x_j | 0 \leqslant x_j \leqslant u_j, \text{integer}, j = 1, 2, \ldots, n\}$

2. Compute z_0, if one is not known *a priori* by

$$z_0 = \sum_{j=1}^{n} \phi_j(u_j)$$

3. Find all combinations of x_j, $j = 1, 2, \ldots, n$, which satisfy

$$\sum_{j=1}^{n} \phi_j(x_j) = z_k$$
$$x_j \in X \qquad (j = 1, 2, \ldots, n)$$

where the sequence $\{z_k\}$ is selected as described subsequently and the z_k are examined in descending order of magnitude.

4. When a z_k is reached, which is less than the greatest feasible lower bound on z, the bound is the optimal solution.

Steps 1 and 2 of the above procedure are self-evident. We shall next consider how to carry out steps 3 and 4. It will be noted that there is no explicit mention of the original constraints of the problem, $h_i(\mathbf{x}) \leqslant 0$, $i = 1, 2, \ldots, m$. These are used, as will be seen, only to check the feasibility of a candidate solution in Step 3, i.e., whether any candidate solution $\mathbf{x}^k$ is such that $h_i(\mathbf{x}^k) \leqslant 0$ for all i.

Let us consider now how step 3 of the hypersurface search algorithm is carried out. It is here that we shall employ dynamic programming solution techniques. The problem we wish to solve in step 3 is as follows.

Find all combinations of x_j, $j = 1, 2, \ldots, n$ which satisfy

$$\sum_{j=1}^{n} \phi_j(x_j) = z_k \qquad (k \in K) \tag{7.7.6}$$
$$x_j \in X \qquad (j = 1, 2, \ldots, n)$$

where K is as yet unspecified as to its members, but there is a definite method for its computation. An equivalent formulation of (7.7.6) is

$$\max \quad z = \sum_{j=1}^{n} \phi_j(x_j)$$

subject to
$$\sum_{j=1}^{n} \phi_j(x_j) \leqslant z_0 \tag{7.7.7}$$
$$x_j \in X \qquad (j = 1, 2, \ldots, n)$$

Problem (7.7.7), if it can be solved efficiently, obviously does what (7.7.6) asks us to do. The way in which we shall solve (7.7.7) is to consider it as a sequence of problems of the form (7.7.7) except that the constraint

$$\sum_{j=1}^{n} \phi_j(x_j) \leqslant z_0 \tag{7.7.8}$$

will be replaced by

$$\sum_{j=1}^{n} \phi_j(x_j) = z_k \tag{7.7.9}$$

and we will solve a sequence of problems of the form

$$\max \quad z = \sum_{j=1}^{n} \phi_j(x_j)$$

subject to

$$\sum_{j=1}^{n} \phi_j(x_j) = z_k \quad (k \in K) \tag{7.7.10}$$

$$x_j \in X \quad (j = 1, 2, \ldots, n)$$

for an appropriate sequence of $z_k \leqslant z_0$. The fact that in (7.7.10), we already know the maximum value of z, viz., z_k, in no way makes this a trivial problem, since we must determine whether or not there exists a set of *feasible* integer values x_j satisfying (7.7.2) which give rise to this maximal value.

If we now apply the principle of optimality to (7.7.10), the following recurrence relations, which we have seen before, obviously provide us with a solution method for (7.7.10):

$$g_1(\lambda_1) = \max_{x_1 = \delta_1} \phi_1(x_1) = \begin{cases} \lambda_1, & \lambda_1 = \phi_1(\delta_1), \quad \delta_1 = 0, 1, \ldots, u_1 \\ -\infty, & \text{otherwise} \end{cases} \tag{7.7.11}$$

$$g_s(\lambda_s) = \max_{0 \leqslant x_s \leqslant \delta_s} [\phi_s(x_s) + g_{s-1}(\lambda_s - \phi_s(x_s))] \quad (s = 2, 3, \ldots, n) \tag{7.7.12}$$

$$(\lambda_s = 0, 1, \ldots, \Lambda_s)$$

where

$$\delta_s = \min(u_s, [\xi_s]), \quad \phi_s(\xi_s) = \lambda_s, \quad \Lambda_s = \sum_{j=1}^{s} \phi_j(u_j)$$

It is a simple matter to see by means of (7.7.11), (7.7.12), and induction that $g_s(\lambda_s) = \lambda_s$ or $g_s(\lambda_s) = -\infty$ for all λ_s and all s. A value of $g_s(\lambda_s) = -\infty$ merely means that there is no finite value of $g_s(\lambda_s)$ because there does not exist an integral value of x_s such that $\phi_s(x_s) = \lambda_s$.

The use of (7.7.11) and (7.7.12) is as we have described in earlier chapters. We calculate $g_s(\lambda_s)$, $x_s^*(\lambda_s)$ for $\lambda_s = 0, 1, \ldots, \Lambda_s$ for $s = 1, 2, \ldots, n-1$. Finally, we calculate $g_n(z_k)$ and $x_n^*(z_k)$, assuming that a solution exists. Using the state variable transformation

$$\lambda_{s-1} = \lambda_s - \phi_s(x_s^*) \quad (s = n, n-1, \ldots, 1)$$

we calculate the values of the remaining variables $x_{n-1}^*, x_{n-2}^*, \ldots, x_1^*$.

Next we consider how to generate the sequence $\{z_k\}$. This is given in the following proposition.

13

PROPOSITION. *The only finite values of the sequence* $\{z_k\}$ *that need be considered in the solution* (7.7.10) *are given by*

$$z_k = \lambda_{n-1} + \phi_n(x_n), \quad x_n = u_n, u_{n-1}, \ldots, 0$$

where λ_{n-1} *are the finite values of the state variable* λ_{n-1} *in the tabulation of* $g_{n-1}(\lambda_{n-1})$. *The calculation is terminated whenever a value of*

$$z_k = \lambda_{n-1} + \phi_n(u_n)$$

is reached which is less than the greatest feasible lower bound.

Proof. We know that:

(1) $g_n(z_k) = \max\limits_{0 \leqslant x_n \leqslant \delta_n} [\phi_n(x_n) + g_{n-1}(z_k - \phi_n(x_n))]$

where $\qquad\qquad \delta_n = \min(u_n, [\xi_n]), \quad \phi_n(x_n) \leqslant z_k.$

(2) $g_s(\lambda_s) = \lambda_s$ or $-\infty.$

(3) $g_{n-1}(\cdot)$ is defined only for finite values of the argument.

Let us now consider $g_{n-1}(z_k - \phi_n(x_n))$. This will be finite only if $z_k - \phi_n(x_n)$ is finite. However, by (2) we see that

$$g_{n-1}(z_k - \phi_n(x_n)) = z_k - \phi_n(x_n) \quad \text{or} \quad -\infty$$

Hence we have that

$$g_n(z_k) = \max\limits_{0 \leqslant x_n \leqslant \delta_n} [\phi_n(x_n) + z_k - \phi_n(x_n) \quad \text{or} \quad \phi_n(x_n) + (-\infty)]$$

$$= z_k.$$

Therefore in order to guarantee finite values we need only consider the finite entries in the tabulation of $g_{n-1}(\cdot)$. The rest of the backward calculation through the tables is guaranteed since the forward calculation of the optimal return functions $g_s(\cdot)$ by recurison considered only finite values of $g_{s-1}(\cdot)$.

The calculation can be terminated when z_k is less than the current feasible lower bound, since

$$z_k = \lambda_{n-1} + \phi_n(u_n)$$

and since successive values of λ_{n-1} are decreasing. Hence, upon the first occurrence of a z_k which satisfies the above condition, the current lower bound is the optimal solution.

Let us apply the foregoing computational method in solving the following problem:

$$\max \quad z = 6x_1^2 + 3x_2 + 2x_2^3 + 2x_3^2 \qquad\qquad (7.7.13)$$

subject to $\qquad\qquad\qquad 3x_1 + 4x_2 + 3x_3 \leqslant 10$

$$2x_1 + 3x_2 + 3x_3 \leqslant 12$$

$$x_1, x_2, x_3 \geqslant 0, \quad \text{integer}$$

We see that

$$\phi_1(x_1) = 6x_1^2$$
$$\phi_2(x_2) = 3x_2 + 2x_2^3$$
$$\phi_3(x_3) = 2x_3^2$$

From the constraints of (7.7.13) we see that

$$0 \leqslant x_1 \leqslant 3 = u_1$$
$$0 \leqslant x_2 \leqslant 2 = u_2$$
$$0 \leqslant x_3 \leqslant 3 = u_3$$

Therefore, from (7.7.11) we have

$$g_1(\lambda_1) = \begin{cases} \lambda_1, & \lambda_1 = 6\delta_1^2, \quad \delta_1 = 0, 1, 2, 3 \\ -\infty, & \text{otherwise} \end{cases}$$

A tabulation of all finite values of $g_1(\lambda_1)$ and $x_1^*(\lambda_1)$ is given in Table 7.7.1.

TABLE 7.7.1. $g_1(\lambda_1)$

λ_1	$g_1(\lambda_1)$	$x_1^*(\lambda_1)$
0	0	0
6	6	1
24	24	2
54	54	3

Using (7.7.12) we next compute $g_2(\lambda_2)$ as

$$g_2(\lambda_2) = \max_{0 \leqslant x_2 \leqslant \delta_2} [3x_2 + 2x_2^3 + g_1(\lambda_2 - 3x_2 - 2x_2^3)]$$

where

$$3\xi_2 + 2\xi_2^3 = \lambda_2 \quad \text{and} \quad \delta_2 = \min(2, [\xi_2])$$

A tabulation of $g_2(\lambda_2)$ and $x_2^*(\lambda_2)$ is given in Table 7.7.2.

TABLE 7.7.2. $g_2(\lambda_2)$

λ_2	$g_2(\lambda_2)$	$x_2^*(\lambda_2)$	λ_2	$g_2(\lambda_2)$	$x_2^*(\lambda_2)$
0	0	0	28	28	2
5	5	1	29	29	1
6	6	0	46	46	2
11	11	1	54	54	0
22	22	2	59	59	1
24	24	0	76	76	2

13*

We note that

$$z_0 = \Lambda_3 = \sum_{j=1}^{3} \phi_j(u_j) = 6(3)^2 + 3(2) + 2(2)^3 + 2(3)^2 = 94$$

The first $z_k = z_0$ and by the proposition, the first z_k to be tried is

$$z_0 = \lambda_2 + \phi_3(u_3) = 76 + 18 = 94$$

which agrees with this calculation. The solution corresponding to $z_0 = 94$ by the usual backward pass through Tables 7.7.2 and 7.7.1 yields the solution

$$x_1^* = 3, \quad x_2^* = 2, \quad x_3^* = 3$$

which is infeasible, i.e., it does not satisfy the constraints of (7.7.13). The next value of the sequence $\{z_k\}$ is

$$z_1 = \lambda_2 + \phi_3(u_3 - 1) = 76 + 8 = 84$$

Again we find that the solution

$$x_1^* = 3, \quad x_2^* = 2, \quad x_3^* = 2$$

is infeasible. Continuing this process we have

$$
\begin{array}{llll}
z_2 = 76 + 2 = 78, & x_1^* = 3, & x_2^* = 2, & x_3^* = 1 \quad \text{(infeasible)} \\
z_3 = 76 + 0 = 76, & x_1^* = 3, & x_2^* = 2, & x_3^* = 0 \quad \text{(infeasible)} \\
z_4 = 59 + 18 = 77, & x_1^* = 3, & x_2^* = 1, & x_3^* = 3 \quad \text{(infeasible)} \\
z_5 = 59 + 8 = 67, & x_1^* = 3, & x_2^* = 1, & x_3^* = 2 \quad \text{(infeasible)} \\
z_6 = 59 + 2 = 61, & x_1^* = 3, & x_2^* = 1, & x_3^* = 1 \quad \text{(infeasible)} \\
z_7 = 59 + 0 = 59, & x_1^* = 3, & x_2^* = 1, & x_3^* = 0 \quad \text{(infeasible)} \\
z_8 = 54 + 18 = 72, & x_1^* = 3, & x_2^* = 0, & x_3^* = 3 \quad \text{(infeasible)} \\
z_9 = 54 + 8 = 62, & x_1^* = 3, & x_2^* = 0, & x_3^* = 2 \quad \text{(infeasible)} \\
z_{10} = 54 + 2 = 56, & x_1^* = 3, & x_2^* = 0, & x_3^* = 1 \quad \text{(infeasible)} \\
z_{11} = 54 + 0 = 54, & x_1^* = 3, & x_2^* = 0, & x_3^* = 0 \quad \textit{(feasible)}
\end{array}
$$

At this point we have a first feasible lower bound. We cannot be sure, however, that a larger feasible solution does not exist until all subsequent $z_k < 54$. Hence we continue the calculation:

$$
\begin{array}{llll}
z_{12} = 46 + 18 = 64, & x_1^* = 2, & x_2^* = 2, & x_3^* = 3 \quad \text{(infeasible)} \\
z_{13} = 46 + 8 = 54, & x_1^* = 2, & x_2^* = 2, & x_3^* = 2 \quad \text{(infeasible)} \\
z_{14} = 29 + 18 = 47 < 54
\end{array}
$$

Hence we have bounded the solution. The optimal solution is

$$z^* = 54, \quad x_1^* = 3, \quad x_2^* = 0, \quad x_3^* = 0$$

The efficiency of the hypersurface search algorithm resides in the fact that the structural constraints (7.7.2), which usually give rise to as many state variables as constraints in a dynamic programming solution, are here used only to check on the feasibility of a candidate solution. All the required optimal return functions depend upon only one state variable.

In [22] computational results are given for problems with varying sizes. For example, problems with 25 variables and 4 constraints were solved in an average of 37 seconds on a CDC CYBER 72. The addition of more constraints would affect this time only linearly with the number of constraints.

Exercises—Chapter 7

7.1. Solve the following problem using a Lagrange multiplier:

$$\min \quad z = 2x_1^2 + 5x_1 + 3x_2^2 + 4x_2 + 4x_3^2 + 3x_3 + 5x_4^2 + 2x_4$$

subject to
$$2x_1 + x_2 + 2x_3 + x_4 \geqslant 10$$
$$x_1 + 2x_2 + 3x_3 + 4x_4 \geqslant 8$$
$$x_1, x_2, x_3, x_4 \geqslant 0, \quad \text{integer}$$

7.2. Solve the following problem using a Lagrange multiplier:

$$\max \quad z = 3x_1^2 + 6x_1 + 5x_2^2 + x_2 + 4x_3^2 + 3x_3$$

subject to
$$2x_1 + 8x_2 + 5x_3 \leqslant 30$$
$$x_1 + x_2 + x_3 \leqslant 6$$
$$x_1, x_2, x_3 \geqslant 0, \quad \text{integer}$$

7.3. Solve the following problem using the method of successive approximations:

$$\max z = x_1^2 y_1 + 3x_2 y_2^2 + 4x_3^2 y_3$$

subject to
$$2x_1 + 3x_2 + 4x_3 \leqslant 24$$
$$3y_1 + 2y_2 + 5y_3 \leqslant 30$$
$$x_1, x_2, x_3, y_1, y_2, y_3 \geqslant 0, \quad \text{integer}$$

7.4. Solve the following problem using successive approximations:

$$\min \quad z = \sum_{j=1}^{3} \phi_j(x_j, y_j)$$

subject to
$$4x_1 + 8x_2 + 6x_3 \geqslant 34$$
$$8y_1 + 6y_2 + 5y_3 \geqslant 23$$
$$x_j, y_j \geqslant 0, \quad \text{integer} \quad (j = 1, 2, 3)$$

where
$$\phi_1(x_1, y_1) = x_1^2 + 6x_1 y_1 + 3y_1^2$$
$$\phi_2(x_2, y_2) = e^{x_1} + 2e^{x_2 + y_2} + e^{y_3}$$
$$\phi_3(x_3, y_3) = 6x_1 + x_1 y_1 + 10y_1$$

7.5. Solve Problem 6.3 by Lagrange multiplier and successive approximations.

7.6. Given the functional equation

$$g(\lambda) = \max_{0 \leqslant x \leqslant \lambda} \left[e^{-10/x} + e^{-15/(\lambda - x)} + g(.8x + .9(\lambda - x)) \right]$$

find the optimal policy and optimal return by policy approximation.

7.7. Solve 7.6 by assuming a stagewise process and letting the number of stages become infinite by using recurrence relations of the form

$$g_1(\lambda_1) = \max_{0 \le x_1 \le \lambda_1} \left[e^{-10/x_1} + e^{-15/(\lambda_1 - x_1)} \right]$$

$$g_s(\lambda_s) = \max_{0 \le x_s \le \lambda_s} \left[e^{-10/x_s} + e^{-15/(\lambda_s x_s)} + g_{s-1}(.8x_s + .9(\lambda_s - x_s)) \right] \qquad (s = 2, 3, \ldots)$$

7.8. Solve by the method of Section 7.7

$$\max \quad z = 3x_1^2 + 4x_1 + 2x_2^2 + 3x_2 + 4x_3^2 + x_3 + 5x_4^2 + 2x_4$$

subject to

$$2x_1^2 + 3x_2 + x_3^2 + 4x_4 \le 32$$

$$x_1 + 2x_2 + 3x_3 + 4x_4 \le 20$$

$$x_1, x_2, x_3, x_4 \ge 0, \quad \text{integer}$$

Chapter 8

Stochastic Processes and Dynamic Programming

8.1. Introduction

With one or two exceptions (e.g., the stochastic gold mining problem in Chapter 6) all of the processes or systems that have been formulated in the previous chapters have been deterministic. What this means is that when a decision is made at some stage, the state resulting from that decision is completely determined and known. The essential difference between that kind of process and a stochastic process is that the state resulting from a decision is not predetermined. It can only be described by some known probability distribution function which depends upon the initial state, and in some cases the decision that has been made.

We can clearly exhibit the differences, as well as the similarities, between the application of dynamic programming to deterministic and stochastic processes by returning to the general description of a dynamic programming process in Chapter 3. We briefly alluded to this difference in Section 3.2.

Consider a deterministic n-stage process in which the state of the system is λ_s. A decision x_s is made and the system undergoes a transformation which results in the state λ_{s-1}. We have seen many examples of this in previous chapters, e.g., $\lambda_{s-1} = \lambda_s - a_s x_s$. In general terms we can describe this as

$$\lambda_{s-1} = T_s(\lambda_s, x_s(\lambda_s)) \tag{8.1.1}$$

The important property of this change from state to state is that it is completely predetermined once T is specified. For example, if T_s is given by

$$\lambda_{s-1} = T_s(\lambda_s, x_s(\lambda_s)) = \lambda_s - a_s x_s \tag{8.1.2}$$

then once λ_s and x_s are specified, λ_{s-1} is completely determined.

Consider now the case of a stochastic process. It is the process of going from one state to the next that can only be described by a probability distribution of some kind. This means that the specification of the current state λ_s and a decision or action to be taken x_s does not determine the resulting state λ_{s-1}. Therefore, the transformation $\tilde{T}_s(\lambda_s, x_s(\lambda_s))$ does not uniquely determine a new state λ_{s-1}. What happens instead is that the new state is a random variable. We shall designate it $\tilde{\lambda}_{s-1}$ and it has associated with it a distribution function $H(\lambda_s, \tilde{\lambda}_{s-1}, x_s(\lambda_s))$. The distribution function depends upon the known state λ_s, the stochastic state vector $\tilde{\lambda}_{s-1}$, and the decision x_s that is made.

The reason H depends upon λ_s is that we always start with a *known* state. It is the transformation that is uncertain. Hence, the transformation is described by a stochastic state $\tilde{\lambda}_{s-1}$. However, before a decision is made at stage $s-1$, the actual state λ_{s-1} will be observed and hence will be known. Hence our *a priori* description of the state resulting from the transformation is in terms of a set of stochastic states $\tilde{\lambda}_{s-1}$, one of which will be the actual state, λ_{s-1}.

To clarify the difference between deterministic and stochastic processes we shall consider a familiar deterministic problem and then consider how one would deal with a stochastic analog of the problem. Suppose we wish to solve

$$\max \quad z = \sum_{j=1}^{n} \phi_j(x_j)$$

subject to $\qquad\qquad x_j \in X_j \qquad (j = 1, 2, \ldots, n)$

(8.1.2a)

The sets X_j are specified in some way, the details of which are not important here.

Let us suppose that the state transformation relations are

$$\lambda_{s-1} = T_s(\lambda_s, x_s(\lambda_s)) \qquad (s = 2, 3, \ldots, n) \tag{8.1.3}$$

Then the recurrence relations that solve (8.1.2) are given by

$$g_1(\lambda_1) = \max_{x_1 \in X_1} \phi_1(x_1) \tag{8.1.4}$$

$$g_s(\lambda_s) = \max_{x_s \in X_s} [\phi_s(x_s) + g_{s-1}(T_s(\lambda_s, x_s(\lambda_s)))] \qquad (s = 2, 3, \ldots, n) \tag{8.1.5}$$

We have explained many times in this book how (8.1.4) and (8.1.5) are employed to solve (8.1.2).

Now let us suppose that the state transformations are stochastic in the sense we have previously discussed. Since a unique transformation from state λ_s result not in a unique state but rather in a vector of possible states $\tilde{\lambda}_{s-1}$, we shall assume that the state transformation relations are

$$\tilde{\lambda}_{s-1} = \tilde{T}_s(\lambda_s, x_s(\lambda_s)) \qquad (s = 2, 3, \ldots, n) \tag{8.1.6}$$

Since the $\tilde{\lambda}_{s-1}$ terms are stochastic, the x_s are also stochastic, since the choice of some specific x_s does not yield a determinate result. If we now consider once more the desire to maximize $\sum_{j=1}^{n} \phi_j(x_j)$ as in (8.1.2), it is quite clear that this objective function is now stochastic in view of the uncertainty inherent in $\tilde{\lambda}_s$ and x_s. Hence it is no longer feasible to maximize the return. What then can we do?

In the face of this kind of uncertainty, where a known probability distribution describes the uncertainty in the transformations, the most common substitute resorted to in probability theory is to maximize the *expectation* or *expected* return. Instead of optimal return, we shall have optimal expected return. We then define

$\tilde{g}_s(\lambda_s)$ = maximum expected return over $\tilde{\lambda}_{s-1}$, over the s remaining stages when the system is in state λ_s and using an optimal policy.

Before proceeding it will be recalled that the expectation $E(y)$ of a random variable y whose probability density function is $f(y)$ is, for the continuous case,

$$E(y) = \int_{-\infty}^{\infty} yf(y)\, dy \tag{8.1.7}$$

and for the case of the discrete density distribution, it is

$$E(y) = \sum_{i=1}^{k} y_i f(y_i) \tag{8.1.8}$$

We see that instead of solving (8.1.2) we seek to

$$\max \quad \tilde{z} = E\left[\sum_{j=1}^{n} \phi_j(x_j)\right] \tag{8.1.9}$$

Since the x_j are also stochastic, we shall emphasize this by rewriting (8.1.9) as

$$\max \quad \tilde{z} = E\left[\sum_{j=1}^{n} \phi_j(\tilde{\lambda}_{j-1}, x_j)\right] \tag{8.1.10}$$

We recall from probability theory that the expectation of a sum is the sum of the expectations, i.e.,

$$E(u+v) = E(u)+E(v) \tag{8.1.11}$$

Using (8.1.10), (8.1.11), and the definition of $\tilde{g}_s(\lambda_s)$ we have for continuous density functions that

$$\tilde{g}_1(\lambda_1) = \max_{x_1 \in X_1} \left[\int_{-\infty}^{\infty} \phi_1(\tilde{\lambda}_0, x_1)\, d\Phi(\lambda_1, \tilde{\lambda}_0, x_1)\right] \tag{8.1.12}†$$

Similarly, the general recurrence relation is

$$\tilde{g}_s(\lambda_s) = \max_{x_s \in X_s} E[\phi_s(\tilde{\lambda}_{s-1}, x_s)+g_{s-1}+(\tilde{\lambda}_{s-1})]$$

$$= \max_{x_s \in X_s} \left[\int_{-\infty}^{\infty} [\phi_s(\tilde{\lambda}_{s-1}, x_s)+g_{s-1}(\tilde{\lambda}_{s-1})]\, d\Phi(\tilde{\lambda}_s, \tilde{\lambda}_{s-1}, x_s)\right]$$
$$(s = 2, 3, \ldots, n) \tag{8.1.13}$$

In the case of discrete density functions, the distribution $d\Phi(\lambda_s, \tilde{\lambda}_{s-1}, x_s)$ will be replaced by a set of probabilities $\{p_k\}$, so that the equivalent expression for (8.1.13) is

$$\tilde{g}_s(\lambda_s) = \max_{x_s \in X_s} \sum_{k=1}^{K} [\phi_s(\tilde{\lambda}_{s-1}, x_s)+g_{s-1}(\tilde{\lambda}_{s-1})]p_k \tag{8.1.14}$$

where
$$0 \leqslant p_k \leqslant 1 \quad (k = 1, 2, \ldots, K)$$

$$\sum_{k=1}^{K} p_k = 1$$

---

† We are using the notation $E(y) = \int_{-\infty}^{\infty} y\, d\Phi(y)$, which is a Riemann–Stieltjes integral, to describe both continuous and discrete expectations.

In this case the probability density function is defined over K possible discrete states that the stochastic state vector $\tilde{\lambda}_{s-1}$ may assume.

In the next several sections we shall discuss, in some detail, problems which illustrate these ideas.

8.2. A Stochastic Allocation Problem—Discrete Case

Consider the problem we examined in Section 7.4 and special cases of which were treated in Section 4.6. We assumed that a certain resource w is to be divided into two parts x and $w-x$. The yields or profits from each of the parts are $f(x)$ and $h(w-x)$, respectively, in some operation or process. In the course of doing this, x is reduced to αx, $\alpha > 0$, and $w-x$ is reduced to $\beta(w-x)$, $0 \leqslant \beta \leqslant 1$. We wish to find the value of x_s at each stage of an n-stage process that results in the greatest overall yield from the operation.

The recurrence relations for the dynamic programming solution are

$$g_1(\lambda_1) = \max_{0 \leqslant x_1 \leqslant \lambda_1} [f(x_1)+h(\lambda_1-x_1)]$$

$$g_s(\lambda_s) = \max_{0 \leqslant x_s \leqslant \lambda_s} [f(x_s)+h(\lambda_s-x_s)+g_{s-1}(\alpha x_s+\beta(\lambda_s-x_s))] \qquad (8.2.1)$$

$$(s = 2, 3, \ldots, n)$$

We shall now present a stochastic version of the above problem. We shall assume, when we choose x_s, that $f(x_s)$ is uncertain to the extent that it may take one of two possible values. With probability p_1 it assumes the value $f_1(x_s)$ and x_s becomes $\alpha_1 x_s$. With probability $p_2 = 1-p_1$, it takes the value $f_2(x_s)$ and x_s is reduced to $\alpha_2 x_s$. There are also two possibilities for $h(\lambda_s-x_s)$. With probability q_1 it assumes the value $h_1(\lambda_s-x_s)$ and λ_s-x_s is reduced to $\beta_1(\lambda_s-x_s)$. Similarly, with probability $q_2 = 1-q_1$, the value of $h_2(\lambda_s-x_s)$ is assumed and λ_s-x_s is reduced to $\beta_2(\lambda_s-x_s)$. We regard the choices which take place as being independent. Hence we have the following probabilities and random variables:

$$\begin{array}{ll} P_1 = p_1q_1, & \alpha_1 x_s+\beta_1(\lambda_s-x_s) \\ P_2 = p_1q_2, & \alpha_1 x_s+\beta_2(\lambda_s-x_s) \\ P_3 = p_2q_1, & \alpha_2 x_s+\beta_1(\lambda_s-x_s) \\ P_4 = p_2q_2, & \alpha_2 x_s+\beta_2(\lambda_s-x_s) \end{array} \qquad (8.2.2)$$

We can observe that

$$P_1+P_2+P_3+P_4 = p_1q_1+p_1q_2+p_2q_1+p_2q_2$$
$$= p_1q_1+p_1(1-q_1)+(1-p_1)q_1+(1-p_1)(1-q_1) = 1$$

and that $$0 \leqslant P_i \leqslant 1$$

Hence this distribution satisfies the requirements for a discrete probability distribution.

In order to formulate the recurrence relations we note that at each stage λ_s is now a stochastic variable $\tilde{\lambda}_s$ and is transformed into $\tilde{\lambda}_{s-1}$ with four different possibilities:

$$\begin{array}{ll} \alpha_1 x_s+\beta_1(\lambda_s-x_s), & \alpha_2 x_s+\beta_1(\lambda_s-x_s) \\ \alpha_1 x_s+\beta_2(\lambda_s-x_s), & \alpha_2 x_s+\beta_2(\lambda_s-x_s) \end{array} \qquad (8.2.3)$$

Using the principle of optimality, (8.2.2) and (8.2.3), we obtain the following counterparts of (8.1.14):

$$\tilde{g}_1(\lambda_1) = \max_{0 \leqslant x_1 \leqslant \lambda_1} [p_1 q_1 \{ f_1(x_1) + h_1(\lambda_1 - x_1) \} + p_1 q_2 \{ f_1(x_1) + h_2(\lambda_1 - x_1) \}$$

$$+ p_2 q_1 \{ f_2(x_1) + h_1(\lambda_1 - x_1) \} + p_2 q_2 \{ f_2(x_1) + h_2(\lambda_1 - x_1) \}] \tag{8.2.4}$$

$$\tilde{g}_s(\lambda_s) = \max_{0 \leqslant x_s \leqslant \lambda_s} [p_1 q_1 \{ f_1(x_s) + h_1(\lambda_s - x_s) + g_{s-1}(\alpha_1 x_s + \beta_1(\lambda_s - x_s)) \}$$

$$+ p_1 q_2 \{ f_1(x_s) + h_2(\lambda_s - x_s) + g_{s-1}(\alpha_1 x_s + \beta_2(\lambda_s - x_s)) \}$$

$$+ p_2 q_1 \{ f_2(x_s) + h_1(\lambda_s - x_s) + g_{s-1}(\alpha_2 x_s + \beta_1(\lambda_s - x_s)) \}$$

$$+ p_2 q_2 \{ f_2(x_s) + h_2(\lambda_s - x_s) + g_{s-1}(\alpha_2 x_s + \beta_2(\lambda_s - x_s)) \}] \tag{8.2.5}$$

We see from (8.2.4) and (8.2.5) that if the p_1, p_2, q_1, q_2 are known, the calculation is no more difficult than the deterministic case, although somewhat lengthier.

8.3. A Stochastic Allocation Problem—Continuous Case

Let us now consider a stochastic version of the grower's problem of Section 4.6. We shall modify our notation slightly for convenience. We assume that in a given year λ_s units of the crop have been grown, some of which will be retained as seed for the succeeding year and the remainder of which will be sold. In the deterministic case, the yield from each unit of the seed crop was $\alpha > 1$ units and the income from y units of crop which are sold is $\phi(y)$. We shall now modify this assumption. Suppose that the grower decides to retain x_s and to sell $\lambda_s - x_s$ in year s. Suppose that the income $\phi(\lambda_s - x_s)$ is deterministic but that there is uncertainty about the amount of crop, $\tilde{\lambda}_{s-1}$ that will be available next year as a result of retaining x_s in year s. This is a common condition in growing, breeding, and investing. Let us assume that this uncertainty can be expressed as

$$\tilde{\lambda}_{s-1} = \tilde{T}_s(\lambda_s, x_s(\lambda_s)) = r_s x_s \tag{8.3.1}$$

The random variable r_s is assumed to have a probability density $p(r_s)$ that is known to the grower. Assuming that the probability density $p(r_s)$ remains constant during the n-year process, we shall assume that

$$p(r_s) = p(r) \tag{8.3.2}$$

The expected value of this density is

$$E(r) = \int_{-\infty}^{\infty} r p(r) \, dr \tag{8.3.3}$$

We assume that $E(r) > 1$. This assumption is equivalent to the assumption of $\alpha > 1$ in the deterministic case. Without such an assumption the grower would sell his entire crop and not preserve some for seed.

The total income from an n-stage process is

$$z = \sum_{j=1}^{n} \phi_j(\lambda_j - x_j) \tag{8.3.4}$$

If the initial amount of crop (for the nth year—the stages are numbered in reverse) was $\lambda_n = q$, the total amount of income from the stochastic process is

$$\tilde{z} = \phi(q - x_n) + \phi(r_n x_n - x_{n-1}) + \ldots + \phi(r_2 x_2 - x_1) \tag{8.3.5}$$

We observe from (8.3.5) that the total income no longer depends only upon the initial amount of crop q and the series of decisions $x_n, x_{n-1}, \ldots, x_1$, as in the deterministic case. The total income also depends upon the sequence of random numbers $r_n, r_{n-1}, \ldots, r_2$. Hence it is not meaningful to ask what values of $x_1, x_2, \ldots, x_n$ maximize z. Instead we shall maximize expected income.

The expected income is calculated by utilizing the known probability distributions of all the random variables that will affect this process. Therefore, at the beginning of the n-year planning period (year 1), the expected total income will be

$$\bar{z} = \phi(q - x_n) + \int_{-\infty}^{\infty} \ldots \int_{-\infty}^{\infty} [\phi(r_n x_n - x_{n-1}) + \ldots + \phi(r_2 x_2 - x_1)] \prod_{j=n}^{2} [p(r_j)\, dr_j] \tag{8.3.6}$$

It must be recognized that the expected value of the total income does not remain constant throughout the process. In year 2 we have already selected some value x_n and so this value is known and the state variable λ_{n-1} is now known, even though we could not predict its value in year 1. Therefore using the values x_n and λ_n in year 2, the total expected income over n years is

$$\bar{z} = \phi(q - x_n) + \phi(\lambda_{n-1} - x_{n-1}) + \int_{-\infty}^{\infty} \ldots \int_{-\infty}^{\infty} [\phi(r_{n-1} x_{n-1} - x_{n-2})$$

$$+ \ldots + \phi(r_2 x_2 - x_1)] \prod_{j=n}^{2} [p(r_j)\, dr_j] \tag{8.3.7}$$

which is not the same as the expected total return at the beginning (year 1) of the process. Similarly, at any stage s, the values of $x_n, x_{n-1}, \ldots, x_{n-s+1}$ will have been observed and the states $\lambda_n, \lambda_{n-1}, \ldots, \lambda_{n-s+1}$ will be known. Consequently, the expected total income is given by

$$\bar{z} = \phi(q - x_n) + \phi(\lambda_{n-1} - x_{n-1}) + \ldots + \phi(\lambda_{n-s+2} - x_{n-s+2})$$

$$+ \phi(\lambda_{n-s+1} - x_{n-s+1}) + \int_{-\infty}^{\infty} \ldots \int_{-\infty}^{\infty} [\phi(r_{n-s+1} x_{n-s+1} - x_{n-s})$$

$$+ \phi(r_2 x_2 - x_1)] \prod_{j=n-s+1}^{2} [p(r_j)\, dr_j] \tag{8.3.8}$$

Although the expected value of income from n years of this stochastic process varies from stage to stage, it has an important property, viz., that at any stage s it is a deterministic function of the current state λ_s and the decisions $x_{n-s}, x_{n-s-1}, \ldots, x_1$ which remain to be made. This, coupled with the separability that is inherent in (8.3.8), allows a dynamic programming solution to be made to this stochastic multistage decision process. By doing so, we shall obtain a solution such that the expected total income is maximized at each stage.

The optimal return functions $\tilde{g}_s(\lambda_s)$ are obtained as follows. For $s = 1$

$$\tilde{g}_1(\lambda_1) = \max_{0 \leqslant x_1 \leqslant \lambda_1} \phi(\lambda_1 - x_1) \tag{8.3.9}$$

Now let us consider the derivation of the general recurrence relation using the principle of optimality. After x_{s-1} is determined, at stage s the state

$$\lambda_s = rx_{s-1} \tag{8.3.10}$$

where r is the value taken by random variable r_{s-1}. When an optimal policy is used the expected return from the previous $s - 1$ stages starting from state rx_{s-1} is

$$\tilde{g}_{s-1}(rx_s)$$

However, the return of the current stage is

$$\phi(\lambda_s - x_s)$$

Therefore the total income when an optimal policy is used over s stages is

$$z = \phi(\lambda_s - x_s) + \tilde{g}_{s-1}(rx_s) \tag{8.3.11}$$

When we now take account of the probability density $p(r)$ for the random variable r, the expected total return

$$\bar{z} = E(z) = \int_{-\infty}^{\infty} zp(r)\,dr = \phi(\lambda_s - x_s) + \int_{-\infty}^{\infty} \tilde{g}_{s-1}(rx_s)\,p(r)\,dr \tag{8.3.12}$$

When the optimal policy is used, this expected value of the total income is maximized with respect to all decisions, including x_s. Therefore we have the general recurrence relation

$$\tilde{g}_s(\lambda_s) = \max_{0 \leqslant x_s \leqslant \lambda_s} \left[\phi(\lambda_s - x_s) + \int_{-\infty}^{\infty} \tilde{g}_{s-1}(rx_s)\,p(r)\,dr \right] \qquad (s = 2, 3, \ldots, n) \tag{8.3.13}$$

Hence, we can obtain the dynamic programming solution to the stochastic version of the grower's problem using (8.3.9) and (8.3.13).

Let us consider a particular case of the stochastic grower's problem in which $\phi(y) = ay^b$, $a > 0$, $0 < b < 1$. Then (8.3.9) and (8.3.13) become

$$\tilde{g}_1(\lambda_1) = \max_{0 \leqslant x_1 \leqslant \lambda_1} a(\lambda_1 - x_1)^b \tag{8.3.14}$$

$$\tilde{g}_s(\lambda_s) = \max_{0 \leqslant x_s \leqslant \lambda_s} \left[a(\lambda_s - x_s)^b + \int_{-\infty}^{\infty} \tilde{g}_{s-1}(rx_s)\,p(r)\,dr \right] \tag{8.3.15}$$

$$(s = 2, 3, \ldots, n)$$

From (8.3.14) we see that $x_1 = 0$ will maximize $a(\lambda_1 - x_1)^b$. Therefore

$$\tilde{g}_1(\lambda_1) = a\lambda_1^b, \qquad x_1^*(\lambda_1) = 0 \tag{8.3.16}$$

Consider now $s = 2$ in (8.3.15):

$$\tilde{g}_2(\lambda_2) = \max_{0 \leq x_2 \leq \lambda_2} \left[a(\lambda_2 - x_2)^b + \int_{-\infty}^{\infty} \tilde{g}_1(rx_2) p(r) \, dr \right] \tag{8.3.17}$$

Substituting (8.3.16) into (8.3.17) we obtain

$$\tilde{g}_2(\lambda_2) = \max_{0 \leq x_2 \leq \lambda_2} \left[a(\lambda_2 - x_2)^b + \int_{-\infty}^{\infty} a(rx_2)^b p(r) \, dr \right] \tag{8.3.18}$$

If we specify some particular $p(r)$, we can then evaluate the integral in (8.3.18). Let us assume that

$$\int_{-\infty}^{\infty} r^b p(r) \, dr = \varrho^b \tag{8.3.19}$$

From (8.3.18) and (8.3.19) we then have

$$\tilde{g}_2(\lambda_2) = \max_{0 \leq x_2 \leq \lambda_2} [a(\lambda_2 - x_2)^b + ax_2^b \varrho^b] \tag{8.3.20}$$

We can find the maximum value of x_2 by differentiating the maximand G_2 of $\tilde{g}_2(\lambda_2)$ in (8.3.20). Thus

$$\frac{\partial G_2}{\partial x_2} = ab(\lambda_2 - x_2)^{b-1}(-1) + a\varrho^b b x_2^{b-1} = 0 \tag{8.3.21}$$

Solving (8.3.21) we obtain

$$x_2^*(\lambda_2) = \frac{\lambda_2}{(\varrho^{b/(b-1)} + 1)} \tag{8.3.22}$$

Substitution of (8.3.22) into (8.3.20) yields

$$\tilde{g}_2(\lambda_2) = a\left(\lambda_2 - \frac{\lambda_2}{\varrho^{b/(b-1)} + 1}\right)^b + a\varrho^b \left(\frac{\lambda_2}{\varrho^{b/(b-1)} + 1}\right)^b$$

which simplifies to

$$\tilde{g}_2(\lambda_2) = \frac{a\varrho^b \lambda_2^b}{(\varrho^{b/(b-1)} + 1)^{b-1}} \tag{8.3.23}$$

Continuation of the recursion process will yield

$$x_3^*(\lambda_3) = \frac{\varrho^{b/(b-1)} + 1}{\varrho^{2b/(b-1)} + \varrho^{b/(b-1)} + 1} \lambda_3 \tag{8.3.24}$$

$$\tilde{g}_3(\lambda_3) = \frac{a\varrho^{2b}}{(\varrho^{2b/(b-1)} + \varrho^{b/(b-1)} + 1)^{b-1}} \tag{8.3.25}$$

It can be shown by mathematical induction that

$$x_s^*(\lambda_s) = \frac{\varrho^{(s-2)b/(b-1)} + \varrho^{(s-3)b/(b-1)} + \ldots + \varrho^{(0)b}}{\varrho^{(s-1)b/(b-1)} + \varrho^{(s-2)b/(b-1)} + \ldots + \varrho^{(0)b/(b-1)}} \lambda_s \tag{8.3.26}$$

$$(s = 2, 3, \ldots, n)$$

and

$$\tilde{g}_s(\lambda_s) = \frac{a\varrho^{(s-1)b}}{\left(\varrho^{(s-1)b/(b-1)} + \varrho^{(s-2)b/(b-1)} + \ldots + ^{(0)b/(b-1)}\right)^{b-1}} \lambda_s^b \qquad (8.3.27)$$

$$(s = 2, 3, \ldots, n)$$

It is important to note how (8.3.16), (8.3.26), and (8.3.27) differ in their use from the deterministic solution of the grower's problem. At the beginning of the n-stage planning period for the grower, we do not know what values will be taken on by $r_1, r_2, \ldots$. We do know, however, that $\lambda_n = q$ and so we can compute the optimal first decision from $\tilde{g}_n(q)$ in the usual way. At any subsequent stage, say stage k, there will be uncertainty about what values the random variables $r_1, r_2, \ldots$, have taken. The optimal decisions are given by (8.3.26) in the same way as in the deterministic case. However, for a stochastic process the sequence of optimal decisions $x_1^*, x_2^*, \ldots, x_n^*$ cannot be calculated in advance because the state transformation relation

$$\lambda_{s-1} = r_s x_s$$

is probabilistic. Hence the result of optimal decision x_s^* is not known until stage $s+1$ after the random variable r_s has assumed some definite value.

8.4. A General Stochastic Inventory Model

Dynamic programming has proven to be of great utility in the solution of inventory problems. A fairly complete treatment of this subject is given in [23]. In this section we shall consider one general formulation based on material in [23].

We consider an inventory system in which some particular item is stocked. In each of n periods we review the inventory and we must decide whether or not to place an order for the item and if an order is placed, how much to order. We shall determine the amounts to be ordered in each of the n periods on the basis of minimizing the sum of all expected costs during the total n periods.

The demand in each period over the total planning period will be considered to be a random variable and will be designated r_j, i.e., the demand in period j. We shall assume that the probability distribution is given by a discrete density function $p_j(r_j)$. The demands in different periods are assumed to be independent of each other.

We assume that in placing an order we incur an ordering cost c_j, independent of the size of the order, if an order is placed in period j. In addition we incur the cost of the number of items we order which is dependent upon the number of items x_j that we order. We shall designate this cost by $\phi_j(x_j)$. In this formulation we shall consider that all demands are filled, i.e., if an order cannot be filled, it is backordered and filled when the stock is replenished. We shall not, however, include the inventory or backorder costs associated with the lead time required when ordering. By the inventory position, which we shall designate λ_j, we mean

$\lambda_j =$ number of items in inventory + number of items on order − number of items on backorder, at the beginning of period j.

The inventory position in period j, after an order has been placed for x_j items, is λ_j+x_j, if x_j is the quantity ordered. The expected cost of carrying inventory will be designated $f_j(\lambda_j+x_j)$.

In selecting x_j, $j \geqslant 2$, we wish to take into account the demands which have occurred in periods 1 to $j-1$. This is done implicitly by use of the inventory position λ_j, which is our state variable. Hence, as usual, x_j depends upon λ_j. We then define as our optimal return function

$\tilde{g}_s(\lambda_s) \equiv$ minimum expected discounted cost for periods s through n, when the inventory position at the beginning of period s, before placing an order, is λ_s.

If the discount factor is α, then a mathematical statement of the definition of $g_s(\lambda_s)$, using our previously defined variables, is

$$\tilde{g}_s(\lambda_s) = \min_{x_s \ldots x_n} \sum_{\text{all } r_j} \left[\prod_{j=s}^{n} p_j(r_j) \right] \left\{ \sum_{j=1}^{n} \alpha^{j-s}[c_j\delta_j+\phi_j(x_j)]+f_s(\lambda_s+x_s) \right.$$

$$\left. + \sum_{j=s+1}^{n} \alpha^{j-s} f_j\left(\lambda_s+ \sum_{k=s}^{j} x_k - \sum_{k=s}^{j-1} r_k\right) \right\} \qquad (s = 1, 2, \ldots, n) \qquad (8.4.1)$$

where
$$\delta_j = \begin{cases} 0, & x_j = 0 \\ 1, & x_j > 0 \end{cases}$$

It is worthwhile recalling that $x_s = x_s(\lambda_s)$, i.e., that the optimal decisions x_s are functions of the inventory positions λ_s. What (8.4.1) tells us, conceptually, is as follows. Suppose we select some policy, i.e., a set of $x_s(\lambda_s)$ and that we also have a set of demands r_s for each period. Then, beginning with the first period, we can sequentially calculate the λ_s and then the x_j. Using the x_j and r_j we can calculate the discounted cost over the planning period for this one set of r_j. We now repeat this calculation for all possible sets of r_j. Then we weight each of these costs by the probability of obtaining that particular set of r_s, i.e., $p_s(r_s)$. The addition of all of these is the expected cost for this one set of $x_s(\lambda_s)$. If we repeat this entire calculation for every allowable set of $x_s(\lambda_s)$, we can then choose the optimal $x_s^*(\lambda_s)$.

We can derive recurrence relations from the definition given by (8.4.1). First, we note that

$$\sum_{\text{all } r_j} \left[\prod_{j=s}^{n} p_j(r_j) \right] F(r_s, r_{s+1}, \ldots, r_n)$$

$$= \sum_{r_s=0}^{\infty} p_s(r_s) \left\{ \sum_{\text{all } r_j} \left[\prod_{j=s+1}^{n} p_j(r_j) \right] F(r_s, r_{s+1}, \ldots, r_n) \right\} \qquad (8.4.2)$$

Using (8.4.2) and (8.4.1) we obtain

$$\tilde{g}_s(\lambda_s) = \min_{x_s} \left\langle \sum_{\text{all } r_j} \left[\prod_{j=s}^{n} p_j(r_j) \right] [c_s\delta_s+\phi_s(x_s)+f_s(\lambda_s+x_s)] \right.$$

$$\times \alpha \sum_{r_s=0}^{\infty} p_s(r_s) \min_{x_{s+1}, \ldots, x_n} \sum_{\text{all } r_j} \left[\prod_{j=s+1}^{n} p_j(r_j) \right]$$

$$\times \left\{ \sum_{j=s+1}^{n} \alpha^{j-s-1}[c_j\delta_j+\phi_j(x_j)]+f_{s+1}(\lambda_s+x_s+x_{s+1}-r_s) \right.$$

$$\left. + \sum_{j=s+2}^{n} \alpha^{j-s-1}f_j\left(\lambda_s+x_s-r_s+ \sum_{k=s+1}^{j} x_k- \sum_{k=s+1}^{j-1} r_k\right) \right\} \qquad (s = 1, 2, \ldots, n-1)$$

$$(8.4.3)$$

Using the definition of $\tilde{g}_{s+1}$ and noting that

$$c_s\delta_s+\phi_s(x_s)+f_s(\lambda_s+x_s)$$

is independent of $r_s, r_{s+1}, \ldots, r_n$ and that

$$\sum_{\text{all } r_j} \left[\prod_{j=s}^{n} p_j(r_j) = 1 \right]$$

we can rewrite (8.4.3) as a recurrence relation

$$\tilde{g}_s(\lambda_s) = \min_{x_s} \left[c_s\delta_s+\phi_s(x_s)+f_s(\lambda_s+x_s) \right.$$

$$\left. + \sum_{r_s=0}^{\infty} p_s(r_s) g_{s+1}(\lambda_s+x_s-r_s) \right] \qquad (s = 1, 2, \ldots, n-1) \qquad (8.4.4)$$

For the nth stage we have

$$\tilde{g}_n(\lambda_n) = \min_{x_n} [c_n\delta_n+\phi_n(x_n)+f_n(\lambda_n+x_n)] \qquad (8.4.5)$$

In actually solving a problem when some probability distribution is given, it is no more difficult to use (8.4.4) and (8.4.5) than the corresponding relations for a deterministic problem. In order to do so, we must choose some finite limit to replace ∞ on the summation in (8.4.4). We replace the upper limit with some number β_s such that the probability of having a demand greater than β_s in period s is small enough to be ignored. Otherwise the calculation is as usual. We compute the $\tilde{g}_s(\lambda_s)$ starting with $\tilde{g}_n(\lambda_n)$. At the end of this sequence we calculate $\tilde{g}_1(\lambda_1)$, where λ_1 is the known initial inventory position. In doing so, we obtain x_1^*. From this we calculate λ_2 and use the $\tilde{g}_2(\lambda_2)$ function to find x_2^*. We proceed this way to calculate the values of all the remaining variables.

8.5. A Stochastic Production Scheduling and Inventory Control Problem

An important problem in the literature of management science is concerned with scheduling the production of some product over a planning horizon so that the combined expected cost of production and carrying inventory will be minimized. The stochastic nature of the problem resides in the fact that the demand in any period has to be considered to be a random variable. We shall make the following reasonable assumptions:

(1) Decisions on how much to produce are made each period.
(2) Each time production decisions are made we plan ahead for n periods.
(3) The demand r_j for the product in period j is a random variable with continuous density function $p_j(r_j)$.

14

The first model of such a situation we shall examine assumes that only one decision is made each period, i.e., how much of the product will be made during that period. All other variables such as material requirements, size of labor force, etc., are assumed to be able to be determined from the production decision. (We shall also consider a more complicated and realistic case further on.)

The inventory at the production facility is the inventory we shall consider. Let λ_j be our state variable. It is defined to be the net inventory at the beginning of period j. It is possible for λ_j to be negative if the unfilled orders exceed the inventory on hand. If we define x_j to be the amount produced in period j and r_j to be the demand in period j then we have

$$\lambda_{j+1} = \lambda_j + x_j - r_j \qquad (8.5.1)$$

The costs associated with period j are several. There will be the normal costs involved in producing an amount x_j, such as labor, raw materials, etc. We denote this cost as the function $A_j(x_j)$, since it depends only on x_j. There will also be a cost incurred when the level of production, is either increased or decreased. These are costs associated with repair, changeover, hiring, firing, etc. This cost, which depends upon the change in the level of production, will be denoted by the function $B_j(x_j - x_{j-1})$. There is also a cost associated with carrying inventory or a cost associated with backorders. We assume that this cost depends upon $\lambda_j + x_j$ and we shall denote it as $C_j(x_j + \lambda_j)$.

We shall now define a state vector $\tilde{g}_s(\xi_s, \lambda_s)$ which depends upon two state variables λ_s and ξ_s. $\tilde{g}_s$ represents the expected cost for periods s through n, discounted to the beginning of period s, when an optimal decision is made at the beginning of each period $s \ldots n$. λ_s is calculated from (8.5.1) and ξ_s is the current value of x_{s-1}. The recurrence relations are easily found, from the principle of optimality, to be

$$\tilde{g}_s(\xi_s, \lambda_s) = \min_{x_s} \left[A_s(x_s) + B_s(x_s - \xi_s) + C_s(x_s + \lambda_s) \right.$$

$$\left. + \alpha \int_0^\infty \tilde{g}_{s+1}(x_s, \lambda_s + x_s - r_s) \, p_j(r_j) \, dr_j \right] \qquad (s = 1, 2, \ldots, n-1) \qquad (8.5.2)$$

α is the discount factor. We also have, for the nth period,

$$\tilde{g}_n(\xi_n, \lambda_n) = \min_{x_n} \left[A_n(x_n) + B_n(x_n - \xi_n) + C_n(x_n + \lambda_n) \right] \qquad (8.5.3)$$

The optimal solution is obtained when we compute $\tilde{g}_1(x_0, \lambda_1)$. The computational solution is straightforward providing the integral in (8.5.2) can be evaluated.

We can complicate the model we have just introduced, in the direction of greater practical import, by changing one assumption. We previously assumed that the amount to be produced uniquely determined the work force. This may not be the case, however. For example, several different sizes of work force could be used for any given amount of production by resorting to various amounts of overtime. Hence there could be several alternatives under consideration for the size of the work force. Let y_s be the size of the work force in period s. We now define the following costs:

$P_s(x_s) \equiv$ cost of production, excluding labor costs in period s, when x_s is produced.

$W_s(y_s) \equiv$ cost of labor in period s when y_s is the size of the work force.

$Q_s(y_s - y_{s-1}) \equiv$ cost associated with changing the size of the work force from y_{s-1} to y_s'.

$R_s(x_s, y_s) \equiv$ cost of deviating from the ideal or correct size of labor force for producing an amount x_s.

$S_s(x_s + \lambda_s) \equiv$ cost of carrying inventory and of backorders.

We shall again require two state variables but they are different than in the previous case since there is no longer an explicit dependence on $x_s - x_{s-1}$. In addition, we shall require two control variables at each stage, viz., x_s and y_s. The state variables ξ_s and λ_s are associated with y_{s-1} and y_s respectively. We define $\tilde{g}_s(\xi_s, \lambda_s)$ as the expected cost for periods s through n, discounted to the beginning of period s, when an optimal decision is made at the beginning of period s. The recurrence relations are

$$\tilde{g}_s(\xi_s, \lambda_s) = \min_{x_s, y_s} \left[P_s(x_s) + W_s(y_s) + Q_s(y_s - \xi_s) + R_s(x_s, y_s) + S_s(x_s + \lambda_s) \right.$$

$$\left. + \alpha \int_0^\infty \tilde{g}_{s-1}(y_s, \lambda_s + x_s - r_s) \, \phi_s(r_s) \, dr_s \right] \qquad (s = 1, 2, \ldots, n-1) \qquad (8.5.4)$$

$$\tilde{g}_n(\xi_n, \lambda_n) = \min_{x_n, y_n} \left[P_n(x_n) + W_n(y_n) + Q_n(y_n - \xi_n) + R_n(x_n, y_n) + S_n(x_n + \lambda_n) \right] \qquad (8.5.5)$$

The computational solution is again straightforward, although it may be quite lengthy because it requires both two state variables and two control variables.

In the stochastic decision problems we have just considered, the costs as well as the density functions for the variables could change from period to period. In such cases, we could only consider solving problems with a finite number of periods, i.e., a finite planning horizon. If one assumes that the costs and density functions do not change, then it is possible to consider an infinite planning horizon, i.e., that the system will continue to operate indefinitely. In such cases, one expects that in some sense future decisions (or the knowledge that the system is to operate indefinitely) affect current decisions. Since most businesses operate (or try to operate) indefinitely, such problems have practical importance. In the next several sections we shall consider the use of Markov processes as models for stochastic decision problems with infinite planning horizons.

8.6. Markov Processes

Consider a system which at any particular time is in one of a finite number of states which we designate $i = 1, 2, \ldots, N$. We further assume that the system undergoes transitions from one state to another state (which may be the same state) at certain discrete intervals of time. If the system is a *simple Markov process*, then the probability of a transition from a state i to a state j during the next time interval depends only upon i and j and not on the previous history of the system before it arrived in state i. Therefore we may specify a set of conditional probabilities p_{ij} that a system which now occupies state i will occupy state j after its next transition. We shall designate the state transition matrix as $P = [p_{ij}]$. Since the p_{ij} are probabilities it must be true that

$$0 \leqslant p_{ij} \leqslant 1 \quad \text{all } i, j \tag{8.6.1}$$

and since the system must be in some state after its next transition, we have that

$$\sum_{j=1}^{N} p_{ij} = 1 \tag{8.6.2}$$

A simple example of a Markov process of the type we have defined above is a very naive weather model. Suppose that we decide to describe the weather in terms of two states. The weather is in state 1 when it is raining and in state 2 when it is not raining. It has been observed that when it is raining there is a 50% chance that it will also be raining tomorrow and a 50% chance that it will not. If it is not raining on any given day, there is a 25% chance that it will be raining tomorrow and consequently, a 75% chance that it will not be raining. Therefore our state transition probabilities p_{ij} are

$$p_{11} = \tfrac{1}{2}, \quad p_{12} = \tfrac{1}{2}, \quad p_{21} = \tfrac{1}{4}, \quad p_{22} = \tfrac{3}{4}$$

or in matrix form

$$P = \begin{bmatrix} \frac{1}{2} & \frac{1}{2} \\ \frac{1}{4} & \frac{3}{4} \end{bmatrix}$$

The matrix P, the state transition matrix, is a complete description of a simple Markov process. It can be used to deduce all the important characteristics of a Markov process. For example, if we wished to know the probability that it would be raining 10 days from now, given that it is not raining today, we could compute this probability using P. In order to do so, we need some additional notation.

Let $s_i(n)$ be the probability that the system will occupy state i after n state transitions, assuming that its initial state $(n = 0)$ is known. We call $s_i(n)$ the *state probabilities*. Since the $s_i(n)$ are probabilities, it must be true that

$$\sum_{i=1}^{N} s_i(n) = 1 \tag{8.6.3}$$

We determine the state probability for state j for the $(n+1)$st transition by multiplying each state probability $s_i(n)$ by p_{ij} and summing over all states, i.e.,

$$s_j(n+1) = \sum_{i=1}^{N} s_i(n)p_{ij} \quad (n = 0, 1, 2, \ldots) \tag{8.6.4}$$

We can express (8.6.4) more compactly using vector notation. If $\mathbf{s}(n)$ is the vector whose components are $s_i(n)$, then

$$\mathbf{s}(n+1) = \mathbf{s}(n)P \tag{8.6.5}$$

If we apply (8.6.5) successively, we have

$$s(1) = s(0)P$$
$$s(2) = s(1)P = s(0)P^2$$
$$s(3) = s(2)P = s(0)P^3$$

$$\cdot$$
$$\cdot$$
$$\cdot$$

The general recursive relationship is

$$s(n) = s(0)P^n \tag{8.6.6}$$

Equation (8.6.6) enables us to find the probability that the system is in each of its states by multiplying the probability vector of its initial state $s(0)$ by the nth power of P.

Let us consider our weather model to illustrate the use of (8.6.5) and (8.6.6). Suppose it is raining, which means that $s_1(0) = 1$ and $s_2(0) = 0$. Therefore $s(0) = [1, 0]$. Hence we have

$$s(1) = s(0)P = [1, 0] \begin{bmatrix} \frac{1}{2} & \frac{1}{2} \\ \frac{1}{4} & \frac{3}{4} \end{bmatrix}$$

and
$$s(1) = [\tfrac{1}{2} \quad \tfrac{1}{2}] \tag{8.6.7}$$

After one day it is equally likely to be raining or not raining. After two days

$$s(2) = s(1)P = [\tfrac{1}{2} \quad \tfrac{1}{2}] \begin{bmatrix} \frac{1}{2} & \frac{1}{2} \\ \frac{1}{4} & \frac{3}{4} \end{bmatrix} \tag{8.6.8}$$

and
$$s(2) = [\tfrac{3}{8} \quad \tfrac{5}{8}]$$

Therefore it is less likely to be raining after two days. We could just as well obtain (8.6.8) by using (8.6.6) directly. Since

$$P^2 = \begin{bmatrix} \frac{1}{2} & \frac{1}{2} \\ \frac{1}{4} & \frac{3}{4} \end{bmatrix} \begin{bmatrix} \frac{1}{2} & \frac{1}{2} \\ \frac{1}{4} & \frac{3}{4} \end{bmatrix} = \begin{bmatrix} \frac{3}{8} & \frac{5}{8} \\ \frac{5}{16} & \frac{11}{16} \end{bmatrix}$$

$$s(2) = s(0)P^2 = [1, 0] \begin{bmatrix} \frac{3}{8} & \frac{5}{8} \\ \frac{5}{16} & \frac{11}{16} \end{bmatrix} = [\tfrac{3}{8} \quad \tfrac{5}{8}]$$

If we continue the calculation of $s(n)$ we obtain the results shown in Table 8.6.1.

TABLE 8.6.1. State probabilities for weather model (rain)

n	0	1	2	3	4	5	6	...
$s_1(n)$	1	0.5	0.375	0.34375	0.33594	0.33398	0.33350	...
$s_2(n)$	0	0.5	0.625	0.65625	0.66406	0.66602	0.66650	...

It can be seen from Table 8.6.1 that as n increases $s_1(n)$ is approaching $\frac{1}{3}$ and $s_2(n)$ appears to be approaching $\frac{2}{3}$. One might wonder what would happen if we had started in initial state 2, i.e., no rain. For this case $s(0) = [0, 1]$ and successive state probabilities would be as appears in Table 8.6.2.

TABLE 8.6.2. State probabilities for weather model (no rain)

n	0	1	2	3	4	5	6	
$s_1(n)$	0	0.25	0.3125	0.328125	0.33203	0.33301	0.33325	...
$s_2(n)$	1	0.75	0.6875	0.671875	0.66797	0.66699	0.66675	...

What Tables 8.6.1 and 8.6.2 seem to indicate is that the state probabilities approach $\frac{1}{3}$ and $\frac{2}{3}$ irrespective of the initial state of the system. Whether we started with $s(0) = [1, 0]$ or $[0, 1]$, we seem to be approaching $s_1(n) = \frac{1}{3}$ and $s_2(n) = \frac{2}{3}$ as n becomes large. This is indeed the case as can be shown by an analysis of the asymptotic form of (8.6.4). A Markov process whose limiting state probability distribution is independent of the initial state of the system is called a *completely ergodic process*. Not all Markov processes are ergodic.

For completely ergodic Markov processes it is possible to find the limiting state probabilities by a direct calculation. If we define s_i as the probability that the system occupies state i after a sufficiently large number of moves, then the vector $s = (s_1, s_2, \ldots, s_n)$ is the vector of limiting state probabilities. When n is large $s(n) \to s$. Therefore, for sufficiently large n we have, from (8.6.5), that

$$s = sP \tag{8.6.9}$$

and in addition

$$\sum_{i=1}^{N} s_i = 1 \tag{8.6.10}$$

Equations (8.6.9) and (8.6.10) can be used to solve for the limiting state probabilities. For the weather model example, we have

$$s_1 = \tfrac{1}{2}s_1 + \tfrac{1}{4}s_2$$
$$s_2 = \tfrac{1}{2}s_1 + \tfrac{3}{4}s_2 \tag{8.6.11}$$
$$s_1 + s_2 = 1$$

Note that (8.6.11) is an overdetermined set of linear equations. Solution of these equations yields $s_1 = \frac{1}{3}$, $s_2 = \frac{2}{3}$, which is what we conjectured from Tables 8.6.1 and 8.6.2.

In the next section we shall add some additional structure and features to a Markov process. The treatment of this subject follows Howard [7], who was responsible for its development.

8.7. Markovian Sequential Decision Processes

We shall now suppose that a Markov process with N states has a reward or economic value structure associated with the transitions from one state to another. We call r_{ij} the reward or profit associated with a transition from state i to state j. The matrix $R = [r_{ij}]$ is the matrix of the rewards associated with all possible state transitions. Negative rewards (profits) indicate a loss on a given transition. The Markov process will generate a sequence of rewards as it moves from state to state. Hence the reward is also a random variable with a probability distribution dependent upon the probabilistic structure of the Markov process.

A Markov process with rewards can be considered to be a crude model of certain kinds of enterprises whose earnings fluctuate because of elements of the operating environment over which the enterprise has no immediate control. Nevertheless, if one has some notion of the probabilities of certain events and factors that may influence them then it is possible to influence or determine longer term profits. A typical desire is to determine, for a Markov process with a reward structure, the expected earnings over the next n transitions given that the system is currently in state i.

We define $v_i(n)$ as the expected total earnings in the next n transitions if the system is currently in state i. We shall now develop a recursive relationship which bears a strong resemblance to, and is one step removed from, a dynamic programming relationship.

Suppose we consider the transitions in reverse. If the system makes a transition from state i to j it will earn an amount r_{ij} plus the amount it expects to earn if it starts in state j with one transition fewer to be made. This total earnings is

$$r_{ij} + v_j(n-1) \tag{8.7.1}$$

However, the probability that the system will go from state i to state j is p_{ij}. Hence the determination of the total expected earnings requires that (8.7.1) be weighted by p_{ij} and summed over all states. Therefore we have that

$$v_i(n) = \sum_{j=1}^{N} p_{ij}[r_{ij} + v_j(n-1)] \qquad (i = 1, 2, \ldots, N) \qquad (8.7.2)$$
$$(n = 1, 2, \ldots)$$

We may rearrange (8.7.2) to yield

$$v_i(n) = \sum_{j=1}^{N} p_{ij} r_{ij} + \sum_{j=1}^{N} p_{ij} v_j(n-1) \qquad (i = 1, 2, \ldots, N) \qquad (8.7.3)$$
$$(n = 1, 2, \ldots)$$

Since the first term on the right-hand side of (8.7.3) does not depend upon n but is a constant for each state i, we may define

$$q_i = \sum_{j=1}^{N} p_{ij} r_{ij} \qquad (i = 1, 2, \ldots, N) \qquad (8.7.4)$$

Hence we may rewrite (8.7.3) as

$$v_i(n) = q_i + \sum_{j=1}^{N} p_{ij} v_j(n-1) \qquad (i = 1, 2, \ldots, N) \qquad (8.7.5)$$
$$(n = 1, 2, \ldots)$$

The quantity q_i may be regarded as the amount of earnings to be expected in the next transition from state i. It is called the expected immediate reward for state i. We may also write equation (8.7.5) in vector form as

$$\mathbf{v}(n) = \mathbf{q} + P\mathbf{v}(n-1) \qquad (n = 1, 2, \ldots) \tag{8.7.6}$$

where $v_i(n)$, q_i are the components of $\mathbf{v}(n)$ and $\mathbf{q}$, respectively.

Let us consider as an example of a Markov process with a reward structure, a manufacturer of several brands of cigarettes who sets as his goal that his combined market share for his brands shall exceed 12% which we shall call state 1. When his market share is below 12% we shall call this state 2. We shall refer to the two states as high market share and low market share, respectively. If the manufacturer has a high market share one quarter and also the following quarter, he earns a profit or reward of 100. If he goes from low market share to low market share during the quarter his profit is 21 units. If, on the other hand, he goes from low market share to high or from high market share to low during the quarter, then his profit is 60 units. Therefore his reward matrix R is

$$R = \begin{bmatrix} 100 & 60 \\ 60 & 21 \end{bmatrix}$$

Suppose the probability transition matrix for this process is

$$P = \begin{bmatrix} \frac{1}{2} & \frac{1}{2} \\ \frac{1}{3} & \frac{2}{3} \end{bmatrix}$$

Then using (8.7.4) we can calculate $\mathbf{q}$ as

$$q_1 = \begin{bmatrix} \frac{1}{2} & \frac{1}{2} \end{bmatrix} \begin{bmatrix} 100 \\ 60 \end{bmatrix} = 80$$

$$q_2 = \begin{bmatrix} \frac{1}{3} & \frac{2}{3} \end{bmatrix} \begin{bmatrix} 60 \\ 21 \end{bmatrix} = 34$$

$$\mathbf{q} = (80, 34)$$

Hence the cigarette manufacturer expects to gain 80 units on leaving state 1 and 34 units on leaving state 2.

Using the data in the foregoing paragraph we can calculate the total expected earnings for the cigarette manufacturer if he has n quarters remaining to be in business. Since most companies wish to remain in business indefinitely, this is a decided shortcoming of the present analysis, which we shall correct subsequently. Nevertheless, the analysis is instructive. We shall arbitrarily decide that $\mathbf{v}(0) = [0, 0]$. This is the "salvage" value of the company, i.e., the value of the company to some hypothetical purchaser on the day the company ceases to operate. We calculate successive total earnings using (8.7.6).

$$v_1(1) = q_1 + \sum_{j=1}^{2} p_{1j} v_j(0) = 80 + \begin{bmatrix} \frac{1}{2} & \frac{1}{2} \end{bmatrix} \begin{bmatrix} 0 \\ 0 \end{bmatrix} = 80$$

$$v_2(1) = q_2 + \sum_{j=1}^{2} p_{2j}v_j(0) = 34 + [\tfrac{1}{3} \quad \tfrac{2}{3}]\begin{bmatrix} 0 \\ 0 \end{bmatrix} = 34$$

$$v_1(2) = q_1 + \sum_{j=1}^{2} p_{1j}v_j(1) = 80 + [\tfrac{1}{2} \quad \tfrac{1}{2}]\begin{bmatrix} 80 \\ 34 \end{bmatrix} = 137$$

$$v_2(2) = q_2 + \sum_{j=1}^{2} p_{2j}v_j(1) = 34 + [\tfrac{1}{3} \quad \tfrac{2}{3}]\begin{bmatrix} 80 \\ 34 \end{bmatrix} = 83.33$$

etc.

A tabulation of the total expected earnings is given in Table 8.7.1.

TABLE 8.7.1. Total expected earnings (n = number of quarters remaining)

n	0	1	2	3	4	5	6	7	...
$v_1(n)$	0	80	137	247.17	463.03	889.54	1736.5	3423.3	...
$v_2(n)$	0	34	83.33	184.56	389.99	804.33	1637.1	3307.3	...

An examination of Table 8.7.1 indicates that as n increases, the ratio of $v_1(n)$ to $v_2(n)$ is approaching unity. Hence, if n is large the relative value of being in state 1 over state 2 is small as a percent of the total expected earnings, but is not zero.

We turn now to a consideration of sequential Markovian decision processes. Let us suppose that our cigarette manufacturer is capable of taking different actions when he is in a low or high market share situation and that these actions will change the probabilities and rewards that govern this Markov process. For example, when the company is in state 1 (high market share) it has two courses of action that it may take; it may employ a high or low advertising budget. However, a larger advertising cost will decrease profits somewhat even though it may help prolong the high market share situation. Similarly, when the company is in state 2 (low market share), it may carry out market research studies to determine what would appeal to its potential customers. It may do this at two different budget levels as well, high and low. Each of the alternatives in state 1 or state 2 has its own associated state transition probabilities and reward matrix.

We shall use a superscript k to indicate the alternatives available in each state, i.e., p_{ij} and r_{ij} will now be designated p_{ij}^k and r_{ij}^k. In the case of our cigarette company, if he is in state 1, he has two alternatives. For alternative 1 (high advertising budget) we will have $\mathbf{p}_1^1 = [p_{11}^1, p_{12}^1] = [0.7 \ 0.3]$ and for alternative 2 (low advertising) we have $\mathbf{p}_1^2 = [0.5 \ 0.5]$. The corresponding reward vectors for each of these alternatives is $\mathbf{r}_1^1 = [r_{11}^1, r_{12}^1] = [80 \ 40]$ and $\mathbf{r}_1^2 = [100 \ 60]$. For state 2 the two alternatives are high and low market research levels. For these alternatives the probabilities and rewards are: $\mathbf{p}_2^1 = [0.6 \ 0.4]$, $\mathbf{p}_2^2 = [0.33 \ 0.67]$ and $\mathbf{r}_2^1 = [40 \ 10]$, $\mathbf{r}_2^2 = [60 \ 21]$. We shall use these data in a subsequent calculation.

In order to clarify the kinds of transitions that may result when there are alternative transition probabilities and rewards, we show the tree of possible transitions in Fig.

8.7.1. In Fig. 8.7.1(a) we have shown the tree of transitions when there is only one alternative between stage transitions. By introducing alternatives in each transition, we have to replace each line in between stages in (a) by K lines, if there are K alternatives in each state transition. As an example, in Fig. 8.7.1(b) we have shown the different transition alternatives between stages 1 and 2 if the system was in state 1 in stage 1 and went to state 2 in stage 2 with the given probabilities and rewards.

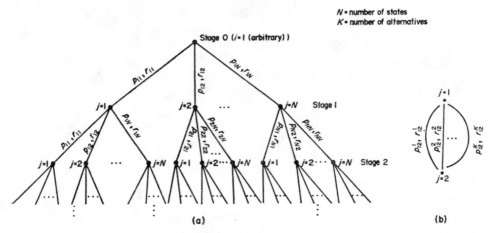

FIG. 8.7.1. State transitions and alternatives.

We now redefine some quantities to take account of the alternatives. Let q_i^k be the expected immediate reward from a single transition from state i under alternative k. Then we have

$$q_i^k = \sum_{j=1}^{N} p_{ij}^k r_{ij}^k \tag{8.7.7}$$

Let n be the number of stages remaining (in the case of the cigarette company, the number of quarters) in the process. Let $d_i(n)$ be the number of the alternative in the ith state that will be used at stage n. Hence $d_i(n)$ is a decision that is made by the policy maker at each stage. A specification of $d_i(n)$ for all i and all n is termed a policy. We define the *optimal policy* as the policy that maximizes total expected earnings or return for each i and n.

We now redefine $v_i(n)$ as the total expected return in n stages starting in state i *under an optimal policy*. This definition and the principle of optimality will allow the derivation of the basic recursion equation. The basic argument is familiar.

Suppose that we have chosen alternatives at stages n, $n-1$, ..., 1, so that we have found $v_j(n)$ for $j = 1, 2, ..., N$. We now wish to find for stage $n+1$ the alternative we should follow in state i, in order to maximize $v_i(n+1)$. The choice is $d_i(n+1)$. If we choose alternative k, then the expected return for $n+1$ stages would be

$$\sum_{j=1}^{N} p_{ij}^k [r_{ij}^k + v_j(n)] \tag{8.7.8}$$

We seek the alternative that will maximize (8.7.8). Hence we determine $v_i(n+1)$ from

$$v_i(n+1) = \max_k \sum_{j=1}^{N} p_i^k [r_i^k + v_j(n)] \tag{8.7.9}$$

Equation (8.7.9) can be rewritten as

$$v_i(n+1) = \max_k \left[q_i^k + \sum_{j=1}^{N} p_{ij}^k v_j(n) \right] \tag{8.7.10}$$

Equation (8.7.10) can be used to find which alternative to use in each state at each stage and will also provide the expected future earnings at each stage. We shall not pursue a calculational example because the limitation of the model to processes that will terminate in a finite number of stages is a severe one. Instead, in the next section, we shall develop a technique that will enable us to deal with processes which continue indefinitely, with no prospect of termination in a given number of transitions.

8.8. The Policy Iteration Method of Howard

We shall be dealing with a completely ergodic N-state Markov process, described by a transition probability matrix P and a reward matrix R. As the system makes transition after transition, the total earnings increases as the number of transitions increases. However, if the system undergoes a very large number of transitions, the average earnings of the process will be a more useful measure of the process.

For an ergodic system, the limiting state probabilities s_i are independent of the initial state. Therefore, the *gain g* of the process will be

$$g = \sum_{i=1}^{N} s_i q_i \tag{8.8.1}$$

where q_i is the expected immediate return.

The gain is a useful means of comparison, between different ergodic Markov processes, of their long-term profitability. The one with the largest gain is the most profitable.

We shall now develop the policy iteration method for finding the optimal policy of a Markov process with rewards and alternatives in each state. The method consists of two parts—a value determination step and a policy improvement step.

We consider first the value determination step. Suppose we are operating the system under some given policy. Hence we have a specified Markov process with rewards. We allow the process to operate for n stages or transitions. We now define $v_i(n)$ as the total expected earnings of the system in n transitions if it starts from state i under the assumed policy.

We have already seen, in Section 8.7, that $v_i(n)$ satisfies the recurrence relations

$$v_i(n) = q_i + \sum_{j=1}^{N} p_{ij} v_j(n-1) \qquad (i = 1, 2, \ldots, N) \tag{8.8.2}$$
$$(n = 1, 2, \ldots)$$

Since we have *assumed* some definite policy there is no need for the superscript k.

For a completely ergodic process an analysis of the limiting form of (8.8.2) as n becomes large gives the result

$$v_i(n) = ng + v_i \quad (n \gg 0) \tag{8.8.3}$$

where g is the gain and v_i is an asymptote of $v_i(n)$.

Since we are concerned with processes that have a very large number of stages we shall use (8.8.3). If we combine (8.8.2) and (8.8.3), we obtain

$$ng + v_i = q_i + \sum_{j=1}^{N} p_{ij}[(n-1)g + v_j] \quad (i = 1, 2, \ldots, N) \tag{8.8.4}$$

Rewriting (8.8.4) we have

$$ng + v_i = q_i + (n-1)g \sum_{j=1}^{N} p_{ij} + \sum_{j=1}^{N} p_{ij}v_j \quad (i = 1, 2, \ldots, N)$$

which simplifies to

$$g + v_i = q_i + \sum_{j=1}^{N} p_{ij}v_j \quad (i = 1, 2, \ldots, N) \tag{8.8.5}$$

Equations (8.8.5) are a set of N linear simultaneous equations in $N+1$ variables (g, v_i, $i = 1, 2, \ldots, N$). Since this is an undetermined system, we may set one of the v_i equal to zero and then determine the values of the remaining v_i as well as g. This will not necessarily be the set of values that satisfy (8.8.3). However, it is a simple matter to show that they will differ from their correct values by some constant value. They will be sufficient for the purpose of the value determination step. The values obtained by setting $v_N = 0$ and solving (8.8.5) will be called *relative values*.

The reason we can use relative values instead of the correct values can be seen by examining (8.8.3). Consider (8.8.3) for two states v_s and v_t. We have from (8.8.3) that for large n

$$v_s(n) = ng + v_s, \quad v_t(n) = ng + v_t \tag{8.8.6}$$

The difference $v_s(n) - v_t(n) = v_s - v_t$. Hence if the correct values of v_s, v_t were $v_s + \alpha$, $v_t + \alpha$, the difference would still be $v_s - v_t$. Since this difference represents the difference in the long-term earnings of the process as a result of starting in state s rather than state t, it will serve our purposes in value determination.

We turn now to the second step of the policy iteration method, viz., the policy improvement step.

We noted in (8.7.10) that if we had an optimal policy up to stage n we could find the best alternative in the ith state at stage $n+1$ by maximizing

$$q_i^k + \sum_{j=1}^{N} p_{ij}^k v_j(n) \tag{8.8.7}$$

over all alternatives k in state i. For large n, we can substitute from (8.8.3) into (8.8.7) to obtain

$$q_i^k + \sum_{j=1}^{N} p_{ij}^k(ng + v_j) \tag{8.8.8}$$

as the quantity that is to be maximized in each state. Rewriting (8.8.8) yields

$$q_i^k + ng \sum_{j=1}^{N} p_{ij}^k + \sum_{j=1}^{N} p_{ij}^k v_j \tag{8.8.9}$$

Since ng is a constant (independent of j) and

$$\sum_{j=1}^{N} p_{ij}^k = 1$$

we need not consider the second term of (8.8.9), when we compare the maximand of (8.8.9) for each alternative k. Hence we may use as a quantity

$$q_i^k + \sum_{j=1}^{N} p_{ij}^k v_j \tag{8.8.10}$$

to be maximized with respect to the alternatives k in state i. The relative values v_i that were determined in the value determination step can be used in (8.8.10) when the maximization is carried out.

The policy improvement step, then, consists in finding, for each state i, the alternative k that maximizes

$$q_i^k + \sum_{j=1}^{N} p_{ij}^k v_j$$

using the relative values v_i, determined under the previous policy. The alternative k becomes d_i, the decision in the state i. The set of d_i then become the new policy. We shall show subsequently that the new policy will have a greater gain than the previous policy.

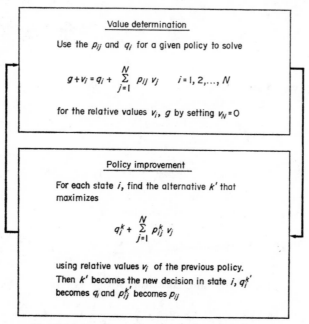

Fig. 8.8.1. Iteration cycle of policy iteration method.

We can put the value determination step and the policy improvement step together to describe the basic iteration cycle of the policy iteration method. Figure 8.8.1 shows the basic iteration cycle.

It is possible to enter the cycle at either step. If we enter at the value determination step, then we must select an initial policy. If we choose to enter the policy improvement step, then we must supply an initial set of relative values. A convenient method of starting is to set all $v_i = 0$ and enter at the policy improvement step.

In order to have a convergent algorithm the policy iteration method must have the following properties:

(1) The successive policies that are found have strictly increasing gains g.
(2) The computation terminates when the policy with the greatest gain has been found. This occurs when the policies on two successive iterations are identical.

We shall now establish that the above properties hold and hence that the policy iteration method will find the optimal policy. This proof is given by Howard [7].

Suppose that our current policy is designated A and that the policy improvement step has produced a new policy B. Then we seek to show, if the gains g^A and g^B designate the gains associated with policies A and B, respectively, that $g^B > g^A$.

Since the test quantity in the policy improvement step is

$$q_i + \sum_{j=1}^{N} p_{ij} v_j \tag{8.8.11}$$

and policy B was chosen as superior to A, then it must be true that

$$q_i^B + \sum_{j=1}^{N} p_{ij}^B v_j^A \geqslant q_i^A + \sum_{j=1}^{N} p_{ij}^A v_j^A \qquad (i = 1, 2, \ldots, N) \tag{8.8.12}$$

Let
$$\gamma_i = q_i^B + \sum_{j=1}^{N} p_{ij}^B v_j^A - q_i^A - \sum_{j=1}^{N} p_{ij}^A v_j^A \tag{8.8.13}$$

Hence $\gamma_i \geqslant 0$ represents the improvement in (8.8.11) for state i. From (8.8.5) we know that for policies A and B we may write

$$g^A + v_i^A = q_i^A + \sum_{j=1}^{N} p_{ij}^A v_j^A \qquad (i = 1, 2, \ldots, N) \tag{8.8.14}$$

$$g^B + v_i^B = q_i^B + \sum_{j=1}^{N} p_{ij}^B v_j^B \qquad (i = 1, 2, \ldots, N) \tag{8.8.15}$$

If we now subtract (8.8.14) from (8.8.15) we obtain

$$g^B - g^A + v_i^B - v_i^A = q_i^B - q_i^A + \sum_{j=1}^{N} p_{ij}^B v_j^B - \sum_{j=1}^{N} p_{ij}^A v_j^A \tag{8.8.16}$$

We now solve (8.8.13) for $q_i^B - q_i^A$ and substitute for $q_i^B - q_i^A$ in (8.8.16). This results in

$$g^B - g^A + v_i^B - v_i^A = \gamma_i - \sum_{j=1}^{N} p_{ij}^B v_j^A + \sum_{j=1}^{N} p_{ij}^A v_j^A + \sum_{j=1}^{N} p_{ij}^B v_j^B - \sum_{j=1}^{N} p_{ij}^A v_j^A$$

which simplifies to

$$g^B - g^A + v_i^B - v_i^A = \gamma_i + \sum_{j=1}^{N} p_{ij}^B (v_j^B - v_j^A) \tag{8.8.17}$$

If we define

$$g' = g^B - g^A \quad \text{and} \quad v_i' = v_i^B - v_i^A$$

then we may rewrite (8.8.17) as

$$g' + v_i' = \gamma_i + \sum_{j=1}^{N} p_{ij}^B v_j' \qquad (i = 1, 2, \ldots, N) \tag{8.8.18}$$

Equations (8.8.18) have the same form as (8.8.5). The solution for g from (8.8.5) was

$$g = \sum_{i=1}^{N} s_i q_i$$

Similarly, the solution for g' in (8.8.18) is

$$g' = \sum_{i=1}^{N} s_i^B \gamma_i \tag{8.8.19}$$

where s_i^B is the limiting state probability of state i under policy B. Since all $s_i^B \geq 0$ and all $\gamma_i \geq 0$, therefore $g' \geq 0$ and $g^B \geq g^A$. Since we are dealing with a completely ergodic Markov process, g^B will be strictly greater than g^A if an improvement, even in only one state, can be made in policy B over policy A. Hence $g^B > g^A$, when an improvement is possible.

Finally, we show that it is not possible for a better policy to exist and not be determined at some iteration in the policy improvement step. Let us assume that, for two policies A and B, $g^B > g^A$ but the policy improvement step has converged on policy A. Then in each state, $\gamma_i \leq 0$, where γ_i is given by (8.8.13). Since $s_i^B \geq 0$ for all i, (8.8.19) yields $g' \leq 0$ and hence $g^B - g^A \leq 0$. However, we assumed that $g^B > g^A$. Hence we have obtained a contradiction. Therefore it is not possible for a superior policy to exist, but not be found, by the policy iteration method.

We shall now solve the problem of the cigarette company, the data for which were presented in Section 8.7. The data are summarized in Table 8.8.1. The last column q_i^k was computed from

$$q_i^k = \sum_{j=1}^{N} p_{ij}^k r_{ij}^k$$

For example, for $i = 1$, $k = 2$, we have

$$q_1^2 = \tfrac{1}{2}(100) + \tfrac{1}{2}(60) = 80$$

We shall begin by choosing $v_1 = v_2 = 0$. Then we enter the policy improvement step. Since $v_1 = v_2 = 0$

$$q_i^k + \sum_{j=1}^{N} p_{ij}^k v_j = q_i^k$$

TABLE 8.8.1. Data for cigarette company

		p_{ij}^k		r_{ij}^k		q_i^k
i	k	$j=1$	2	$j=1$	2	
1	1	$\frac{7}{10}$	$\frac{3}{10}$	80	40	68
	2	$\frac{1}{2}$	$\frac{1}{2}$	100	60	80
2	1	$\frac{3}{5}$	$\frac{2}{5}$	40	10	28
	2	$\frac{1}{3}$	$\frac{2}{3}$	60	21	34

Hence we choose the alternative in each state that maximizes q_i^k. Therefore our first policy is the second alternative in each state, i.e.,

$$\mathbf{d} = \begin{bmatrix} 2 \\ 2 \end{bmatrix}$$

The transition probability matrix and expected immediate rewards corresponding to this policy are

$$P = \begin{bmatrix} \frac{1}{2} & \frac{1}{2} \\ \frac{1}{3} & \frac{2}{3} \end{bmatrix} \qquad \mathbf{q} = \begin{bmatrix} 80 \\ 34 \end{bmatrix}$$

We now carry out the value determination step using the P and q corresponding to th previous policy. Hence we wish to solve

$$\begin{aligned} g + v_1 &= 80 + \tfrac{1}{2}v_1 + \tfrac{1}{2}v_2 \\ g + v_2 &= 34 + \tfrac{1}{3}v_1 + \tfrac{2}{3}v_2 \end{aligned} \qquad (8.8.20)$$

We set $v_2 = 0$ and obtain for the solution to (8.8.20)

$$v_1 = 55.2, \qquad v_2 = 0, \qquad g = 52.4$$

Using the new relative values v_i, we enter the policy improvement step and calculate

$$q_i^k + \sum_{j=1}^{N} p_{ij}^k v_j$$

for each state.

For $i = 1$, $k = 1$ we have

$$q_1^1 + \sum_{j=1}^{N} p_{1j}^1 v_j = 68 + \tfrac{7}{10}(55.2) + \tfrac{3}{10}(0) = 106.64$$

and for $k = 2$ we have

$$80 + \tfrac{1}{2}(55.2) + \tfrac{1}{2}(0) = 107.6$$

Hence we choose alternative 2 in state 1. For $i = 2$, $k = 1$ we have

$$28 + \tfrac{3}{5}(55.2) + \tfrac{2}{5}(0) = 61.12$$

and for $k = 2$

$$34 + \tfrac{1}{3}(55.2) + \tfrac{2}{3}(0) = 52.40$$

Hence we choose alternative 1 in state 2. Therefore, our new policy is

$$\mathbf{d} = \begin{bmatrix} 2 \\ 1 \end{bmatrix}$$

The transition probability matrix and expected immediate earnings corresponding to the new policy are

$$P = \begin{bmatrix} \tfrac{1}{2} & \tfrac{1}{2} \\ \tfrac{3}{5} & \tfrac{2}{5} \end{bmatrix} \qquad q = \begin{bmatrix} 80 \\ 28 \end{bmatrix}$$

We again enter the value determination step and solve

$$\begin{aligned}
g + v_1 &= 80 + \tfrac{1}{2}v_1 + \tfrac{1}{2}v_2 \\
g + v_2 &= 28 + \tfrac{3}{5}v_1 + \tfrac{3}{5}v_2
\end{aligned} \tag{8.8.21}$$

Setting $v_2 = 0$, we find the solution to (8.8.21) to be

$$v_1 = 47.27, \qquad v_2 = 0, \qquad g = 56.36$$

Using the new relative values we calculate

$$g_i^k + \sum_{j=1}^{N} p_{ij}^k v_j$$

for each state. We then have

$$\begin{aligned}
i = 1,\ k = 1 \quad & 68 + \tfrac{7}{10}(47.27) + \tfrac{3}{10}(0) = 101.09 \\
i = 1,\ k = 2 \quad & 80 + \tfrac{1}{2}(47.27) + \tfrac{1}{2}(0) = 103.64 \\
i = 2,\ k = 1 \quad & 28 + \tfrac{3}{5}(47.27) + \tfrac{2}{5}(0) = 56.36 \\
i = 2,\ k = 2 \quad & 34 + \tfrac{1}{3}(47.27) + \tfrac{2}{3}(0) = 49.76
\end{aligned}$$

The new policy is $\mathbf{d} = \begin{bmatrix} 2 \\ 1 \end{bmatrix}$ which is the same as the previous policy. Hence we have converged. The optimal policy for the cigarette company is to use alternative 2 (low advertising) when the company is in state 1 (a larger market share) and to use alternative 1 (larger market research activity) when the company is in state 2 (smaller market share).

As the example indicates, the calculation converged very rapidly (2 iterations). In Howard [7], an example is presented with 40 states and 41 alternatives in each state. Hence there are $(41)^{40}$ possible policies, which is approximately 3.25×10^{64} policies, an incredibly large number. However, the policy iteration method found the optimal policy in only seven iterations, which indicates the great efficiency of the method.

Exercises—Chapter 8

8.1. For the problem of Section 8.2, suppose that when we choose x_s, with probability $p_1, f(x)$ assumes the value $f_1(x_s)$ and x_s becomes $\alpha_1 x_s$; with probability p_2, $f(x)$ takes the value $f_2(x_s)$ and x_s becomes $\alpha_2 x_s$; and finally, with probability $p_3 = p - p_1 - p_2$, $f(x)$ takes the value $f_3(x_s)$ and x_s becomes $\alpha_3 x_s$. Similarly, with probability q_1, $h(\lambda_s - x_s)$ becomes $h_1(\lambda_s - x_s)$ and $\lambda_s - x_s$ is reduced to $\beta_1(\lambda_s - x_s)$; with probability q_2, we have $h_2(\lambda_s - x_s)$ and $\beta_2(\lambda_s - x_s)$; with probability $q_3 = 1 - q_1 - q_2$, we have $h_3(\lambda_s - x_s)$ and $\beta_3(\lambda_s - x_s)$. Derive the recurrence relations for the optimal solution.

8.2. Suppose the cigarette manufacturer of Sections 8.7 and 8.8 analyzes his data more closely and allows for three states: 1 (high market share), 2 (average market share), and 3 (low market share) and allows for several alternatives in each state. In state 1, low, average and high advertising are the three alternatives. In state 2 the company may also use two alternatives, i.e., average advertising and low market research. In state 3 we have three alternatives, low, average, or high market research activities. A summary of the data is

State alternative		p_{ij}^k			r_{ij}^k		
i	k	$j = 1$	2	3	1	2	3
1	1	.5	.3	.2	80	60	40
	2	.4	.3	.3	85	75	50
	3	.3	.4	.3	100	80	60
2	1	.4	.6		60	20	
	2	.3	.7		40	10	
3	1	.5	.3	.2	40	20	10
	2	.4	.3	.3	50	30	15
	3	.2	.4	.4	60	40	20

Find the optimal policy.

8.3. Derive recurrence relations for the solution of

$$\max \quad \prod_{j=1}^{n} \phi_j(x_j)$$

subject to

$$x_j \in X_j \qquad (j = 1, 2, \ldots, n)$$

where the X_j are given as in Section 8.3.

8.4. Develop a dynamic programming algorithm for the following problem. We are given a network with nodes numbered from 1 through N and arc (ij) connects pairs of nodes i and j. Associated with each arc is a nonnegative distance or cost c_{ij}. We assume there are no loops in the network. Suppose now that once a particular arc is chosen, there is a finite probability that an adjacent arc will be traversed instead. Therefore you cannot be certain of traveling along the arc you desire. Determine the optimal choice of arcs, to minimize the total *expected* distance from node 1 to node N.

Chapter 9

Dynamic Programming and the Calculus of Variations

9.1. Introduction

The optimization problems we have discussed in this book previously, no matter what their origin, all had a common mathematical description. In brief, we defined a set of feasible points, X and a function $f(\mathbf{x})$, $\mathbf{x} \in X$ where $\mathbf{x} = (x_1, x_2, \ldots, x_n)$. The optimization problem was to find a *point* $\mathbf{x}^* \in X$ such that $f(\mathbf{x}^*) \geqslant f(\mathbf{x})$, all $\mathbf{x} \in X$ or $f(\mathbf{x}^*) \leqslant f(\mathbf{x})$, all $\mathbf{x} \in X$.

We now wish to consider an optimization problem of quite a different kind. The set X will now contain, not points $\mathbf{x}$, but instead will consist of a set of *functions*. We now define a *functional* on X as a function $J(\cdot)$ such that to each function in X, we associate a single real number. It is the optimization of functionals that constitutes the class of problems that is analyzed and solved by the *calculus of variations*.

There are many different kinds of functionals. A few examples will illustrate some of the types. The reader of this book has met functionals throughout this book. For example, let X be a set of bounded functions on a real interval $[a, b]$. For $G \in X$, we define the functional:

$$J(G) = \max_{[a, b]} \{G(x)\} \tag{9.1.1}$$

Most of the dynamic programming calculations of $g_s(\lambda_s)$ are of this basic type.

Another kind of functional is most often considered in elementary calculus of variations. Let X be a set of functions integrable on $[a, b]$. Then define the functional

$$J(F) = \int_a^b F(x) \, dx \tag{9.1.2}$$

If we are given a set of functions X and a functional J, a typical problem of the calculus of variations is to:

$$\max_{F \in X} \ J(F) \quad \text{or} \quad \min_{F \in X} \ J(F) \tag{9.1.3}$$

Constrained problems involving functionals also are common. For example, a problem of this type is

$$\max_{f \in X} \ J_1(f)$$

subject to

$$J_2(f) \leqslant 0 \tag{9.1.4}$$

The fundamental problem of the calculus of variations is to select the function $y(x)$ which maximizes or minimizes

$$J(y) = \int_{x_1}^{x_2} F(x, y, y')\, dx \qquad (9.1.5)$$

The integral of F is, in general, to be considered as both an implicit and an explicit function of x, since it depends directly on x and it also depends on x indirectly through the function $y(x)$ and its derivative $y'(x)$.

We shall derive, in the next section, a set of conditions that $y(x)$ must satisfy in order that $J(y)$ be a minimum. In order to do so we first introduce the concept of a *variation*. Suppose $y_0(x)$ is the function that makes $J(y)$ as small as possible and $y(x)$ is another function of x which is infinitesimally different from $y_0(x)$ at all points x in the open interval (x_1, x_2). We then define the variation of $y(x)$ as

$$\delta y = y(x) - y_0(x) \qquad (9.1.6)$$

δ is the symbol for variation. It is important to understand how a variation differs from a differential, with which we have more experience. The variation of a function represents an infinitesimal change in both the function and its derivative at a fixed value of x. Though $y(x)$ can be changed by changing x, the variation symbol implies that x is fixed. It is the function itself that is altered, as is indicated in Figure 9.1.1. At $x = x_c$, we have

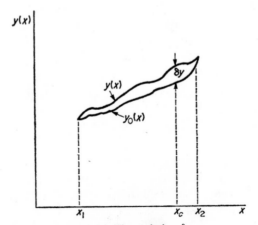

FIG. 9.1.1. The variation δy.

shown the variation δy. The variation is often represented alternatively as

$$\delta y(x) = y(x) - y_0(x) = \varepsilon \phi(x) \qquad (9.1.7)$$

where $\phi(x)$ is an arbitrary continuous and differentiable function of x and ε is a scalar tending to zero.

We consider now some properties of the variation. Since the variation operator changes $y(x)$ for fixed x, it is clear that:

$$\delta x = 0 \qquad (9.1.8)$$

Another important property of the variation is that the variation operator is commutative with both the differentiation and integration operators. We see this as follows.

Consider the derivative of a variation, using (9.1.7),

$$\frac{d}{dx}(\delta y(x)) = \frac{d}{dx}(\varepsilon \phi(x)) = \varepsilon \frac{d\phi}{dx} \tag{9.1.9}$$

and the variation of a derivative

$$\delta\left(\frac{dy(x)}{dx}\right) = \frac{dy(x)}{dx} - \frac{dy_0(x)}{dx} = \frac{d}{dx}(y(x) - y_0(x)) = \varepsilon \frac{d\phi}{dx} \tag{9.1.10}$$

Since (9.1.9) and (9.1.10) yield the same result, we have

$$\frac{d}{dx}(\delta y(x)) = \delta\left(\frac{dy(x)}{dx}\right) \tag{9.1.11}$$

Similarly, we show that for integration

$$\delta \int_{x_1}^{x_2} y(x)\,dx = \int_{x_1}^{x_2} y(x)\,dx - \int_{x_1}^{x_2} y_0(x)\,dx$$

$$= \int_{x_1}^{x_2} [y(x) - y_0(x)]\,dx = \int_{x_1}^{x_2} \delta y(x)\,dx$$

which yields

$$\delta \int_{x_1}^{x_2} y(x)\,dx = \int_{x_1}^{x_2} \delta y(x)\,dx \tag{9.1.12}$$

Using (9.1.12) we see that the change of a functional resulting from a variation in $y(x)$ is

$$\delta J(y) = J(y) - J(y_0) = \int_{x_1}^{x_2} [F(x, y, y') - F(x, y_0, y_0')]\,dx \tag{9.1.13}$$

9.2. Necessary and Sufficient Conditions for Optimality

We now wish to find the function $y(x)$ which minimizes an objective function of the form given in (9.1.5), i.e., solve the problem

$$\min_{y(x)} \; J(y) = \int_{x_1}^{x_2} F(x, y, y')\,dx \tag{9.2.1}$$

It is useful to recall the general strategy used, in classical optimization, in searching for a local minimum (or maximum) of a function of one or more independent variables. A local neighborhood of the function at a point is examined to see if the first derivatives of the function, with respect to each of the variables, vanish. A point where this condition holds is called a stationary point, and the vanishing of the first partial derivative. is a necessary (but not sufficient) condition for the existence of a minimum at the point.

We employ the same notion in the calculus of variations. A *stationary point* is defined as a point such that

$$\delta J(y) = 0 \tag{9.2.2}$$

for a sufficiently small ε. Hence a necessary condition for a minimum (which will be derived in more detail subsequently) is that (9.2.2) holds at a point.

In order to determine whether the stationary point is a minimum, maximum, or neither, one must examine higher order terms in ε (about the point). We can do this by expanding the first integral of (9.1.13) by means of a Taylor series:

$$F(x, y, y') = F(x, y_0, y_0') + \frac{\partial F}{\partial y}(y - y_0) + \frac{\partial F}{\partial y'}(y' - y_0') + \frac{1}{2}\frac{\partial^2 F}{\partial y^2}(y - y_0)^2$$

$$+ \frac{\partial^2 F}{\partial y\, \partial y'}(y - y_0)(y' - y_0') + \frac{1}{2}\frac{\partial^2 F}{2y'^2}(y' - y_0')^2 + \cdots \tag{9.2.3}$$

A word needs to be said about the partial derivatives in (9.2.3). x is of course constant. The partial derivatives are to be interpreted as

$$\frac{\partial F}{\partial y} \equiv \left(\frac{\partial F}{\partial y}\right)_{x, y'} \quad \text{and} \quad \frac{\partial F}{\partial y'} \equiv \left(\frac{\partial F}{\partial y'}\right)_{x, y}$$

i.e., x, y, y' are treated as independent variables for purposes of partial differentiation, the total differential being given by

$$dF = \frac{\partial F}{\partial x}\, dx + \frac{\partial F}{\partial y}\, dy + \frac{\partial F}{\partial y'}\, dy'$$

If we substitute from (9.2.3) into (9.1.13) and use the definition of variation from (9.1.7), we obtain

$$J(y) - J(y_0) = \varepsilon \int_{x_1}^{x_2} \left(\phi \frac{\partial F}{\partial y} + \phi' \frac{\partial F}{\partial y'}\right) dx$$

$$+ \frac{\varepsilon^2}{2} \int_{x_1}^{x_2} \left(\phi^2 \frac{\partial^2 F}{\partial y^2} + 2\phi\phi' \frac{\partial^2 F}{\partial y\, \partial y'} + \phi'^2 \frac{\partial^2 F}{\partial y'^2}\right) dx + \cdots \tag{9.2.4}$$

We shall now use (9.2.4) in deriving the necessary conditions we seek. For sufficiently small ε, we shall neglect all terms in the Taylor expansion of $J(y) - J(y_0)$, (9.2.4), except the first. Therefore, for sufficiently small ε we have from (9.2.4) that

$$\delta J(y) = J(y) - J(y_0) = \varepsilon \int_{x_1}^{x_2} \left(\phi \frac{\partial F}{\partial y} + \phi' \frac{\partial F}{\partial y'}\right) dx \tag{9.2.5}$$

If $J(y_0)$ is to be an optimum, then $\delta J(y)$ must vanish, since ε can be either positive or negative. Therefore, $J(y_0)$ can be a minimum or maximum only if

$$\int_{x_1}^{x_2} \left(\phi \frac{\partial F}{\partial y} + \phi' \frac{\partial F}{\partial y'}\right) dx = 0 \tag{9.2.6}$$

This is analogous to the vanishing of first partial derivatives in the classical theory of the maxima and minima of ordinary functions of a real variable.

The second term of the integrand of (9.2.6) can be integrated by parts, which yields

$$\int_{x_1}^{x_2} \phi' \frac{\partial F}{\partial y'} \, dx = \phi \frac{\partial F}{\partial y'} \Big|_{x_1}^{x_2} - \int_{x_1}^{x_2} \phi \frac{d}{dx} \left(\frac{\partial F}{\partial y'} \right) dx \qquad (9.2.7)$$

In the simplest case we consider, it is assumed that the boundary conditions are such that the function $y(x)$ is fixed at the limits of integration. Hence the function $\phi(x)$ must vanish at the boundaries. Therefore the first term on the right-hand side of (9.2.7) will vanish. (With other boundary conditions, we must evaluate the first term differently.) If no variation is allowed at the end points, and using (9.2.7) with (9.2.6), we have

$$\int_{x_1}^{x_2} \left[\frac{\partial F}{\partial y} - \frac{d}{dx} \left(\frac{\partial F}{\partial y'} \right) \right] \phi \, dx = 0 \qquad (9.2.8)$$

Since $\phi(x)$ is arbitrary, if (9.2.8) is to be satisfied for all admissible $\phi(x)$, then it must be true that

$$\boxed{\frac{\partial F}{\partial y} - \frac{d}{dx} \left(\frac{\partial F}{\partial y'} \right) = 0} \qquad (9.2.9)$$

The differential equation (9.2.9) is called the *Euler–Lagrange equation*. It is a necessary condition for the function $y(x)$ to be an optimum solution of (9.2.1).

We shall give two simple examples of the use of the Euler–Lagrange equation.

Consider the problem of determining the curve of minimum length connecting two points in the Euclidean plane. Figure 9.2.1 shows several paths connecting the points $(x_1, y(x_1))$ and $(x_2, y(x_2))$.

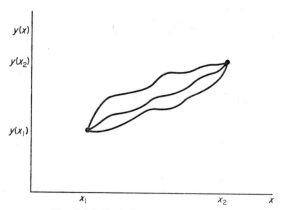

FIG. 9.2.1. Paths between two points.

An element of arc length ds, along any arc, is given by

$$ds = \sqrt{dx^2 + dy^2} = (y'^2 + 1)^{1/2} \, dx$$

and the distance along the curve connecting the two points will be

$$J(y) = \int_{x_1}^{x_2} ds = \int_{x_1}^{x_2} (y'^2 + 1)^{1/2} \, dx \qquad (9.2.10)$$

We wish to find the $y(x)$ that minimizes $J(y)$. To use the Euler–Lagrange equation, we have

$$F(x, y, y') = (y'^2+1)^{1/2}$$

$$\frac{\partial F}{\partial y} = \frac{\partial}{\partial y}(y'^2+1)^{1/2} = 0 \qquad (9.2.11)$$

$$\frac{\partial F}{\partial y'} = \frac{\partial}{\partial y'}(y'^2+1)^{1/2} = y'(y'^2+1)^{-1/2} \qquad (9.2.12)$$

Substituting (9.2.11) and (9.2.12) into (9.2.9) yields

$$-\frac{d}{dx}\left[\frac{y'}{(1+y'^2)^{1/2}}\right] = 0 \qquad (9.2.13)$$

Integrating (9.2.13) gives us

$$y'(1+y'^2)^{-1/2} = c_1 \qquad (9.2.14)$$

where c_1 is a constant. It is easy to see that (9.2.14) implies that

$$y' = c_2$$

and therefore $y = c_2x+c_3$; a straight line is the shortest distance between the two given points. The constants c_2 and c_3 can be evaluated from the points $(x_1, y(x_1))$ and $(x_2, y(x_2))$. Since we have not considered sufficient conditions as yet, the curve $y = c_2x+c_3$ is really an extremal curve. In this case, however, it is well known that the extremal curve is a minimum curve.

As a second example, let us find the extremals of

$$J(y) = \int_{-1}^{1} (y'^2-2xy) \, dx \qquad (9.2.15)$$

where $y(-1) = -1$ and $y(1) = 1$. For this problem

$$F = y'^2-2xy$$

and

$$\frac{\partial F}{\partial y} = -2x \qquad (9.2.16)$$

$$\frac{\partial F}{\partial y'} = 2y'$$

Substituting (9.2.16) into (9.2.9) yields

$$-2x-\frac{d}{dx}(2y') = 0 \qquad (9.2.17)$$

A first integral of (9.2.17) results in

$$-2y' = x^2+a_1 \qquad (9.2.18)$$

where a_1 is a constant of integration. Integrating (9.2.18) we then obtain

$$y = -\tfrac{1}{6}x^3 + c_1 x + c_2 \tag{9.2.19}$$

Using the boundary conditions, we find that $c_1 = \tfrac{7}{6}$, $c_2 = 0$. Hence the extremal of (9.2.15) is

$$y = -\frac{1}{6}x^3 + \frac{7x}{6} \tag{9.2.20}$$

We now consider the matter of sufficient conditions for a function $y(x)$ to be a minimum or a maximum extremal. We previously defined the first variation $\delta J(y)$ in (9.2.5) to be

$$\delta J(y) = \varepsilon \int_{x_1}^{x_2} \left(\phi \frac{\partial F}{\partial y} + \phi' \frac{\partial F}{\partial y'} \right) dx \tag{9.2.21}$$

If we re-examine (9.2.4), then by analogy to (9.2.21) we can define the second variation $\delta^2 J(y)$ as

$$\delta^2 J(y) = \frac{\varepsilon^2}{2} \int_{x_1}^{x_2} \left(\phi^2 \frac{\partial^2 F}{\partial y^2} + 2\phi\phi' \frac{\partial^2 F}{\partial y \, \partial y'} + \phi'^2 \frac{\partial^2 F}{\partial y'^2} \right) dx \tag{9.2.22}$$

Then it is easily shown that if

$$\delta^2 J(y) > 0 \tag{9.2.23}$$

for all possible admissible variations, the stationary value of $J(y)$ will be a minimum. This is similar to the result of the minimum in the case of a function of a single variable. Similarly, the condition

$$\delta^2 J(y) < 0 \tag{9.2.24}$$

indicates that the stationary value is a maximum. If $\delta^2 J(y)$ is positive for some variations and negative for others, the stationary value is not an extremum. If $\delta^2 J(y) = 0$, for all variations, then the nature of the stationary point requires further investigation.

Because the second variation is so difficult to use, other sufficient conditions have been developed. One will be mentioned here. It is called the Legendre condition. It states that if

$$\frac{\partial^2 F}{\partial y'^2} \geqslant 0 \quad x_1 \leqslant x \leqslant x_2 \tag{9.2.25}$$

then the solution is a minimum. If

$$\frac{\partial^2 F}{\partial y'^2} \leqslant 0 \quad x_1 \leqslant x \leqslant x_2 \tag{9.2.26}$$

then the solution is a maximum.

We can demonstrate the use of these sufficient conditions on our examples. For the case of the solution to (9.2.10) which was the straight line $y = c_2 x + c_3$, we shall evaluate the second variation given by (9.2.22).

$$F = (y'^2 + 1)^{1/2}$$

$$\frac{\partial^2 F}{\partial y^2} = 0$$

$$\frac{\partial F}{\partial y'} = y'(1 + y'^2)^{-1/2} \qquad (9.2.27)$$

$$\frac{\partial^2 F}{\partial y \, \partial y'} = 0$$

$$\frac{\partial^2 F}{\partial y'^2} = \frac{1}{(1 + y'^2)^{3/2}}$$

Substituting from (9.2.27) into (9.2.22) we obtain

$$\delta^2 J(y) = \frac{\varepsilon^2}{2} \int_{x_1}^{x_2} \phi'^2 \left[\frac{1}{(1 + y'^2)^{3/2}} \right] dx \qquad (9.2.28)$$

It is readily seen from (9.2.28) that for $0 \leqslant x_1 \leqslant x \leqslant x_2$, $\delta^2 J(y) > 0$. Hence, the result we obtained was a minimum.

As an example of the use of the Legendre condition, consider our second example. For this problem

$$F = y'^2 - 2xy$$

$$\frac{\partial F}{\partial y'} = 2y'$$

$$\frac{\partial^2 F}{\partial y'^2} = 2 > 0 \quad \text{for all} \quad x$$

Therefore the extremal $y = -\frac{1}{6}x^3 + \frac{7}{6}x$ is a minimum.

We can generalize all of the above results for functions F, which depend on several different functions $y_1(x), y_2(x), \ldots, y_m(x)$ which will be indicated by the vector function $\mathbf{y}(x)$. We must now determine $\mathbf{y}(x)$ so that the objective function

$$J(\mathbf{y}(x)) = \int_{x_1}^{x_2} F(x, \mathbf{y}, \mathbf{y}') \, dx \qquad (9.2.29)$$

is stationary. We again define variations

$$\delta y_i(x) = y_i(x) - y_0(x) = \varepsilon_i \phi_i(x) \qquad (i = 1, 2, \ldots, m) \qquad (9.2.30)$$

The variation of the objective function $J(\mathbf{y}(x))$, displaced from the optimal path, will then be given by

$$\delta J(\mathbf{y}(x)) = J(\mathbf{y}(x)) - J(\mathbf{y}_0(x)) = \int_{x_1}^{x_2} F(x, \mathbf{y}, \mathbf{y}') \, dx - \int_{x_1}^{x_2} F(x, \mathbf{y}_0, \mathbf{y}_0') \, dx \qquad (9.2.31)$$

Expanding the first term on the right-hand side by a Taylor series, we obtain

$$\int_{x_1}^{x_2} (F(x, \mathbf{y}, \mathbf{y}')) \, dx = \int_{x_1}^{x_2} F(x, \mathbf{y_0}, \mathbf{y_0'}) \, dx + \sum_{i=1}^{m} \varepsilon_i \left(\frac{\partial F}{\partial y_i} \phi_i + \frac{\partial F}{\partial y_i'} \phi_i' \right) dx \quad (9.2.32)$$

We then obtain that $\delta J(y)$ is, to the first order terms in ε, given by

$$\delta J(\mathbf{y}) = \sum_{i=1}^{m} \varepsilon_i \int_{x_1}^{x_2} \left(\frac{\partial F}{\partial y_i} \phi_i + \frac{\partial F}{\partial y_i'} \phi_i' \right) dx \quad (9.2.33)$$

Integrating by parts results in

$$\delta J(\mathbf{y}) = \sum_{i=1}^{m} \varepsilon_i \int_{x_1}^{x_2} \left[\frac{\partial F}{\partial y_i} - \frac{d}{dx} \left(\frac{\partial F}{\partial y_i'} \right) \right] \phi_i \, dx \quad (9.2.34)$$

under the assumption that the $y_i(x)$ are given as fixed at x_1 and x_2.

Since all the ε_i in (9.2.34) are independent and each can be either positive or negative we then have

$$\int_{x_1}^{x_2} \left[\frac{\partial F}{\partial y_i} - \frac{d}{dx} \left(\frac{\partial F}{\partial y_i'} \right) \right] \phi_i \, dx = 0 \quad (i = 1, 2, \ldots, m) \quad (9.2.35)$$

if $\delta J(\mathbf{y})$ is to be zero for all ε_i. Since the ϕ_i are arbitrary, (9.2.35) has to be satisfied for all ϕ_i. Hence we have that

$$\frac{\partial F}{\partial y_i} - \frac{d}{dx} \left(\frac{\partial F}{\partial y_i'} \right) = 0 \quad (i = 1, 2, \ldots, m) \quad (9.2.36)$$

Equations (9.2.36) are the Euler–Lagrange equations for functions F which depend on several independent functions $y_i(x)$. Each such function must, according to (9.2.36), satisfy an Euler–Lagrange equation, as a necessary condition for the existence of an optimum value of $J(\mathbf{y}(x))$.

In the same fashion, sufficient conditions, analogous to (9.2.22) for the case of one independent function, can also be developed.

9.3. Boundary Conditions and Constraints

In the problems considered previously, we restricted ourselves to functions which had fixed values at two boundary points, as well as fixed limits of integration. There are important classes of problems for which neither of these assumptions is valid. When different assumptions are made we must consider the problems *de novo* and rederive the conditions that a solution will satisfy.

Before considering a general analysis, let us consider some examples. Consider the variational problem

$$\min_y \quad J(y) = \int_{x_1}^{x_2} [\alpha y'^2 - y f(x)] \, dx \quad (9.3.1)$$

where $f(x)$ is a known function of x. We shall not specify the boundary conditions as yet. Hence when we consider the variation:

$$\delta y(x) = y(x) - y_0(x) = \varepsilon \phi(x) \tag{9.3.2}$$

we cannot specify that $\phi(x)$ vanishes at the boundaries $x = x_1$ and $x = x_2$. The first variation of $J(y)$ given by (9.3.1) is

$$\delta J(y) = \varepsilon \int_{x_1}^{x_2} \left(\phi \frac{\partial F}{\partial y} + \phi' \frac{\partial F}{\partial y'} \right) dx$$

$$= \varepsilon \int_{x_1}^{x_2} [2\alpha \phi' y' - \phi f(x)] \, dx \tag{9.3.3}$$

If we integrate the first term of the integrand of (9.3.3) by parts we obtain

$$\delta J(y) = -\varepsilon \int_{x_1}^{x_2} \left[2\alpha \frac{d^2 y}{dx^2} + f(x) \right] \phi \, dx + \varepsilon (2\alpha) \frac{dy}{dx} \phi \Big|_{x_1}^{x_2} \tag{9.3.4}$$

We can see from (9.3.4) that if the variation $\delta J(y)$ is to be zero for all admissible variations, then both the Euler–Lagrange equation and the boundary conditions must be satisfied:

$$2\alpha \frac{d^2 y}{dx^2} + f(x) = 0 \tag{9.3.5}$$

$$\frac{dy}{dx} \phi \Big|_{x=x_1} = \frac{dy}{dx} \phi \Big|_{x=x_2} = 0 \tag{9.3.6}$$

We may note that since (9.3.5) is a second-order differential equation, two boundary conditions must be specified; otherwise the solution is not unique. We also note from (9.3.6) that at x_1 and x_2, the derivative must vanish if the variation does not. Since no boundary conditions have been prescribed and since (9.3.6) must hold for all values of $\phi(x_1)$ and $\phi(x_2)$, we must have that

$$\frac{dy}{dx} = 0 \quad \text{at} \quad x = x_1, x_2 \tag{9.3.7}$$

Boundary conditions such as (9.3.7) are often called *natural boundary conditions*.

In order to determine under what conditions a solution will exist, we integrate (9.3.5) to obtain

$$\frac{dy}{dx} = -\frac{1}{2\alpha} \int_{x_1}^{x} f(t) \, dt \tag{9.3.8}$$

We can see that the first boundary condition

$$\frac{dy}{dx} = 0 \quad \text{when} \quad x = x_1$$

is satisfied. The satisfaction of the second boundary condition requires that

$$-\frac{1}{2\alpha} \int_{x_1}^{x_2} f(t) \, dt = 0 \tag{9.3.9}$$

It is clear that (9.3.9) is a very restrictive condition. Hence, we see that when we failed to specify boundary conditions, a set of "natural" boundary conditions are found in the course of examining the variational solution.

There are other kinds of boundary conditions that may be specified. Therefore, let us consider the matter of boundary conditions more generally. We have the problem

$$\min_{y} \quad J(y) = \int_{x_1}^{x} F(x, y, y') \, dx \tag{9.3.10}$$

where $y(x)$, unrestricted by boundary conditions, is to be determined so as to minimize y. It will be noted that we have left the upper limit of the integral unspecified. We shall treat the upper limit in terms of variation as well. Suppose there is an optimal value of x, called x_0. Then we consider the difference between the optimal value of the objective function and its value when an infinitesimal change in $y(x)$ and x is made. We have

$$\delta J(y) = J(y) - J(y_0) = \int_{x_1}^{x} F(x, y, y') \, dx - \int_{x_1}^{x} F(x, y_0, y_0') \, dx \tag{9.3.11}$$

Figure 9.3.1 shows this variation in both $y(x)$ and x.

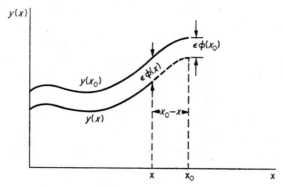

FIG. 9.3.1. Variation of upper limit.

We may write the first integral of (9.3.11) as

$$\int_{x_1}^{x} F(x, y, y') \, dz = \int_{x_1}^{x_0} F(x, y, y') \, dx + \int_{x_0}^{x} F(x, y, y') \, dx \tag{9.3.12}$$

Combining (9.3.11) and (9.3.12) results in

$$\delta J(y) = \int_{x_1}^{x_0} F(x, y, y') \, dx + \int_{x_0}^{x} F(x, y, y') \, dx - \int_{x_1}^{x} F(x, y_0, y_0') \, dx \tag{9.3.13}$$

Using $y(x) - y_0(x) = \varepsilon \phi(x)$, we shall again expand the first term of (9.3.13) in a Taylor series to obtain

$$\int_{x_1}^{x_0} F(x, y, y') \, dx \approx \int_{x_1}^{x_0} \left[F(x, y_0, y_0') + \frac{\partial F}{\partial y} (\varepsilon \phi) + \frac{\partial F}{\partial y'} (\varepsilon \phi') \right] dx \tag{9.3.14}$$

if we neglect the higher order terms. Providing the difference $x - x_0$ is of the same order as ε, we may write that

$$\int_{x_0}^{x} F(x, y, y')\, dx \approx (x - x_0)\, F(x_0, y_0, y_0') \tag{9.3.15}$$

from the mean value theorem of integrals. Combining (9.3.13), (9.3.14), and (9.3.15) results in

$$\delta J(y) = \varepsilon \int_{x_1}^{x_0} \left(\frac{\partial F}{\partial y}\phi + \frac{\partial F}{\partial y'}\phi' \right) dx + (x - x_0)\, F(x_0, y_0, y_0') \Big|_{x_0} \tag{9.3.16}$$

We integrate (9.3.16) by parts to give

$$\delta J(y) = \varepsilon \int_{x_1}^{x_0} \left[\frac{\partial F}{\partial y} - \frac{d}{dx}\left(\frac{\partial F}{\partial y'} \right) \right] \phi\, dx - \varepsilon \frac{\partial F}{\partial y'}\phi \Big|_{x_1} + \varepsilon \frac{\partial F}{\partial y'}\phi \Big|_{x_0}$$
$$+ (x - x_0)\, F(x, y_0, y_0') \Big|_{x_0} \tag{9.3.17}$$

The terms evaluated at $x = x_1$ and $x = x_0$ are the ones that lead to natural boundary conditions. The Euler–Lagrange equation is still a necessary condition for the existence of an optimum. However, the boundary conditions can now be considered as part of the variation.

We turn now to the matter of including explicit restrictions or constraints in the statement of problems that are to be solved by a variational approach. Let us consider the approach to solving the following problem:

$$\min_{y} \quad J(y) = \int_{x_1}^{x_2} F(x, y, y')\, dx \tag{9.3.18}$$

subject to

$$I(y) = \int_{x_1}^{x_2} Y(x, y, y')\, dx = C \tag{9.3.19}$$

where C is a given constant. What we must do is construct a function $y(x)$ which satisfies the constraint (9.3.19) and also differs infinitesimally from y_0. For this purpose we define a variation which depends on two functions ϕ_1, ϕ_2 which are arbitrary differentiable functions of x which vanish at $x = x_1$ and $x = x_2$. Therefore

$$\delta y = y - y_0 = \varepsilon_1 \phi_1 + \varepsilon_2 \phi_2 \tag{9.3.20}$$

If we substitute from (9.3.20)

$$y = y_0 + \varepsilon_1 \phi_1 + \varepsilon_2 \phi_2$$

into (9.3.19) we have

$$I(\varepsilon_1, \varepsilon_2) = \int_{x_1}^{x_2} Y(x, y, y')\, dx \tag{9.3.21}$$

where ε_1 and ε_2 are now related by (9.3.21). Since this may be too complicated a relationship to deal with explicitly, we make use of the well-known method of Lagrange multipliers.

As in the case of the unconstrained problem, a necessary condition for the existence of an optimum is that

$$\delta J(y) = \int_{x_1}^{x_2} [F(x, y, y') \, dx - F(x, y_0, y_0') \, dx] = 0 \qquad (9.3.22)$$

The admissible variations must also satisfy

$$\delta I = \int_{x_1}^{x_2} [Y(x, y, y') - Y(x, y_0, y_0')] \, dx = 0 \qquad (9.3.23)$$

Now we introduce a Lagrange multiplier μ in order to convert (9.3.19) into an unconstrained problem. We therefore seek to find $y(x)$ which yields

$$\delta \hat{J}(y) = \delta J(y) + \mu \, \delta I = 0 \qquad (9.3.24)$$

for sufficiently small ε_1 and ε_2. We expand (9.3.24) in a Taylor series to obtain

$$\delta \hat{J}(y) = \int_{x_1}^{x_2} \left[\varepsilon_1 \left(\frac{\partial F}{\partial y} - \frac{d}{dx} \left(\frac{\partial F}{\partial y'} \right) \right) \phi_1 + \varepsilon_2 \left(\frac{\partial F}{\partial y} - \frac{d}{dx} \left(\frac{\partial F}{\partial y'} \right) \right) \phi_2 \right] dx$$

$$+ \mu \int_{x_1}^{x_2} \left[\varepsilon_1 \left(\frac{\partial Y}{\partial y} - \frac{d}{dx} \left(\frac{\partial Y}{\partial y'} \right) \right) \phi_1 + \varepsilon_2 \left(\frac{\partial Y}{\partial y} - \frac{d}{dx} \frac{\partial Y}{\partial y'} \right) \phi_2 \right] dx \quad (9.3.25)$$

A repetition of the same arguments we previously employed in deriving Euler–Lagrange equations will yield, as a necessary condition for $\delta \hat{J}(y)$ to vanish, a new Euler–Lagrange equation

$$\left(\frac{\partial F}{\partial y} + \mu \frac{\partial Y}{\partial y} \right) - \frac{d}{dx} \left(\frac{\partial F}{\partial y'} + \mu \frac{\partial Y}{\partial y'} \right) = 0 \qquad (9.3.26)$$

Formally, we can obtain the same result by employing a modified objective function

$$\hat{J}(y) = J(y) + \mu I = \int_{x_1}^{x_2} (F + \mu Y) \, dx \qquad (9.3.27)$$

and finding a stationary point of (9.3.27). Therefore, a necessary condition that $y(x)$ minimizes $J(y)$ is that (9.3.26) and (9.3.19) be satisfied.

The above results generalize to the case of $J(\mathbf{y}(x))$ and to the case of multiple constraints. For the general case of

$$\min_{\mathbf{y}} \ J(\mathbf{y}(x)) = \int_{x_1}^{x_2} F(x, \mathbf{y}, \mathbf{y}') \, dx \qquad (9.3.28)$$

subject to

$$I_p(\mathbf{y}) = \int_{x_1}^{x_2} Y(x, \mathbf{y}, \mathbf{y}') \, dx = C_p \qquad (p = 1, 2, \ldots, m) \qquad (9.3.29)$$

The Euler–Lagrange equations are

$$\left(\frac{\partial F}{\partial y_i} + \mu_i \frac{\partial Y}{\partial y_i} \right) - \frac{d}{dx} \left(\frac{\partial F}{\partial y'} + \mu_i \frac{\partial Y}{\partial y_i'} \right) = 0 \qquad (i = 1, 2, \ldots, m) \qquad (9.3.30)$$

where $\mu_i(x)$ are Lagrange multipliers.

As an example of a constrained problem we seek to find the shortest distance between the points $(1, -1, 0)$ and $(2, 1, -1)$ which lies on the surface $15x-7y+z = 22$. The distance between two points in E^3 is given by

$$J(y, z) = \int_{x_1}^{x_2} (1+y'^2+z'^2)^{1/2} \, dx \tag{9.3.31}$$

where $y = y(x)$ and $z = z(x)$. We seek to find the minimum of $J(y, z)$ provided that

$$h(x, y, z) = 15x-7y+z-22 = 0 \quad \text{and} \quad x_1 = 1, \quad x_2 = 2$$

We form the Lagrangian

$$\hat{J} = \int_1^2 [(1+y'^2+z'^2)^{1/2}+\mu(x)\,(15x-7y+z-22)] \, dx \tag{9.3.32}$$

and write down the Euler–Lagrange equations for it:

$$-7\mu-\frac{d}{dx}\left(\frac{y'}{(1+y'^2+z'^2)^{1/2}}\right) = 0 \tag{9.3.33}$$

$$\mu-\frac{d}{dx}\left(\frac{z'}{(1+y'^2+z'^2)^{1/2}}\right) = 0 \tag{9.3.34}$$

and the constraint equation
$$15x-7y+z-22 = 0 \tag{9.3.35}$$

Equations (9.3.33)–(9.3.35) are the necessary conditions that $y(x)$ and $z(x)$ must satisfy. We also have that

$$y(1) = -1, \quad y(2) = 1, \quad z(1) = 0, \quad z(2) = -1 \tag{9.3.36}$$

If we multiply (9.3.34) by 7 and add it to (9.3.33) we obtain

$$\frac{d}{dx}\left(\frac{y'+7z'}{(1+y'^2+z'^2)^{1/2}}\right) = 0$$

and by integrating, we have

$$\frac{y'+7z'}{(1+y'^2+z'^2)^{1/2}} = \hat{C}_1 \tag{9.3.37}$$

From (9.3.35) we have that
$$z' = 7y'-15 \tag{9.3.38}$$

Substituting from (9.3.38) into (9.3.37) and solving the resulting differential equation gives us

$$y(x) = C_1x+C_2 \tag{9.3.39}$$

Using (9.3.36) and (9.3.39) we obtain

$$y(x) = 2x-3 \tag{9.3.40}$$

From (9.3.38) and (9.3.40) we find that

$$z(x) = 1 - x \qquad (9.3.41)$$

From (9.3.33) or (9.3.34) we find that $\mu(x) \equiv 0$.
Hence the minimum distance we seek is

$$d = \int_1^2 (1 + y'^2 + z'^2)^{1/2} \, dx$$

$$= \int_1^2 (1 + 4 + 1)^{1/2} \, dx = \sqrt{6}x \Big|_1^2 = \sqrt{6}$$

Another problem type to which the Lagrange multiplier technique can be applied is as follows. We wish to minimize

$$J(y, z) = \int_{x_1}^{x_2} F(y, z) \, dx \qquad (9.3.42)$$

subject to

$$\frac{dy}{dx} = f(y, z) \qquad (9.3.43)$$

We seek to find $y(x)$ and $z(x)$ so as to minimize $J(y, z)$ when y and z are related through (9.3.43). We again introduce a Lagrange multiplier $\mu(x)$ and form the Lagrangian function

$$\hat{J} = \int_{x_1}^{x_2} \left\{ F(y, z) - \mu(x) \left[\frac{dy}{dx} - f(y, z) \right] \right\} dx \qquad (9.3.44)$$

In the usual way, we determine that if $y(x)$ and $z(x)$ are to minimize $\hat{J}$, necessary conditions are the Euler–Lagrange equations

$$\frac{\partial F}{\partial z} + \mu(x) \frac{\partial f}{\partial z} = 0, \qquad \frac{\partial F}{\partial y} + \frac{d\mu(x)}{dx} \frac{\partial f}{\partial y} = 0 \qquad (9.3.45)$$

with appropriate boundary conditions.

Problems of the forms (9.3.42) and (9.3.43) are of great importance in applications such as optimal control.

9.4. Practical Difficulties of the Calculus of Variations

The foregoing material on the calculus of variations is intended only as a very incomplete introduction to the subject. An excellent treatment of this subject can be found in [24].

Now that we have some idea of the methodology that is employed by the classical theory of the calculus of variations, we may note that in fact, solutions to calculus of variations problems are often very difficult to obtain. Let us consider some of the difficulties.

16

Problems with certain kinds of inequality constraints present very great difficulties. For example, suppose we wish to minimize

$$J(y) = \int_0^C F(x, y, y')\, dx \qquad (9.4.1)$$

subject to
$$y_L \leqslant y \leqslant y_U \qquad (9.4.2)$$

If we only know the lower and upper bounds of y but not the corresponding values of x where these values hold, then the calculus of variations approach is beset with difficulties. Figure 9.4.1 indicates the difficulty. We do not know the points x_L, x_U. However, the use of the Euler–Lagrange equation implies that we have a free variation between the limits $x = 0$ and $x = C$ and not between x_L and x_U. This is a serious problem and it is not difficult to imagine situations a good deal more complicated than that depicted in Fig. 9.4.1.

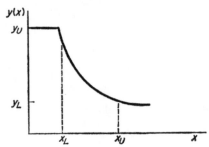

FIG. 9.4.1. Inequality constraint.

Another significant problem in the use of the calculus of variations is that the Euler–Lagrange equations are second order or higher nonlinear differential equations. This means that two (or more) boundary conditions must be specified in order to find a unique solution. As long as an analytic solution to the Euler–Lagrange equations can be found, then the nature of these boundary conditions is not important. However, as is very often the case, no analytic solution can be found; it is then necessary to resort to numerical methods of solving the resulting differential equation(s). If the boundary values are given at each end of the interval of integration, then what results is known as a two-point boundary value problem. Solving such problems is one of the more difficult and challenging areas of numerical analysis research.

Still a third difficulty involves the use of nonanalytic functions, which are common in application areas such as optimal control problems, approximation problems, etc. For example, one might wish to optimize

$$J(y) = \int_{x_1}^{x_2} |y(x) - p(x)|\, dx \qquad (9.4.3)$$

subject to one or more constraints. It is not possible to deal with (9.4.3) in the context of the calculus of variations since the basic theory requires that the function $F(x, y, y')$ have continuous derivatives.

In summary, it is frequently very difficult, if not impossible, to obtain solutions to the Euler–Lagrange equations and constraints of the problem under consideration.

In the next several sections of this chapter we shall consider the application of dynamic programming to variational problems.

9.5. Dynamic Programming in Variational Problems

There is a marked difference of approach to solving variational problems between the calculus of variations and dynamic programming. In the calculus of variations the optimal function (extremal) is determined by finding a solution to one or more differential equations that satisfy the boundary conditions. This is done, not in a point by point calculation, but is found all at once, or a sequence of approximations to the total function.

In the dynamic programming approach, we do not find the optimal function all at once, but rather we move from point to point, evaluating the next point from the previous point on the extremal and a knowledge of its derivative.

Despite these differences there is a close connection between the two approaches. In fact, it is possible, as we shall see, to derive the Euler–Lagrange equation from the basic linear partial differential equation of dynamic programming.

We shall now derive a typical dynamic programming approach. We consider the problem

$$\max_{z} \quad J(z) = \int_{x_1}^{x_2} F(x, y, z)\, dx \tag{9.5.1}$$

subject to

$$\frac{dy}{dx} = f(x, y, z) \tag{9.5.2}$$

with the initial condition

$$y(x_1) = C \tag{9.5.3}$$

As is usual in dynamic programming, we shall define an optimal return function. It will differ slightly from the kinds of functions we have used in previous chapters, because we are dealing with an integral of a continuous variable instead of a summation of discrete stages. We shall defer consideration of computational aspects of the approach. We are interested for the present in the theoretical results that the utilization of the dynamic programming approach yields.

We define

$$g(x, y(x)) = \max_{z[x,\, x_2]} \int_{x}^{x_2} F(x, y, z)\, dx \tag{9.5.4}$$

where the notation $z[x, x_2]$ indicates that $z(x)$ is restricted to the interval $[x, x_2]$. Note that x and $y(x)$ are to be considered state variables in this problem with an *infinite* number of stages.

16*

We now derive the basic recursion relationship. We divide the interval $[x, x_2]$ into two intervals $[x, x+\xi]$ and $[x+\xi, x_2]$. Then we may write

$$g(x, y(x)) = \max_{z[x,\, x_2]} \left[\int_x^{x+\xi} F(x, y, z)\, dx + \int_{x+\xi}^{x_2} F(x, y, z)\, dx \right] \qquad (9.5.5)$$

and then dividing the maximization into two intervals, we obtain

$$g(x, y(x)) = \max_{z[x,\, x+\xi]} \max_{z[x+\xi,\, x_2]} \left[\int_x^{x+\xi} F(x, y, z)\, dx + \int_{x+\xi}^{x_2} F(x, y, z)\, dx \right] \qquad (9.5.6)$$

Since the first integral does not require maximization over $[x+\xi, x_2]$, we may rewrite (9.5.6) to obtain

$$g(x, y(x)) = \max_{z[x,\, x+\xi]} \left[\int_x^{x+\xi} F(x, y, z)\, dx + \max_{z[x+\xi,\, x_2]} \int_{x+\xi}^{x_2} F(x, y, z)\, dx \right] \qquad (9.5.7)$$

However, using the definition (9.5.4) we see that

$$\max_{z[x+\xi,\, x_2]} \int_{x+\xi}^{x_2} F(x, y, z)\, dx = g(x+\xi, y(x+\xi)) \qquad (9.5.8)$$

Combining (9.5.7) and (9.5.8), we obtain the basic recursion relationship for the variational problem (9.5.1)–(9.5.3):

$$g(x, y(x)) = \max_{z[x,\, x+\xi]} \left[\int_x^{x+\xi} F(x, y, z)\, dx + g(x+\xi, y(x+\xi)) \right] \qquad (9.5.9)$$

Equation (9.5.9) is the continuous analog of the basic recursion equations we developed in earlier chapters for discrete multistage problems. The term $g(x+\xi, y(x+\xi))$ is the optimal return from $x+\xi$ to x_2 when the result of the previous stages was $y(x+\xi)$. This corresponds to $g_{s-1}(\lambda_{s-1})$ in the discrete process. Note that unlike the discrete case the return function $g(\cdot)$ is the same function on both sides of (9.5.9). We used such a functional equation in Section 7.4. Subsequently, we shall use (9.5.9) to find numerical solutions to variational problems.

We shall now use (9.5.9) to derive a further result of importance. For small values of ξ, we can replace

$$\int_x^{x+\xi} F(x, y, z)\, dx$$

by $F(x, y, z)\xi$. Therefore, (9.5.9) can be written

$$g(x, y(x)) = \max_{z[x,\, x+\xi]} [F(x, y, z)\xi + g(x+\xi, y(x+\xi))] \qquad (9.5.10)$$

We now wish to expand $g(x+\xi, y(x+\xi))$ in a Taylor series about $(x, y(x))$ and use this expansion to eliminate $g(x, y(x))$ from (9.5.10). A Taylor series expansion of a function $h(u)$ about a point $u = u_0$ is

$$h(u) = h(u_0) + (u-u_0)\, h'(u_0) + \frac{(u-u_0)^2}{2!} h''(u_0) + \cdots \qquad (9.5.11)$$

For our function $g(x, y(x))$ we have

$$h'(u_0) = g'(x, y(x)) = \frac{\partial g}{\partial x} + \frac{\partial g}{\partial y}\frac{dy}{dx}$$

Therefore
$$g'(x, y(x)) = \frac{\partial g}{\partial x} + \frac{\partial g}{\partial y}f \qquad (9.5.12)$$

Therefore we may write

$$g(x+\xi, y(x+\xi)) = g(x, y(x)) + \xi\left(\frac{\partial g}{\partial x} + \frac{\partial g}{\partial y}f(x, y, z)\right) \qquad (9.5.13)$$

where, in (9.5.13), we have neglected terms in ξ^2 and higher. We now substitute (9.5.13) into (9.5.10) to obtain

$$g(x, y(x)) = \max_{z[x,\, x+\xi]}\left[F(x, y, z)\xi + g(x, y(x)) + \xi\left(\frac{\partial g}{\partial x} + \frac{\partial g}{\partial y}f(x, y, z)\right)\right] \quad (9.5.14)$$

We are justified in ignoring the higher order terms in ξ, since we shall be taking a limit involving $\xi \to 0$. We may now subtract $g(x, y(x))$ from both sides of (9.5.14) since z is not an argument in $g(x, y(x))$. This results in

$$0 = \max_{z[x,\, x+\xi]}\left[F(x, y, z)\xi + \xi\left(\frac{\partial g}{\partial x} + \frac{\partial g}{\partial y}f(x, y, z)\right)\right] \qquad (9.5.15)$$

We now divide both sides of (9.5.15) by ξ and take the limit as $\xi \to 0$. This results in

$$0 = \max_{z(x)}\left[F(x, y, z) + \frac{\partial g}{\partial x} + f\frac{\partial g}{\partial y}\right] \qquad (9.5.16)$$

From (9.5.16) we see that the original variational problem has been converted to an ordinary maximization problem. We know that a necessary condition for a maximum is that the first partial derivative with respect to z vanishes, i.e.,

$$\frac{\partial F}{\partial z} + \frac{\partial g}{\partial y}\frac{\partial f}{\partial z} = 0 \qquad (9.5.17)$$

Also at the maximum point, the maximand of (9.5.16) is zero. Therefore

$$F + \frac{\partial g}{\partial x} + \frac{\partial g}{\partial y}f = 0 \qquad (9.5.18)$$

We can now eliminate the optimal return function g from (9.5.17) and (9.5.18) to yield a partial differential equation in the original variables x, y, z, f and F and whose solution will, therefore, satisfy the necessary conditions for a maximum. We do so as follows. From (9.5.17) we obtain

$$\frac{\partial g}{\partial y} = -\frac{\partial F/\partial z}{\partial f/\partial z} \equiv U(x, y, z) \qquad (9.5.19)$$

Substituting from (9.5.19) into (9.5.18) and solving for $\partial g/\partial x$, we have

$$\frac{\partial g}{\partial x} = \frac{(\partial F/\partial z)f}{\partial f/\partial z} - F \equiv V(x, y, z) \tag{9.5.20}$$

Since $\dfrac{\partial}{\partial x}\left(\dfrac{\partial g}{\partial y}\right) = \dfrac{\partial}{\partial y}\left(\dfrac{\partial g}{\partial x}\right)$, we see from (9.5.19) and (9.5.20) that

$$\frac{\partial}{\partial x} U(x, y, z) = \frac{\partial}{\partial y} V(x, y, z) \tag{9.5.21}$$

We know that

$$\frac{\partial}{\partial x} U(x, y, z) = \frac{\partial U}{\partial x} + \frac{\partial U}{\partial y}\frac{\partial y}{\partial x} + \frac{\partial U}{\partial z}\frac{\partial z}{\partial x} \tag{9.5.22}$$

and that

$$\frac{\partial}{\partial y} V(x, y, z) = \frac{\partial V}{\partial y} + \frac{\partial V}{\partial x}\frac{\partial x}{\partial y} + \frac{\partial V}{\partial z}\frac{\partial z}{\partial y} \tag{9.5.23}$$

However, $y(x)$ is a state variable that must vary independently of x. Hence we have that $\partial y/\partial x = \partial x/\partial y = 0$. Therefore, combining this with (9.5.21)–(9.5.23) we have

$$\frac{\partial U}{\partial x} + \frac{\partial U}{\partial z}\frac{\partial z}{\partial x} = \frac{\partial V}{\partial y} + \frac{\partial V}{\partial z}\frac{\partial z}{\partial y} \tag{9.5.24}$$

Equation (9.5.24) is a necessary condition that the function $z(x)$ must satisfy in order to maximize (9.5.1)–(9.5.3).

What is significant about (9.5.24) is that this partial differential equation was derived by applying the principle of optimality of dynamic programming. One can frequently solve such partial differential equations by the method of characteristics. We shall not explore that solution methodology since it is relatively straightforward when it can be applied.

An interesting question is whether the partial differential equation (9.5.24) is related in any way to the Euler–Lagrange equation or whether this is a quite different condition. In fact, we shall show their equivalence by deriving the Euler–Lagrange equation from (9.5.24).

The Euler–Lagrange equation is a necessary condition for a function $y(x)$ to optimize

$$J(y) = \int_{x_1}^{x_2} F(x, y, y')\, dx \tag{9.5.25}$$

Therefore, referring to (9.5.1)–(9.5.3) if we consider the case where $z = f = y'$ we have the maximization (or minimization) of (9.5.25) as a special case of (9.5.1)–(9.5.3). Under these conditions we have that $\partial f/\partial z = 1$ and, therefore, from (9.5.19) we have

$$U(x, y, y') = -\frac{\partial F}{\partial y'} \tag{9.5.26}$$

and from (9.5.20) that

$$V(x, y, y') = y' \frac{\partial F}{\partial y'} - F \tag{9.5.27}$$

Equation (9.5.24) for $z = y'$ is

$$\frac{\partial U}{\partial x} + \frac{\partial U}{\partial y'} \frac{\partial y'}{\partial x} = \frac{\partial V}{\partial y} \tag{9.5.28}$$

We shall now show that (9.5.28) is the Euler–Lagrange equation. We can evaluate the necessary partial derivatives of (9.5.28) from (9.5.26) and (9.5.27) as

$$\frac{\partial U}{\partial x} = -\frac{\partial^2 F}{\partial x \, \partial y'} \tag{9.5.29}$$

$$\frac{\partial U}{\partial y'} = -\frac{\partial^2 F}{\partial y'^2} \tag{9.5.30}$$

$$\frac{\partial V}{\partial y} = y' \frac{\partial^2 F}{\partial y \, \partial y'} - \frac{\partial F}{\partial y} \tag{9.5.31}$$

Substitution of (9.5.29)–(9.5.31) into (9.5.28) yields

$$-\frac{\partial^2 F}{\partial x \, \partial y'} - \frac{\partial^2 F}{\partial y'^2} \frac{\partial y'}{\partial x} = \frac{y' \, \partial^2 F}{\partial y \, \partial y'} - \frac{\partial F}{\partial y} \tag{9.5.32}$$

Noting that

$$\frac{d}{dx} \left(\frac{\partial F}{\partial y'} \right) = \frac{\partial^2 F}{\partial x \, \partial y'} + \frac{\partial^2 F}{\partial y \, \partial y'} y' + \frac{\partial^2 F}{\partial y'^2} \frac{\partial y'}{\partial x} \tag{9.5.33}$$

we obtain from (9.5.32) and (9.5.33)

$$\frac{\partial F}{\partial y} - \frac{d}{dx} \left(\frac{\partial F}{\partial y'} \right) = 0 \tag{9.5.34}$$

which is the Euler–Lagrange equation.

9.6. Computational Solution of Variational Problems by Dynamic Programming

As we have noted previously, most variational problems which arise in practical applications are likely to be of such complexity that it is not possible to solve the Euler–Lagrange equations analytically. Furthermore, the numerical solution of these partial differential equations may be extremely difficult. Hence, it is of considerable importance that dynamic programming offers a direct computational approach that often is fairly simple to apply.

Let us return to the variational problem we considered in Section 9.5, viz.,

$$\max_{z} \quad J(z) = \int_{x_1}^{x_2} F(x, y, z)\, dx \tag{9.6.1}$$

subject to

$$\frac{dy}{dx} = f(x, y, z) \tag{9.6.2}$$

$$y(x_1) = c \tag{9.6.3}$$

In Section 9.5 we also developed a functional equation, (9.5.9),

$$g(x, y(x)) = \max_{z|x, x+\xi]} \left[\int_{x}^{x+\xi} F(x, y, z)\, dx + g(x+\xi, y(x+\xi)) \right] \tag{9.6.4}$$

In order to develop an approximate numerical calculation, we must convert (9.6.4) to a discrete n-stage model, such as we have used in previous chapters. We approximate the interval $[x_1, x_2]$ by a discrete set of $n+1$ points, $s = 0, 1, \ldots, n$ and ordered in reverse, i.e., $0 = x_2$, $1 = x_2 - \xi$, $\ldots$, $n-1 = x_1 + \xi$, $n = x_1$. The boundary condition $y(x_1) = y_1$ will then be $y_n = c$.

At any stage s, (9.6.2) can be written as

$$y'_s = f_s(y_s, z_s) \tag{9.6.5}$$

where y_s, y'_s, z_s are understood to stand for y, y', and z at the sth stage. We use the usual difference approximation for the derivative

$$y'_s \approx \frac{y_{s-1} - y_s}{\xi} \tag{9.6.6}$$

Then, from (9.6.5) and (9.6.6), we have

$$\frac{y_{s-1} - y_s}{\xi} = f_s(y_s, z_s) \tag{9.6.7}$$

We solve (9.6.7) for y_{s-1}

$$y_{s-1} = y_s + \xi f_s(y_s, z_s) \tag{9.6.8}$$

The integral in (9.6.4) is approximated by

$$\int_{x}^{x+\xi} F(x, y, z)\, dx \approx F_s(y_s, z_s)\xi \tag{9.6.9}$$

where $F_s(y_s, z_s) = F(x, y, z)$ at stage s.

If we designate $g(x, y(x))$ as $g_s(y_s)$ when $x = x_s$, then we can substitute from (9.6.8) and (9.6.9) into (9.6.4), (9.6.2), (9.6.3) to obtain

$$g_s(y_s) = \max_{z_s} [F_s(y_s, z_s)\xi + g_{s-1}(y_{s-1})]$$

$$y_{s-1} = y_s + \xi f_s(y_s, z_s) \qquad (s = 1, 2, \ldots, n) \tag{9.6.10}$$

and

$$g_0(y_0) = 0, \quad y_n = c$$

The optimal solution to (9.6.10) is given by $g_n(y_n) = g_n(c)$. This value will be an approximation to $J(z)$, i.e.,

$$g_n(c) \approx \max_{z[x_1, x_2]} \int_{x_1}^{x_2} F(x, y, z) \, dx \qquad (9.6.11)$$

The function $z(y)$ which yields the value $g_n(c)$ in (9.6.11) is given by the points z_s, $z_{s-1}, \ldots, z_1$ which are determined in the course of the maximization which is carried out at each stage. As is usual, in numerical approximations, we can make $g_n(c)$ as close an approximation to $J(z)$ by choosing a sufficiently small ξ, i.e., increasing the number of points in the interval $[x_1, x_2]$.

The use of equations such as (9.6.10) should be fairly familiar by now. After establishing the grid of points in x, i.e., the number of stages, we choose a grid of points in both y and z. Then the typical stage calculation, say for $s = k$, is to compute $g_k(y_k)$ for each y_k in the range $[y(x_1), y(x_2)]$ over the grid of points set up for y. We must also determine a grid of points for z, over which we will maximize. Therefore for y_k, we calculate $F_k(y_k, z_k)$. We also need $g_{k-1}(y_{k-1})$. First we calculate y_{k-1} from

$$y_{k-1} = y_k + \xi f_k(y_k, z_k)$$

and then calculate $g_{k-1}(y_{k-1})$ from the previous stage table entries. We then compute the sum $F_k(y_k, z_k)\xi + g_{k-1}(y_{k-1})$ and repeat this for the same y_k and all values of z_k. We then choose the maximum sum as $g_k(y_k)$ and note the $z_k(y_k)$ that led to $g_k(y_k)$. We repeat this procedure for all values of y_k and so construct a table of $g_k(y_k)$ for all values of y_k. At the last stage, we need only calculate $g_n(c)$.

We have previously considered the following problem in some detail:

$$\min_{y'} \quad J(y') = \int_{x_1}^{x_2} F(x, y, y') \, dx \qquad (9.6.12)$$

with $y(x_1) = c$. Therefore, we shall indicate how the numerical solution to (9.6.12) is performed. It is a special case of (9.6.1)–(9.6.3), (assuming (9.6.1)–(9.6.3) was a minimization problem), where

$$z = y' = f$$

Hence, we can rewrite (9.6.10) as

$$g_s(y_s) = \min_{y_s} [F_s(y_s, y_s')\xi + g_{s-1}(y_{s-1})]$$
$$y_{s-1} = y_s + \xi y_s' \qquad (s = 1, 2, \ldots, n) \qquad (9.6.13)$$
$$g_0(y_0) = 0, \quad y_n = c$$

We may note that in (9.6.10) and (9.6.13) it was fairly easy to accommodate a fixed boundary condition at x_1 and a natural boundary condition at x_2. This is one of the principal advantages of the dynamic programming approach. If there was also a fixed boundary condition at x_2, then in terms of our reverse grid, suppose it was $y_0 = b$. We have the same recursion equations as in (9.6.10) except that in stage 1, we have that

$$y_0 = b = y_1 + \xi f_1(y_1, z_1) \qquad (9.6.14)$$

We then solve (9.6.14) for z_1 to obtain, say,

$$z_1 = \psi(b, y, \xi)$$

and
$$g_1(y_1) = F(y_1, \psi)\xi \tag{9.6.15}$$

Similarly, for the problem of (9.6.12), we have the same recursion equations as in (9.6.13) except that in stage 1, we have

$$y_0 = b = y_1 + \xi y_1'$$

Therefore
$$y_1' = \frac{b - y_1}{\xi}$$

and
$$g_1(y_1) = F\left(y_1, \frac{b - y_1}{\xi}\right)\xi \tag{9.6.16}$$

9.7. A Computational Example

In order to illustrate the use of the computational method given in Section 9.6, we shall solve a problem for which we can solve the Euler–Lagrange equation and then compare the exact solution with the numerical solution.

We consider the following problem in production scheduling. At a given initial time, say $t = 0$, the production rate $p(t) = 100$ units per unit time. It is required that 10 time units hence, the production rate $= 300$. We define $R(t, p, p')$ to be the cost of changing production which results from changes in the production machines, raw material changes and other costs associated with any non-personnel costs. Suppose this cost is proportional to the square of the rate of change of the production rate and that our accountants determine that

$$R(t, p, p') = 2p'(t)^2 \tag{9.7.1}$$

Similarly, there are personnel costs associated with changing the production rate. These are a result of increasing or decreasing the size of the labor force and are designated $P(t, p, p')$. Suppose these have been determined to be

$$P(t, p, p') = 4tp'(t) \tag{9.7.2}$$

Our objective is to minimize the sum of the costs given in (9.7.1) and (9.7.2). Hence we wish to

$$\min_p \; J(p) = \int_0^{10} [2p'(t)^2 + 4tp'(t)] \, dt \tag{9.7.3}$$

when
$$p(0) = 100, \quad p(10) = 300$$

The problem given by (9.7.3) is sufficiently simple that an analytic solution is easily found. We shall find this solution and compare it with the numerical solution we subsequently find.

The Euler–Lagrange equation (9.2.9) for (9.7.3) is

$$\frac{\partial F}{\partial p} - \frac{d}{dt}\left(\frac{\partial F}{\partial p'}\right) = 0 \tag{9.7.4}$$

We have that

$$F = 2p'^2 + 4tp'$$

$$\frac{\partial F}{\partial p} = 0$$

$$\frac{\partial F}{\partial p'} = 4p' + 4t$$

Therefore, the Euler–Lagrange equation is

$$\frac{d}{dt}(4p' + 4t) = 0 \qquad (9.7.5)$$

After differentiation, we have

$$4p'' + 4 = 0 \qquad (9.7.6)$$

Integrating (9.7.6) we have

$$p(t) = \frac{-t^2}{2} + C_1 t + C_2 \qquad (9.7.7)$$

We determine C_1 and C_2 from the boundary conditions. Since $p(0) = 100$, $C_2 = 100$. Using $p(10) = 300$, we have

$$\frac{-100}{2} + 10C_1 + 100 = 300$$

$$C_1 = 25$$

Therefore

$$p(t) = \frac{-t^2}{2} + 25t + 100, \qquad 0 \leqslant t \leqslant 10 \qquad (9.7.8)$$

is the solution.

Now let us determine the solution to (9.7.3) by the numerical computational approach of the previous section. The equations we shall use are (9.6.13). We shall choose a spacing $\xi = 1$ and divide the interval $[0, 10]$ into 10 sub-intervals of length equal to 1. Because we have specified a value of $p(t)$ at $t = 10$, the upper limit of the integral, we note that

$$g_1(p_1) = \min_{p_1} [F_1(p_1, p_1')] \qquad (9.7.9)$$

where

$$F(t, p, p') = 2p'^2 + 4tp'$$

and

$$p_1' = \frac{300 - p_1}{\xi} = 300 - p_1$$

Therefore

$$g_1(p_1) = F_1(p_1, 300 - p_1) \qquad (9.7.10)$$

and no minimization is required to determine $g_1(p_1)$. We have chosen to evaluate p_1 in the range $[100, 300]$ at intervals of 50. Table 9.7.1 gives $g_1(p_1)$ and the value of p_1' that yields $g_1(p_1)$.

TABLE 9.7.1. Optimal return: $g_1(p_1)$

p_1	$g_1(p_1)$	p_1'
100	87,200	200
150	50,400	150
200	23,600	100
250	6,800	50
300	0	0

We now calculate $g_2(p_2)$ using (9.6.13). The general equation is

$$g_2(p_2) = \min_{p_2'} [2p_2'^2 + 4(8)p_2' + g_1(p_1)] \tag{9.7.11}$$

where
$$p_1 = p_2 + p_2' \tag{9.7.12}$$

Therefore we substitute (9.7.12) into (9.7.11) to obtain

$$g_2(p_2) = \min_{p_2'} [2p_2'^2 + 32p_2' + g_1(p_2 + p_2')] \tag{9.7.13}$$

We illustrate in detail the calculation of $g_2(100)$. We shall allow p_2', the rate of change of p_2, to vary from 0 to 35, in increments of 5. Therefore we have

$$g_2(100) = \min_{p_2'} [2p_2'^2 + 32p_2' + g_1(100 + p_2')]$$

$$= \min_{p_2'} [G_2(100, p_2')]$$

$$G_2(100, 0) = 0 + g_1(100) = 87,200$$
$$G_2(100, 5) = 2(25) + 32(5) + g_1(105) = 210 + 83,520 = 83,730$$

In the computation of $G_2(100, 5)$ we required $g_1(105)$ which is not tabulated in Table 9.7.1. This is a frequent problem in dynamic programming calculations. We shall use linear interpolation in Table 9.7.1 to obtain $g_1(105)$ and throughout the numerical calculation in subsequent tables to obtain g_{s-1} in the calculation of g_s. We now continue:

$$G_2(100, 10) = 2(100) + 32(10) + g_1(110) = 520 + 79,840 = 80,360$$
$$G_2(100, 15) = 2(225) + 32(15) + g_1(115) = 930 + 76,160 = 77,090$$
$$G_2(100, 20) = 2(400) + 32(20) + g_1(120) = 1440 + 72,480 = 73,920$$
$$G_2(100, 25) = 2(625) + 32(25) + g_1(125) = 2050 + 68,800 = 70,850$$
$$G_2(100, 30) = 2(900) + 32(30) + g_1(130) = 2760 + 65,120 = 67,880$$
$$G_2(100, 35) = 2(1225) + 32(35) + g_1(135) = 3570 + 61,440 = 65,010$$

Then $g_2(100) = \min_{p_2'} [G_2(100, p_2')]$

$$= \min[87200, 83730, 80360, 77090, 73920, 70850, 67880, 65010]$$
$$= 65,010; \qquad p_2' = 35$$

We must repeat the above calculation for $p_2 = 150, 200, 250, 300$. If we do so, we obtain the results shown in Table 9.7.2.

TABLE 9.7.2. Optimal return: $g_2(p_2)$

p_2	$g_2(p_2)$	p_2'
100	65,010	35
150	35,210	35
200		35
250	5,450	25
300	0	0

In the same fashion we calculate $g_3(p_3)$, $g_4(p_4)$, ..., $g_9(p_9)$. The results of these calculations are given in Table 9.7.3. Finally, we calculate $g_{10}(p_{10}) = g_{10}(100)$. Since this value has been prescribed we compute only $g_{10}(100)$ from:

$$g_{10}(100) = \min_{p_{10}'} [2p_{10}'^2 + 0 + g_9(100 + p_{10}')]$$

$$= \min_{p_{10}'} [G_{10}(100, p_{10}')]$$

$G_{10}(100, \ 0) = 0 + g_9(100) = 15,184$

$G_{10}(100, 10) = 2(10)^2 + g_9(110) = \ \ 200 + 14,138 = 14,338$

$G_{10}(100, 20) = 2(20)^2 + g_9(120) = \ \ 800 + 13,093 = 13,893$

$G_{10}(100, 25) = 2(25)^2 + g_9(125) = 1250 + 12,570 = 13,820$

$G_{10}(100, 30) = 2(30)^2 + g_9(130) = 1800 + 12,047 = 13,847$

$g_{10}(100) = \min[15184, 14338, 13893, 13820, 13847]$

$\qquad = 13,820; \qquad p_{10}' = 25$

We now move backwards through the tables of $g_s(p_s)$ to calculate the optimal solution $p(t)$ in terms of the tabulated values of p_s. When $s = 10$, $p_{10}' = 25$, $p_{10} = 100$.

Therefore
$$p_9 = p_{10} + p_{10}' = 100 + 25 = 125$$

We again have an interpolation problem. Since all the tables have p_s given in increments of 50, $p_9 = 125$ does not appear in the table of $g_9(p_9)$. Of course, this value could be calculated if the table was given in smaller increments. We shall guess that p_9' is 30 when $p_9 = 125$. The subsequent backward calculation and the values of p_9' that appeared in the tables (or were estimated) are:

$$p_8 = p_9 + p_9' = 125 + 30 = 155; \qquad p_8' = 25$$
$$p_7 = p_8 + p_8' = 155 + 25 = 180; \qquad p_7' = 25$$
$$p_6 = p_7 + p_7' = 180 + 25 = 205; \qquad p_6' = 20$$
$$p_5 = p_6 + p_6' = 205 + 20 = 225; \qquad p_5' = 20$$
$$p_4 = p_5 + p_5' = 225 + 20 = 245; \qquad p_4' = 15$$
$$p_3 = p_4 + p_4' = 245 + 15 = 260; \qquad p_3' = 15$$
$$p_2 = p_3 + p_3' = 260 + 15 = 275; \qquad p_2' = 15$$
$$p_1 = p_2 + p_2' = 275 + 15 = 290$$

TABLE 9.7.3. Optimal returns: $g_3(p_3) - g_9(p_9)$

p_3	$g_3(p_3)$	p'_3	p_4	$g_4(p_4)$	p'_4	p_5	$g_5(p_5)$	p'_5	p_6	$g_6(p_6)$	p'_6	p_7	$g_7(p_7)$	p'_7	p_8	$g_8(p_8)$	p'_8	p_9	$g_9(p_9)$	p'_9
100	47,580	35	0	33,161	35	0	25,272	35	100	21,085	35	100	18,558	35	100	16,724	30	100	15,184	30
150	22,281	35	150	17,391	35	150	14,991	35	150	13,375	30	150	12,102	30	150	10,957	25	150	9,956	20,25
200	10,595	25	200	9,462	25	200	8,498	20	200	7,653	20	200	6,912	20	200	6,255	20	200	5,661	15
250	4,630	20	250	4,051	15	250	3,586	15	250	3,200	15	250	2,870	15	250	2,576	10	250	2,301	10
300	0	0	300	0	0	300	0	0	300	0	0	300	0	0	300	0	0	300	0	0

Hence, the optimal return function has been found to be $p(t)$ where p is given for the following values of t:

t	0	1	2	3	4	5	6	7	8	9	10
$p(t)$	100	125	155	180	205	225	245	260	275	290	300

If an analytic representation is desired, the above data can be fit by a smooth curve. A comparison of the numerical calculation with the analytic solution previously obtained is shown in Fig. 9.7.1. If a larger grid of points and more accurate interpolation

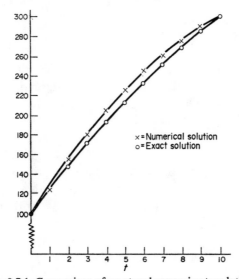

FIG. 9.7.1. Comparison of exact and approximate solutions.

had been employed, any arbitrary degree of accuracy could be obtained. Even for the relatively crude approximation employed, the agreement obtained in this example is quite adequate for many purposes.

It is important to understand why the numerical solution we have just obtained is superior to treating (9.6.12) directly by a numerical solution procedure. Let us then consider how we would solve

$$\min_{y} \ J(y) = \int_{x_1}^{x_2} F(x, y, y') \, dx \qquad (9.7.14)$$

$$y(x_1) = c$$

If F satisfies the proper conditions, then we know that the solution must satisfy the Euler–Lagrange equation

$$\frac{\partial F}{\partial y} - \frac{d}{dx}\left(\frac{\partial F}{\partial y'}\right) = 0 \qquad (9.7.15)$$

This will be a second order differential equation of the form

$$\frac{d^2y}{dx^2} = \psi(x, y, y')$$ (9.7.16)

which means that we must specify two boundary conditions in order to obtain a unique solution. The two boundary conditions that we have are

$$y(x_1) = c$$ (9.7.17)

which was given originally, and the other is

$$\left.\frac{\partial F}{\partial y'}\right|_{x=x_2} = 0$$ (9.7.18)

which we required in the course of the variational procedure that led to the Euler–Lagrange equation.

We see from (9.7.17) and (9.7.18) that we have a two-point boundary problem. If we apply any numerical integration technique to (9.7.16), the various methods all do something of the following sort. One must guess an initial value of $y'(x)$ in order to begin the numerical integration and continue until $y(x_2)$ is reached. Based on the disparity between what is obtained at $x = x_2$ and the condition given by (9.7.18), we obtain a correction to $y'(x)$ and begin the integration over. This may have to be repeated many times. There are many problems associated with these procedures. At best, they are many problems associated with these procedures. At best, they are time consuming and at worst, may have serious problems of stability associated with them.

9.8. Additional Variational Problems

We consider the problem

$$\max_{z} \quad J(z) = \int_0^\infty F(x, y, z)\, dx$$ (9.8.1)

subject to

$$\frac{dy}{dx} = f(y, z)$$ (9.8.2)

$$y(0) = c$$ (9.8.3)

We can proceed in much the same fashion as we did in Section 9.5. We define

$$g(y) = \max_{z[0,\,\infty]} \int_0^\infty F(x, y, z)\, dx$$ (9.8.4)

We now divide the interval $[0, \infty]$ into two parts and write

$$g(y) = \max_{z[0,\,\infty]} \left[\int_0^\xi F(x, y, z)\, dx + \int_\xi^\infty F(x, y, z)\, dx \right]$$ (9.8.5)

from which we may write

$$g(y) = \max_{z[0,\,\xi]} \left[\max_{z[\xi,\,\infty]} \int_0^\xi F(x, y, z)\, dx + \int_\xi^\infty F(x, y, z)\, dx \right] \tag{9.8.6}$$

We may remove the first integral from the inner maximization to obtain

$$g(y) = \max_{z[0,\,\xi]} \left[\int_0^\xi F(x, y, z)\, dx + \max_{z[\xi,\,\infty]} \int_\xi^\infty F(x, y, z)\, dx \right] \tag{9.8.7}$$

Using the definition (9.8.4) we observe that

$$\max_{z[\xi,\,\infty]} \int_\xi^\infty F(x, y, z)\, dx = g(y(\xi)) \tag{9.8.8}$$

Combining (9.8.7) and (9.8.8) we obtain the fundamental recursion relationship for the solution of problem (9.8.1)–(9.8.3)

$$g(y) = \max_{z[0,\,\xi]} \left[\int_0^\xi F(x, y, z)\, dx + g(y(\xi)) \right] \tag{9.8.9}$$

For small values of ξ, we may rewrite (9.8.9) as

$$g(y) = \max_{z[0,\,\xi]} \left[F(y, z(0))\xi + g(y + \xi f(y, z(0))) + 0(\xi) \right] \tag{9.8.10}$$

As the interval $[0, \xi]$ goes to zero, to select z over $[0, \xi]$ is to select $z(0)$. Let us define $w \equiv z(0)$ and expand the second term of (9.8.10) in a Taylor series. Substituting in (9.8.10) we have

$$g(y) = \max_w \left[F(y, w)\xi + g(y) + \xi f(y, w) g'(y) \right] + 0(\xi) \tag{9.8.11}$$

If we assume that the limits exist then as $\varepsilon \to 0$, we obtain from (9.8.11), after removing $g(y)$,

$$0 = \max_w \left[F(y, w) + f(y, w) g'(y) \right] \tag{9.8.12}$$

The necessary conditions on w that a maximum must satisfy are

$$F(y, w) + f(y, w) \frac{\partial g}{\partial y} = 0$$
$$\frac{\partial F}{\partial w} + \frac{\partial f}{\partial w} \frac{\partial g}{\partial y} = 0 \tag{9.8.13}$$

If we eliminate $\partial g/\partial y$ from the two equations (9.8.13) we obtain

$$f(y, w) \frac{\partial F}{\partial w} - F(y, w) \frac{\partial f}{\partial w} = 0 \tag{9.8.14}$$

Equation (9.8.14) gives a relationship between w and y or z as a function of y. Using this relationship, say $z = \psi(y)$, and substituting in (9.8.2), we obtain

$$\frac{dy}{dx} = f(y, \psi(y))$$

$$y(0) = c \qquad (9.8.15)$$

Hence, the dynamic programming approach gives us, in principle, a way to obtain a solution, analytic or numerical, to (9.8.1)–(9.8.3).

In considering the optimal control of certain processes, it is often desired to maximize or minimize a function at the end of a time period. Such problems are called terminal control processes. What we seek is the greatest or least value of a function at the end of the time period, irrespective of the path taken to reach the terminal condition.

Consider a function $F(y(t))$ whose final value $F(y(T))$ we wish to maximize. Consider then the problem

$$\max_{z(t)} \quad J(z) = F(y(T)) \qquad (9.8.16)$$

subject to

$$\frac{dy}{dt} = f(y, z) \qquad (9.8.17)$$

$$\int_0^T H(y, z)\, dt = b \qquad (9.8.18)$$

$$y(0) = c \qquad (9.8.19)$$

Equation (9.8.18) is an additional constraint on the function $F(y(t))$. We seek a function $z(t)$ which maximizes (9.8.16) subject to (9.8.17)–(9.8.19).

We introduce a Lagrange multiplier μ to bring (9.8.18) into the objective function. Hence we now seek to solve

$$\max_{z(t)} \quad \hat{J}(z) = F(y(T)) + \mu \int_0^T H(y, z)\, dt \qquad (9.8.20)$$

subject to

$$\frac{dy}{dt} = f(y, z) \qquad (9.8.21)$$

$$y(0) = c \qquad (9.8.22)$$

We shall now subdivide the interval $[0, T]$ into n equal intervals ξ such that $n\xi = T$. We shall number the stages (time intervals) backward so that $s = n$ is the initial time and $s = 0$ is the final time. We can approximate (9.8.17) and (9.8.18) over the n time intervals by

$$y_{s+1} - y_s = f(y_s, z_s)\xi \qquad (s = 0, 1, \ldots, n) \qquad (9.8.23)$$

$$\sum_{s=1}^n H(y_s, z_s)\xi = b \qquad (9.8.24)$$

The initial condition is

$$y_n = c \qquad (9.8.25)$$

We now define an optimal return function as:

$g_s(y_s)$ = maximum value of $\hat{J}_s(z_s)$ over the S remaining stages of the process, when in state y_s, subject to (9.8.23)–(9.8.25) and using an optimal policy.

Therefore we have

$$g_s(y_s) = \max_{z_s} \hat{J}_s(z_s) = \max \left[F(y_0) + \mu \sum_{s=1}^{n} H(y_s, z_s)\xi \right] \tag{9.8.26}$$

where y_0 is the final value of y corresponding to $y(T)$.

Applying the principle of optimality and (9.8.26) we can drive the following recursion relationships:

$$g_1(y_1) = \max_{z_1} \left[\mu H(y_1, z_1)\xi + F(y_1 + f(y_1, z_1)\xi) \right] \tag{9.8.27}$$

$$g_s(y_s) = \max_{z_s} \left[\mu H(y_s, z_s)\xi + g_{s-1}(y_s + f(y_s, z_s)\xi) \right] \quad (s = 2, 3, \ldots, n) \tag{9.8.28}$$

where

$$y_0 = y_1 + f(y_1, z_1)\xi \tag{9.8.29}$$

Therefore, (9.8.27) can also be written

$$g_1(y_1) = \max_{z_1} \left[\mu H(y_1, z_1)\xi + g_0(y_1 + f(y_1, z_1)\xi) \right] \tag{9.8.30}$$

where

$$g_0(y_1 + f(y_1, z_1)) = [F(y_1 + f(y_1, z_1)\xi)] = F(y_0) \tag{9.8.31}$$

The calculation would proceed in the usual way. Equation (9.8.27) would be used to calculate a table of $g_1(y_1)$ vs. y_1, as well as the z, that led to the solution. The remaining tables would be calculated from (9.8.28). At the last stage, we calculate $g_n(c)$ and then thread our way through the tables to find the optimal z values in each table. The set of values $\{z_s\}$ is the approximate optimal policy $z(t)$, for the assumed value μ of the Lagrange multiplier. The entire calculation would then be repeated for other values of μ until (9.8.18) is satisfied.

Exercises—Chapter 9

9.1. Solve the problem

$$\min \quad J(y) = \int_0^T [y^2 + 2xy^2 + (y')^2] \, dx$$

using the Euler–Lagrange equation.

9.2. Solve the problem

$$\min \quad J(y) = \int_0^\Theta (y')^2 \, dx$$

subject to

$$\int_0^\Theta y^2 \, dx = 1$$

$$y(0) = y(\Theta) = 0$$

9.3. Show that if $y(x)$ is the function which optimizes

$$J(y) = \int_0^\Theta (p^2 y'^2 + q^2 y^2) \, dx$$

where $p(x)$ and $q(x)$ are known functions, then

$$J(y) = p^2 y' y \big|_{x=\Theta} - p^2 y' y \big|_{x=0}$$

9.4. Solve the problem

$$\min \quad J(y) = \int_1^2 x^2 y' 2 \, dx$$

subject to

$$y(0) = y(1) = 1$$

using dynamic programming.

9.5. Solve the problem

$$\min \quad J(y) = \int_0^\Theta (y^2 + a^2) \, dx$$

subject to

$$\frac{dy}{dx} = a - 4y$$

$$y(0) = 1$$

using dynamic programming.

9.6. Solve the problem

$$\min \quad J(y) = \int_0^\Theta (y^2 + a^2) \, dx$$

subject to

$$\frac{dy}{dx} = a - y$$

$$y(0) = 1, \quad y(\Theta) = 0$$

using dynamic programming.

9.7. Solve the problem

$$\min \quad J(y) = \int_0^\Pi (y'^2 + 2y \sin x) \, dx$$

$$y(0) = 0, \quad y(\Pi) = 0$$

by the variational approach and also by dynamic programming.

Chapter 10

Applications of Dynamic Programming

10.1. Introduction

The principal purpose of this chapter is to present a number of actual applications of dynamic programming to practical problems, as well as some new potential applications. The applications reported on are for the purpose of emphasizing the variety of different kinds of problems and different areas of endeavor, to which dynamic programming methodology has been applied and can be applied.

The different applications are of varying degrees of detail and complexity. Enough detail will be presented, as well as references, to enable the reader to understand the ways in which models are formulated and dynamic programming principles are applied.

The notational conventions used in dynamic programming are far from uniform and differ widely in different books and papers. In the application studies described in the succeeding sections of this chapter, we shall use the same notation as the original reference, so that those readers who wish to consult the original source may do so without the burden of notational inconsistency. Readers are urged to consult these references for greater detail than is possible here.

10.2. Municipal Bond Coupon Schedules [25]

An underwriting syndicate for a municipal bond issue attempts to select a schedule of bond coupons, one for each maturity in the series, so as to minimize the net interest cost to the issuer, subject to a constraint on expected profit from successful sale of the bond issue and to a marketability constraint on each of the coupons, which is based on the expected reoffering yield for each maturity.

There are also a variety of other constraints which may be imposed. Generally, they relate to conditions which the municipality which issues the bonds imposes on a qualifying bid by the underwriters. For example, one requirement might be that the combined debt-service and retirement cash flow be constant. See [25] for others.

In order to develop the model for this problem, we first define some notation.

NIC = net interest cost.

t = the number of years from the date of issue until a particular set of bonds (those with a t year maturity) will be repaid. t assumes values F, $F+1$, ..., L and is an integer.

$F =$ the earliest maturity (in number of years from the delivery date) of any bonds in the issue.

$L =$ the latest maturity (in number of years from the delivery date) of any bonds in the issue.

$A_t =$ the total face amount (in dollars) of all bonds in the issue having a t year maturity.

$A =$ the total face amount (in dollars) of the issue.

$c_t =$ the nominal annual coupon rate (in dollars/dollar/year) on all bonds in the issue having a t year maturity. c_t is the decision variable.

$P_t =$ the price per dollar of face amount at which the underwriters expect to resell all bonds in the issue having a t year maturity.

$\Pi =$ the total number of dollars desired by the underwriters to cover their expenses and profits.

$B =$ the number of bond-years in the issue

$$\left(B = \sum_{t=F}^{L} tA_t \right)$$

$\underline{c}_t =$ minimum permissible nominal annual coupon rate consistent with bonds in the issue having a t year maturity being marketable at the lowest possible yield.

$\bar{c}_t =$ maximum permissible nominal annual coupon rate consistent with bonds in the issue having a t year maturity being marketable at the lowest possible yield.

$r_t =$ the yield at which the underwriters expect to resell all bonds in the issue having a t year maturity.

The net interest cost (NIC) is the criterion which is used to decide the winning bid. It is the sum of the required outlay for interest by the issuing municipality less any surplus payment over the par value of the issue as proposed by the bidder, all stated on a per bond year basis. Accordingly, we have

$$\text{NIC} = \frac{1}{B} \left\{ \sum_{t=F}^{L} tA_t c_t - \left[\sum_{t=F}^{L} P_t A_t - (A + \Pi) \right] \right\} \tag{10.2.1}$$

The price of a bond is given as the sum of the present value of an annuity of the coupon payments plus the present value of the par value to be received at the bond's maturity. Therefore, we have

$$P_t = \sum_{i=1}^{2t} \frac{\frac{1}{2}c_t}{\left(1 + \frac{r_i}{2}\right)^i} + \frac{1}{\left(1 + \frac{r_t}{2}\right)^{2t}} \tag{10.2.2}$$

In (10.2.2) semi-annual compounding is used. We now define

$$\alpha_t = \frac{1}{\left(1 + \frac{r_t}{2}\right)^{2t}} \tag{10.2.3}$$

$$\beta_t = \frac{1 - \alpha_t}{r_t} \tag{10.2.4}$$

We express the price of a bond maturing after t years as a linear function of c_t, the decision variable. Therefore

$$P_t = \alpha_t + \beta_t c_t \tag{10.2.5}$$

Substituting (10.2.5) into (10.2.1) we obtain as the objective function for the problem

$$\min \quad \text{NIC} = \frac{1}{B} \left\{ \sum_{t=F}^{L} (t - \beta_t) A_t c_t - \left[\sum_{t=F}^{L} \alpha_t A_t - A - \Pi \right] \right\} \tag{10.2.6}$$

The second term (in square brackets) in (10.2.6) does not involve c_t and is a constant which, therefore, can be ignored for purposes of optimization of NIC. Similarly, we can ignore $1/B$ in the optimization process. Therefore, we can consider as the objective function

$$\min \quad \sum_{t=F}^{L} (t - \beta_t) A_t c_t \tag{10.2.7}$$

Marketability considerations limit the choice of the coupon rates to certain values. Hence we have constraints of the form

$$\underline{c}_t \leq c_t \leq \bar{c}_t \quad t = F, F+1, \ldots, L \tag{10.2.8}$$

In addition, there is the requirement that no bid be "below par", together with the requirement that the bid, if won and sold according to the proposed set of yields, produce the desired profit and overhead. This is expressed as

$$\sum_{t=F}^{L} P_t A_t \geq A + \Pi \tag{10.2.9}$$

which, after combining with (10.2.5) and rewriting, becomes

$$\sum_{t=F}^{L} \beta_t A_t c_t \geq A + \Pi - \sum_{t=F}^{L} \alpha_t A_t \tag{10.2.10}$$

The problem that we wish to solve is, therefore, given by (10.2.7), (10.2.8), and (10.2.10), i.e.,

$$\min \quad \sum_{t=F}^{L} (t - \beta_t) A_t c_t$$

subject to
$$\sum_{t=F}^{L} \beta_t A_t c_t \geq A + \Pi - \sum_{t=F}^{L} \alpha_t A_t \tag{10.2.11}$$

$$\underline{c}_t \leq c_t \leq \bar{c}_t \quad t = F, F+1, \ldots, L$$

We shall now express (10.2.11) in terms of a dynamic programming formulation. We define the stages to be the bonds of the given maturity being considered. At stage i we consider bonds with a maturity of t_i years, with $t_{i-1}, t_{i-2}, \ldots, t_1$ still to be considered and where $i = 1, 2, \ldots, n$ where $n = L - F$.

The state variable, designated p_i, is the amount of "production" (equation (10.2.10) is often called the production constraint) still to be obtained at stage i during the remainder of the process to satisfy the production constraint.

If we designate the right-hand side of (10.2.10) by H, i.e.,

$$H = A + \Pi - \sum_{t=F}^{L} \alpha_t A_t \tag{10.2.12}$$

then H is the total amount of production required. At stage n, with c_{t_n}, the contribution to production is $\beta_{t_n} A_{t_n} c_{t_n}$. Therefore the amount required from stages $n-1$ through 1 will be

$$p = H - \beta_{t_n} A_{t_n} c_{t_n} \tag{10.2.13}$$

Hence there will be a value of p at stage n for every value of c_{t_n}. We designate $p(c_{t_n})$ by p_n. The general relationship, between state variables at successive stages, is, therefore,

$$p_i = p_{i+1} - \beta_{t_i} A_{t_i} c_{t_i} \tag{10.2.14}$$

where $p_i = p(c_{t_n}, c_{t_{n-1}}, \ldots, c_{t_i})$. The contribution to the net interest cost by coupon c_{t_i} is seen to be, from (10.2.7),

$$(t_i - \beta_{t_i}) A_{t_i} c_{t_i}$$

We define

$f_i^*(p) =$ net interest cost contribution from optimally selecting coupons $c_{t_i}, c_{t_{i+1}}, \ldots, c_{t_n}$ with contribution to production of p_i still to be obtained when maturities $t_{i-1}, t_{i-2}, \ldots, t_1$, remain to be considered.

Then, applying the principle of optimality, we obtain the recursion relations

$$f_i^*(p_i) = \min_{\underline{c}_{t_i} \leq c_{t_i} \leq \bar{c}_{t_i}} [(t_i - \beta_{t_i}) A_{t_i} c_{t_i} + f_{i+1}^*(p_{i+1} + \beta_{t_i} A_{t_i} c_{t_i})]$$

$$f_{n+1}^*(H) = 0 \tag{10.2.15}$$

$$p_1 \leq 0$$

Additional complications such as requiring that the number of distinct coupons used in a bid be not greater than some stipulated number can also be included. This results in the necessity of introducing another state variable. However, it is no more difficult to derive the recursion relations, even though the computational chore is now greater.

Details of these extensions, as well as a discussion of the computational strategies and experience, are given in [25].

10.3. Expansion of Electric Power Systems [26]

An electric power system consists of a certain number of hydro, thermal, and nuclear generation plants connected by an extensive network to all the customers of the system. The total electric demand (or load) on the system is a stochastic process which increases with time over the planning horizon. The problem is to determine the optimal additions of capacity of varying kinds so that the total discounted expected costs are minimized.

Since the cost characteristics and ability of the different kinds of plants to service peak loads or long term loads varies considerably, the determination of the optimal mix of plants for expansion is not a simple problem.

In order to formulate a mathematical description of the problem we wish to solve, we define the following. The state of the system at any time t will be given by the vector $S_t = (H_t, T_t, N_t, P_t)$ where:

H_t = a measure of the system's hydro-electric capability at time t (since the number of new hydro-electric projects is limited, H_t will take on values of allowable reasonable combinations of new projects).

T_t = number of megawatts of thermal capacity that have been added to the initial system by time t.

N_t = number of megawatts of nuclear capacity that have been added to the initial system by time t.

P_t = number of megawatts of peaking turbine capacity that have been added to the initial system by time t.

The task of the planner is to choose the level of each of the variables given above for all periods t such that the discounted expected capital, operating, maintenance and penalty costs incurred during the planning horizon are minimized.

We further define:

D = number of periods considered $(1 \leqslant t \leqslant D)$.

$f_t(S_t)$ = present worth at time t of expected future cost if the system is in state S_t and an optimal expansion plan is followed to the end of period D.

If we now apply the principle of optimality and the definition of $f_t(S_t)$, we obtain the recursion relations

$$f_t(S_t) = \min_{\Delta s \geqslant 0} [C_t(\Delta S) + \alpha f_{t+1}(S_{t+1})] + \alpha a_t(S_t) \tag{10.3.1}$$

$$t = D, D-1, \ldots, 1$$

where
$$S_{t+1} = S_t + \Delta S$$

$$f_{D+1}(S_{D+1}) \equiv 0$$

and

ΔS = change of state or capacity additions during period t.

$C_t(\Delta S)$ = present worth of the capital carrying costs and the fixed operating costs associated with the expansion ΔS, summed to the end of period D and discounted to the start of period t.

α = discount factor.

$a_t(S_t)$ = expected variable operating cost incurred if the system is operated optimally during period t.

Further details on the evaluation of costs $a_t(S_t)$ and $C_t(\Delta S)$ may be found in [26].

The difficulty with the formulation given by (10.3.1) is that, while it is completely general, it involves four state variables and four decision variables. For practical problems, this involves n^8 computations per period where n is the average number of values each decision and state variable can assume. It turns out, however, that because of the nature of the state variables a great reduction in the amount of computation can be made.

We may observe that the fixed cost function $C_t(\Delta S)$ is additively separable with respect to the state changes ΔH, ΔT, ΔN, ΔP. This means, in effect, that the capital and fixed operating and maintenance costs for each type of plant are independent. Therefore, we have

$$C_t(\Delta S) = C_{H,t}(\Delta H) + C_{T,t}(\Delta T) + C_{N,t}(\Delta N) + C_{P,t}(\Delta P) \qquad (10.3.2)$$

Using (10.3.2) with (10.3.1) we can write

$$f(S) = \min_{\Delta H \geqslant 0} \left[C_{H,t}(\Delta H) + \min_{\Delta T \geqslant 0 \,|\, \Delta H} \left[C_{T,t}(\Delta T) + \min_{\Delta N \geqslant 0 \,|\, \Delta H, \Delta T} \left[C_{N,t}(\Delta N) \right. \right. \right.$$

$$\left. \left. \left. + \min_{\Delta P \geqslant 0 \,|\, \Delta H, \Delta T, \Delta N} \left[C_{P,t}(\Delta P) + \alpha f_{t+1}(S_{t+1}) \right] \right] \right] \right] + \alpha a_t(S_t) \qquad (10.3.3)$$

where the successive minimizations are with respect to holding previous state variables fixed. Equation (10.3.3) can be written in terms of a sequence of functional recursion equations which reveals the computational process more clearly. This sequence is:

$$g_t^{(1)}(H_{t+1}, T_{t+1}, N_{t+1}, P_t) = \min_{\Delta P \geqslant 0} C[P,t(\Delta P) + \alpha f_{t+1}(S_{t+1})] \qquad (10.3.4)$$

$$g_t^{(2)}(H_{t+1}, T_{t+1}, N_t, P_t) = \min_{\Delta N \geqslant 0} [C_{N,t}(\Delta N) + g_t^{(1)}(H_{t+1}, T_{t+1}, N_{t+1}, P_t)] \qquad (10.3.5)$$

$$g_t^{(3)}(H_{t+1}, T_t, N_t, P_t) = \min_{\Delta T \geqslant 0} [C_{T,t}(\Delta T) + g_t^{(2)}(H_{t+1}, T_{t+1}, N_t, P_t)] \qquad (10.3.6)$$

$$f(S_t) = \min_{\Delta H \geqslant 0} [C_{H,t}(\Delta H) + g_t^{(3)}(H_{t+1}, T_t, N_t, P_t)] + \alpha a_t(S_t) \qquad (10.3.7)$$

for all $t = D, D-1, \ldots, 1$.

The advantage of the form given by (10.3.4)–(10.3.7) is that in each functional equation, the minimization is with respect to a single variable. This reduces the computational chore greatly.

The above model was used by the National Energy Board of Canada to study the expansion of the Maritime Power Pool System in Canada and to compare the results with an existing 17-year expansion plan. In addition, a hypothetical power system, for which cost data and expansion data are given, is examined in [26] and the results of the calculation are given.

10.4. The Design of a Hospital Ward [27]

The design of actual hospital wards is usually accomplished by trial and error procedures which are inefficient and generally non-optimal. In order to include all possible relevant costs and find a very close approximation to an optimal solution, the following dynamic programming approach has been developed.

The only restrictions on the geometric design of the ward are as follows:

1. Total ward space must be allocated between patients' rooms, service rooms and a linear corridor separating room types (Fig. 10.4.1).

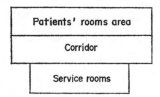

FIG. 10.4.1. Ward scheme.

2. Patients' rooms consist of standard rectangular bed modules (Fig. 10.4.2).

FIG. 10.4.2. Bed module.

3. The service room has a fixed area and must be rectangular in shape.

These assumptions are actually less restrictive than those specified in designs generated by conventional design methods.

The problem then consists in finding, for some overall shape of ward, e.g.,

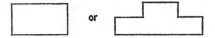

the geometrical layout of the ward so that the associated cost function is minimized. This entails finding:

(1)   the optimal number of rows of standard modules.
(2)   the optimal number of standard modules in each row.
(3)   the optimal position of the rows relative to each other.
(4)   the dimensions of the service room area.

We shall employ the following notation:

z = value of the cost objective function.
k = maximum number of rows permitted.
m_i = number of standard modules in the ith row ($i = 1$ is the first row near the corridor) $i = 1, 2, \ldots, k$.
M = total number of beds in the ward. (M is even since each module has two beds.)
L = total length of service room area, in units of standard-module length.
W = width of service room area.
A = total area of service rooms.

a = half the width of standard module.

b = length of standard module.

C_p, $p = 1, 2, \ldots, 13$ = cost coefficients.

$\tilde{C}_i$, $i = 1, 2, \ldots, k$ = cost coefficients associated with ith row.

In [27] a detailed derivation of the cost functions, under a variety of assumptions, is given. In general, the optimization problem takes the form

$$\min \quad z = C_1 + C_2 L + \frac{C_3}{L} + C_4 m_1 + C_5 \frac{(-1)^{m_1}}{m_1} + \sum_{i=1}^{k} \tilde{C}_i m_i + C_6 \sum_{i=1}^{k} m_i^2$$

$$+ C_7 \sum_{i=1}^{k} m_i^3 + C_8 \sum_{i=1}^{k} \sum_{j=1}^{i} m_i^2 m_j + C_9 \sum_{i=1}^{k} m_i i + C_{10} \sum_{i=1}^{k} m_i i^2$$

$$+ C_{11} \sum_{i=1}^{k} m_i^3 i + C_{12} \sum_{i=1}^{k} (-1)^{m_i} + K C_{13} \tag{10.4.1}$$

subject to
$$\sum_{i=1}^{k} m_i = \frac{M}{2} \tag{10.4.2}$$

$$m_i \geqslant m_{i+1} \quad (i = 1, 2, \ldots, k-1) \tag{10.4.3}$$

$$A = 2aLW \tag{10.4.4}$$

Frequently, other constraints, e.g., limits on L, are added. These do not, in any way, affect the general method for finding a solution, although the details change slightly. (See [27].)

The objective function z can be separated into two parts: a function which includes all the terms which are not dependent on at least one of the m_i, $i = 1, 2, \ldots, k$, which we call F_1, and a function which includes all the other terms, which we call F_2. Therefore, we can optimize with respect to F_1 and F_2 separately.

F_1 depends upon the variable L and some other constant coefficients. Let us define

$$g_{F_1} = \min_{L>0} F_1(L) = \min_{L>0} \left[C_1 + C_2 L + \frac{C_3}{L} \right] \tag{10.4.5}$$

We also define

$$z_i(m_1 + m_2 + \ldots + m_{i-1}, m_i) = m_i(C_i + C_9 i + C_{10} i^2)$$
$$+ m_i^2(C_6 + C_8(m_1 + m_2 + \ldots + m_{i-1})) + m_i^3(C_7 + C_{11} i)$$
$$+ (-1)^{m_i} C_{12} + C_{13} \quad (i = 1, 2, \ldots, k) \tag{10.4.6}$$

and

$$z_1(m_1) = m_1(C_4 + \tilde{C}_1 + C_9 + C_{10}) + m_1^2 C_6 + m_1^3(C_7 + C_8 + C_{11})$$
$$+ (-1)^{m_1} C_{12} + C_{13} + \frac{(-1)^{m_1} C_5}{m_1} \tag{10.4.7}$$

Using (10.4.1) and (10.4.5)–(10.4.7) we have

$$z = z_1(m_1) + F_1(L) + \sum_{i=2}^{k} z_i(m_1 + m_2 + \ldots + m_{i-1}, m_i) \tag{10.4.8}$$

Applying the principle of optimality to (10.4.8) and (10.4.2)–(10.4.4) we can obtain the recurrence relations

$$g_i(y) = \min_{m_i} [z_i(y-m_i, m_i) + g_{i-1}(y-m_i)] \qquad (10.4.9)$$

where
$$m_i = 0, 1, \ldots, \left[\frac{y}{i}\right]$$

$$y = i, i+1, \ldots, \frac{M}{2}$$

and

$$g_1(y) = \min_{m_1} [z_1(m_1) + F_1(L)] = g_{F_1} + \min_{m_1} z_1(m_1) \qquad (10.4.10)$$

In the use of (10.4.9) and (10.4.10) it can be seen that

$$y = m_1 + m_2 + \ldots + m_i$$

i.e., y equals the total amount of the resource (standard modules) used up to and including the ith stage. The control or decision variables are L and m_i, $i = 1, 2, \ldots, k$, as well as the relative positioning of two successive rows. In [28] it is shown that the problem of determining the optimal positioning of successive rows of modules can be solved independently of the number of modules in each row without impairing the ability to find a global optimum to the original problem. The method for handling the relative positioning of rows is as follows.

Let i and j be row numbers and let $i < j$. Then $\tilde{D}_{ij} = m_i - m_j = 0$, odd or even number. Define D_{ij} to be the left-hand displacement, in units of standard modules, between rows i and j. (See Fig. 10.4.3.)

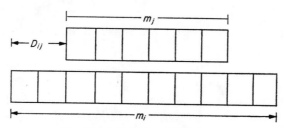

FIG. 10.4.3. Relative positioning.

Then it has been shown in [28] that if we define:

CASE 1: $\tilde{D}_{ij} = 0$

There is no relative positioning.

CASE 2: $\tilde{D}_{ij}$ is an odd number.

Then D_{ij} given by

$$D_{ij} = \frac{m_i - m_j + 1}{2}$$

will provide the optimal solution.

CASE 3: $\tilde{D}_{ij}$ is an even number.

Then D_{ij} given by

$$D_{ij} = \frac{m_i - m_j}{2}$$

will provide the optimal solution.

If we use the D_{ij} given in the preceding, with the optimal values of L and m_i, $i = 1, 2, \ldots, k$, we obtain the optimal solution to the original problem.

In [27] the derivation of the form of the cost factors in the objective function is given as well as equations for other special cases. A numerical example is also provided.

10.5. Optimal Scheduling of Excess Cash Investment [29]

We shall be concerned in this analysis with the *scheduling* of a company's investments of its predictable, short-term, excess cash. The investment of operating cash will be considered as a scheduling problem. This is different from stock investment or capital budgeting where the return from investment is uncertain. We assume, and this is the case, that operating cash reserves must be scheduled optimally, but that the timing and amounts of receipts are predictable in a stable business. How this excess operating capital is invested can affect overall returns markedly.

We shall limit our concern to the daily scheduling of excess cash resulting from predictable cash flows and we assume that all planned cash flows are feasible (no negative cash balance). A number of other assumptions will be made for purposes of analysis and need to be stated:

1. We have a perfect forecast of total receipts and total disbursements for each day of the planning period.
2. We know what set of investment opportunities will be available for each day of the planning period. For example, treasury bills have a predictable maturity structure as do other securities.
3. Yield rates of all the securities considered within the planning period are considered to be perfectly predictable.
4. All securities considered are available in integral numbers of units, all having the same lowest denomination, d_0. For simplicity, all securities are treated as if they were of the interest bearing type, so that the cost of any investment is d_0.
5. If one specific security is available, e.g., a treasury bill starting on day 17 with 23 days to maturity, then any number of similar investments are available.
6. All securities are assumed to be bought or sold at the end of a given day.

We now define the following notation:

N = the number of days in the planning period.
a_i = the forecast of receipts for day i, $i = 1, 2, \ldots, N$.
b_i = the forecast of disbursements for day i, $i = 1, 2, \ldots, N$.

c_0 = the book bank balance prior to starting day 1 of the planning period.

f_i = the forecast of the bank balance on day i if no investments were made. Therefore

$$f_i = c_0 + \sum_{k=1}^{i} (a_k - b_k) \qquad (i = 1, 2, \dots, N)$$

and $$f_i \geqslant 0 \qquad (i = 1, 2, \dots, N).$$

In Fig. 10.5.1 a typical graph of the function f_i is shown over a planning period. The area below the "curve" represents the availability of cash forecasted, f_i, on each day. The return on the investments is *not* shown in Fig. 10.5.1. It is not included in a_i. An investment starting at day i, of length L days, and of amount d_0 can be represented as a box of length L and height d_0, lying anywhere below the function f_i. Such a box is shown in Fig. 10.5.1.

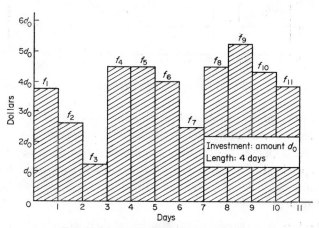

FIG. 10.5.1. Availability of cash resources.

The problem we wish to solve, in terms of the graphical depiction of Fig. 10.5.1, is to pack the resource space (the area under the curve) with the available investments in the best possible way. In other words, we seek to find the best placement of boxes of all allowed configurations. Investments are possible only in discrete lengths (days) and discrete heights (units of d_0). At first glance, the problem appears complicated because the resource height differs from day to day and the investments which are available on different days also vary from day to day.

In order to make the problem more tractable, two simplifying assumptions are introduced. We assume, first, that there is a lowest denomination d_0 common to all investments and second, that there is unlimited availability of investments. With these assumptions we can partition the problem into a number of resource layers of height d_0 which do not interact. Hence each layer becomes an independent one-dimensional problem.

It is possible to further divide up each layer into separate problems since we are interested only in those parts of the layers which lie below the resource boundary. The separate parts of the layers are treated as independent problems. They are called "longest rectangles". They represent the useful periods during which idle cash is generated by the business' activities. This partitioning also reveals certain areas which are too small to be utilized for investment.

In Fig. 10.5.2, we have shown the 11 day period of Fig. 10.5.1 partitioned into eight longest rectangles and several waste areas which are shaded.

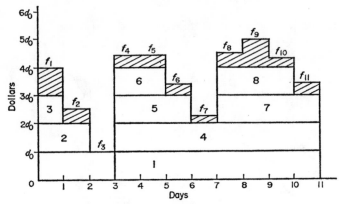

FIG. 10.5.2. Longest rectangles and waste areas.

Since we have reduced the problem of packing the resource area to that of packing the longest rectangles, we will now consider a dynamic programming formulation of the latter problem. We suppose that we have a resource (investment opportunity) which is available for a specific, limited period of time, starting at time point K and of length L days. The investment availability changes with time in a known way and is described by a matrix of returns available. The matrix of returns available is defined as:

$a_i(l) =$ total return from the *best* available investment which starts at point i and has length l days. If none is available, there is a zero entry.

Hence we need values of $a_i(l)$ for

$$K \leqslant i \leqslant K+L-1$$
$$1 \leqslant l \leqslant L+K-i$$

in order to pack the rectangle which begins at point K and has length L days.

The stages of the dynamic programming formulation are each day. Hence we have stages $L, L-1, \ldots, 1$. Our state variable is

$x_n =$ the current scheduled investment backlog (in days) from the start of stage n.

The decision process is to select the net investment to add on to the current schedule. It will start at a point $K+L-n+x_n$ and last d_n days where d_n is the decision variable. The stage return is $a_{K+L-n+x_n}(d_n)$. Therefore

$$x_{n-1} = x_n + d_{n-1}$$

We define:

$f_n(x_n) =$ optimal return from the investment period starting at point $K+L-n$ and of length n days, when starting in state x_n.

Then the dynamic programming formulation, using the principle of optimality, is

$$f_n(x_n) = \max_{1 \le d_n \le n - x_n} [a_{K+L-n+x_n}(d_n) + f_{n-1}(x_n + d_n - 1)] \quad (n = 1, 2, \ldots, L) \quad (10.5.1)$$

and
$$x_n = 0, 1, \ldots, n-1$$
$$f_n(n) = 0 \quad \text{all } n \quad (10.5.2)$$

We can show that this formulation has redundant subproblems and that the state variable x_n is unnecessary. Hence (10.5.1) can be simplified. We proceed as follows. Rewrite (10.5.1) for $n+1$ and $x_{n+1} = x_n + 1$. We have

$$f_{n+1}(x_n + 1) = \max_{1 \le d_{n+1} \le n - x_n} [a_{K+L-n+x_n}(d_{n+1}) + f_n(d_{n+1} + x_n)] \quad (10.5.3)$$

If we compare (10.5.1) and (10.5.3) we can see that if $f_n(m) = f_{n-1}(m-1)$ for all values of m, then both maximizations are equivalent problems and

$$d_{n+1}(m+1) = d_n(m)$$
$$f_{n+1}(m+1) = f_n(m), \quad \text{all } m \quad (10.5.4)$$

The relations (10.5.4) hold for $n = 1, 2, \ldots, L$ and also for $n = 0$ since by (10.5.2) $f_n(n) = 0$, all n. Therefore we can define the following:

$$V_n = f_n(0) = f_{n+1}(1) = \ldots = f_K(K-n)$$
$$d_n = n - d_n(0) = n - d_n(1) = \ldots = n - d_n(K-n) - K + n, \quad \text{all } n \quad (10.5.5)$$

Substituting (10.5.5) into (10.5.1) we obtain

$$V_1 = a_{K+L-1}(1)$$
$$V_n = \max_{1 \le d_n \le n} [a_{K+L-n}(d_n) + V_{n-d_n}] \quad (n = 2, 3, \ldots, L) \quad (10.5.6)$$

Equations (10.5.6) are a simple set of recursion relations which consider all possible ways of partitioning rectangles into subrectangles and allocating them to investments. At the conclusion of the calculation with (10.5.6), the values of $d_1, d_2, \ldots, d_L$ give the optimal investment decision for the rectangle and also for all other rectangles which have equal or smaller length and end at the same point. The entire algorithm is then repeated for each other rectangle.

In [29] consideration is also given to using discounting as a way of dealing with some uncertainty in the predicted transactions of the company. Additional constraints are also considered such as one on the bank balance to be maintained in a given bank.

10.6. Animal Feedlot Optimization [30]

Feedlots are places to which beef cattle are shipped and kept for a period of time for feeding under controlled conditions to get them to a final weight before they are slaughtered. The general problem faced by feedlot managers is to find answers to the following questions:

1. What initial weight should be purchased?
2. At what final weight should the animal be sold?
3. How long should the completion time be?
4. Into how many subperiods should this total time be divided for feeding purposes?
5. How long should each feeding period be?
6. What ration, and how much, should be fed in each period?

The answers to these questions are closely tied to one another and cannot be considered independently.

Consider Fig. 10.6.1. At time zero, animals weighting W_0 pounds are purchased. We have arbitrarily divided T days into five periods, as an example. During a time of t_1 days, animals of weight W_0 are fed ration R_1 in amount X_1 and during a time interval of t_1. This process is continued until the fifth period is completed and a final weight W_F is achieved.

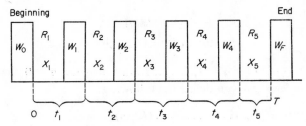

FIG. 10.6.1. Weight, feeding, and time relationships.

The total profit for the feedlot is given by

$$Z = SP(T, W_F)W_F - \sum_{j=1}^{n} c_j - (FC)T - BP(W_0)W_0 \qquad (10.6.1)$$

where
$$T = \text{completion time in days.}$$
$$SP(T, W_F) = \text{selling price per pound at time } T \text{ for animals of weight } W_F.$$
$$c_j = \text{cost of feed in period } j.$$
$$n = \text{number of periods.}$$
$$FC = \text{fixed costs per day.}$$
$$BP(W_0) = \text{purchase price for animals of weight } W_0.$$

The nutritional aspects of feeding cattle and the mathematical relationships involved are fairly complicated and they are discussed in terms of one model in [30]. They will not be discussed in detail here. A few words are in order, however. The amount of feed consumed is assumed to be divided into two portions: the first for maintenance of current weight and the remainder for production (weight gain). The major characteristics of any ration can then be described by:

$$NE_m = \text{net energy for maintenance.}$$
$$NE_p = \text{net energy for production.}$$
$$C(X_i) = \text{cost per unit of ration } i.$$

It is assumed that only least cost rations are considered (determined by a separate calculation) and that a least cost ration is uniquely determined by its NE_m and NE_p values. Therefore if $\tilde{X}_i$ = ration vector for ration i, then

$$\tilde{X}_i = [NE_m, NE_p, C(X_i)]$$

completely describes a ration for mathematical purposes.

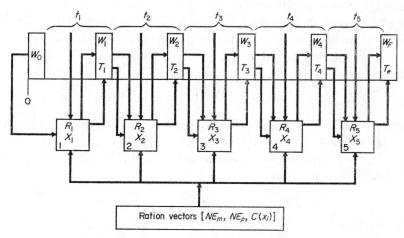

FIG. 10.6.2. Mathematical model of feedlot.

The mathematical model of the feedlot, to be used in deriving the dynamic programming formulation, is shown in Fig. 10.6.2. The dynamic programming state functions are represented by the boxes:

$$\boxed{\begin{array}{c} R_i \\ X_i \\ i \end{array}}$$

The state functions depend upon two state variables, weight, and cumulative time. The state variables for period i are W_i, the animal weight at the end of period i (which is input for period $i+1$), and the cumulative time T_i at the end of period i. The input weight to period i is W_{i-1} and the cumulative time up to period i is T_{i-1}. The decision variables in period i are R_i, the ration fed, and t_i, the length of period i. The amount of ration fed, X_i, is not a decision variable but is required information. T_e is a reasonable upper bound for the completion time.

We define

$\Lambda_i(W_{i-1}, T_{i-1})$ = optimal contribution to the total profit and requires the optimal ratio, quantity and period length in its evaluation.

We also define

$$Z^* = \max_{t_i, \tilde{X}_k, W_0} \left[SP(T^*, W_F) W_F - \sum_{j=1}^{n} c_j - (FC)T^* - PB(W_0)W_0 \right] \quad (10.6.2)$$

where $\tilde{X}_k$ is the ration vector for ration k and the maximization is carried out over all rations $\tilde{X}_k$, $k = 1, 2, \ldots, N$ where N is the total number of rations and all values $t_i = 1, 2, \ldots, n$. It must be true that

$$\sum_{i=1}^{n} t_i = T^* \leqslant T_e \tag{10.6.3}$$

and T^* is the optimal completion time.

Before giving the mathematically precise form of the recurrence relations, it is useful to consider the general computational strategy. Suppose we have calculated functions $\Lambda_k(W_{k-1}, T_{k-1})$ for each period $k = 1, 2, \ldots, n$. Suppose we also calculate another function

$$\Lambda_{n+1}(T) = SP(T, W_F)W_F - (FC)T$$

for values of T which are candidates for T^*. These state functions are used in the maximization of the profit equation. As an example, suppose we consider five rations $\tilde{X}_i$ $i = 1, 2, \ldots, 5$ and three periods. Then we calculate $\Lambda_4(T)$ for all the values of T we wish to consider. Then we have

$$\Lambda_3(W_2, T_2) = \max_{t_3, \tilde{X}_i} [\Lambda_4(T_2 + t_3) - c(\tilde{x}_i)X] \tag{10.6.4}$$

where X is the amount of optimal ration fed, and the maximization is over all five rations and possible values of t_3. A ration and time is only considered in the maximization if from W_2 the final weight is attainable, consistent with energy and consumption relationships, which must be considered in the calculation. Then we calculate

$$\Lambda_2(W_1, T_1) = \max_{t_2, \tilde{X}_i} [\Lambda_3(W', T_1 + t_2) - c(\tilde{X}_i)X] \tag{10.6.5}$$

where X and W' are determined from the consumption and energy equations, given an input of W_1 and time T_1. Finally,

$$\Lambda_1(W_0, T_1) = \max_{\tilde{X}_i} [\Lambda_2(W', t_1 = T_1) - c(\tilde{X}_i)X] \tag{10.6.6}$$

$\Lambda_1(W_0, T_1)$ is the maximum profit for animals beginning with weight W_0 and whose first feeding period has length $t_1 = T_1$ days. From this and the other functions, we can determine the optimal rations, ration quantities, and period lengths. By summing the individual period length, we obtain the total completion time. Therefore

$$Z^*(n, W_0, W_F, T_1) = \Lambda_1(W_0, T_1) - PB(W_0)W_0 \tag{10.6.7}$$

Equation (10.6.7) says that Z^* depends on the number of periods, the initial and final weights, as well as the length of the first feeding period. The optimal first period length uniquely defines the successive period length, and therefore, the optimal completion time. Hence we can write the maximum profit for all time as

$$Z^*(n, W_0, W_F) = \max_{T_1} [\Lambda_1(W_0, T_1) - BP(W_0)W_0] \tag{10.6.8}$$

If we find $\Lambda_1(W_0, T_1)$ for a range of initial weights, we can make use of (10.6.8). Then the maximum profit over all time and initial weights is

$$Z^*(n, W_F) = \max_{W_0} \left\{ \max_{T_1} [\Lambda_1(W_0, T_1) - BP(W_0)W_0] \right\} \qquad (10.6.9)$$

If we also vary the parameters n and W_F on successive entire calculations of the type given by (10.6.9) we can find

$$Z^* = \max_{n} \left\{ \max_{W_F} [Z^*(n, W_F)] \right\} \qquad (10.6.10)$$

Before giving the complete dynamic programming formulation we shall require some additional notation and definitions of some auxiliary state functions used in the calculation.

$R_k(W_{k-1}, T_1)$ = optimal ration in period k for given values of W_{k-1} and T_{k-1}.

$X_k(W_{k-1}, T_{k-1})$ = optimal quantity of $R_k(W_{k-1}, T_{k-1})$ (that value of X for which $\Lambda_k(W_{k-1}, T_{k-1})$ attains its value).

$T_k(W_{k-1}, T_{k-1})$ = optimal length of period k (that value of t_k for which $\Lambda_k(W_{k-1}, T_{k-1})$ attains its value).

$Q_k(W_{k-1}, T_{k-1})$ = ending weight of period k when $X_k(W_{k-1}, T_{k-1})$ of $R_k(W_{k-1}, T_{k-1})$ is fed for $T_k(W_{k-1}, T_{k-1})$ (that value of W_k at which to enter Λ_{k+1}).

T_b = minimum total time to completion.

T_0 = minimum length of any time period (step size).

t^* = recursion time within t_k (in steps of T_0) for updating consumption–energy.

W_{0_b} = minimum initial weight considered.

W_{0_e} = maximum initial weight considered.

ε = user-defined tolerance within which the specified final weight and computed final weight must agree.

W_I = initial weight increment.

w^* = weight increment for spacing values of W_0.

K_0, K_1, K_2, K_3, K_4 = constants in energy–consumption relationships.

We may now apply the principle of optimality to the definitions of state functions to arrive at the following mathematical description of the recurrence relations and auxiliary calculations (also included are consumption–energy relationships):

$$\Lambda_{n+1}(T) = SP(T, W_F)W_F - (FC)T, \quad T = T_b + jT_0, \quad j = 1, 2, \ldots, \frac{T_e}{T_0}$$

$$\Lambda_n(W_{n-1}, T_{n-1}) = \max_{t_n, \tilde{X}_i} [\Lambda_{n+1}(T_{n-1} + t_n) - c(\tilde{X}_i)X], \quad i = 1, 2, \ldots, N \quad \text{on} \quad \tilde{X}_i$$

$$t_n = T_b - T_{n-1} + jT_0, \quad j = 0, 1, \ldots, \frac{T_e - T_b}{T_0} \quad \text{for} \quad T_{n-1} \geqslant T_b$$

$$t_n = jT_0, \quad j = 1, 2, \ldots, \frac{T_e - T_{n-1}}{T_0} \quad \text{for} \quad T_{n-1} \geqslant T_b$$

and where

$$X = \sum_{p=1}^{t_n/t^*} X^{(p)}, \quad \text{if} \quad |W'-W_F| < \varepsilon \quad \text{for } W' \text{ determined from}$$

$$X^{(p)} = \frac{K_0 W^{(p)} NE_{m_i}}{NE_{p_i}}$$

$$W^{(p+1)} = W^{(p)} + \frac{NE_{p_i}[X^{(p)}-(K_1 W^{(p)}+K_2)t^*/NE_{m_i}]}{K_3 W^{(p)}+K_4}$$

$$W^{(1)} = W_{n-1} \quad p = 1, 2, \ldots, \frac{t_n}{t^*}$$

$$W' = W^{(t_n/t^*+1)}$$

$\varLambda_n(W_{n-1}, T_{n-1})$ is constructed for

$$W_{n-1} = W_F-qw^*, \quad q = 1, 2, \ldots, \frac{W_F-W_{0_b}}{w^*}$$

$$T_{n-1} = (n-1)T_0+lT_0, \quad l = 0, 1, \ldots, \frac{T_e-nT}{T_0}$$

For $k = n-1, n-2, \ldots, 2$ we calculate $\varLambda_k(W_{k-1}, T_{k-1})$ from

$$\varLambda_k(W_{k-1}, T_{k-1}) = \max_{t_k, \tilde{X}_i} [\varLambda_{k-1}(W', T_{k-1}+t_k)-c(\tilde{X}_i)X] \quad i = 1, 2, \ldots, N \quad \text{on} \quad \tilde{X}_i$$

$$t_k = jT_0, \quad j = 1, 2, \ldots, \frac{T_e-(n-k)T_0-T_{k-1}}{T_0}$$

and where

$$X = \sum_{p=1}^{t_k/t^*} X^{(p)}, \quad W' = W^{(t_k/t^*+1)}$$

for W' determined from

$$X^{(p)} = \frac{K_0 W^{(p)} NE_{m_i}}{NE_{p_i}}$$

$$W^{(p+1)} = W^{(p)} + \frac{NE_{p_i}[X^{(p)}-(K_1 W^{(p)}+K_2)t^*/NE_{m_i}]}{K_3 W^{(p)}+K_4}$$

$$W^{(1)} = W_{k-1}, \quad p = 1, 2, \ldots, \frac{t_k}{t^*}$$

$\varLambda_k(W_{k-1}, T_{k-1})$ is calculated for

$$W_{k-1} = W_F-qw^*, \quad q = 1, 2, \ldots, \frac{W_F-W_{0_b}}{w^*}$$

$$T_{k-1} = (k-1)T_0+lT_0, \quad l = 1, 2, \ldots, \frac{T_e-nT_0}{T_0}$$

$$\varLambda_1(W_0, t_1) = \max_{\tilde{X}_i} [\varLambda_2(W', t_1)-c(\tilde{X}_i)X], \quad i = 1, 2, \ldots, N \quad \text{on} \quad \tilde{X}_i$$

and where

$$X = \sum_{p=1}^{t/t^*} X^{(p)}, \qquad W' = W^{(t_1/t^*+1)}$$

and W' is found from the recurrence relations used above for $p = 1, 2, \ldots, t_1/t^*$. $\Lambda_1(W_0, t_1)$ is calculated for

$$W_0 = W_{0_b} + qW_I, \qquad q = 0, 1, \ldots, \frac{W_{0_e} - W_{0_b}}{W_I}$$

$$t_1 = lT_0, \qquad l = 1, 2, \ldots, \frac{T_e - (n-1)T}{T_0}$$

After calculating all the optimal return functions $\Lambda_k(W_{k-1}, T_{k-1})$, $k = 1, 2, \ldots, n$ and $\Lambda_{n+1}(T)$ we are ready to perform the backward pass through our tables in order to calculate the optimal solution. This calculation is done in two phases. First $Z^*(n, W_F)$ is obtained, along with the optimal initial weight, first period length and total completion time. Then the functions Λ_k are traversed in order $k = 2, 3, \ldots, n$ in conjunction with the auxiliary functions $R_k, X_k, T_k,$ and Q_k to find the complete solution for all n periods.

The backward pass may be formally described as follows:

Let

$$W_0 = W_{0_b} + qW_I, \qquad q = 0, 1, \ldots, \frac{W_{0_e} - W_{0_b}}{W_I}$$

For each W_0, let

$$t_1 = lT_0, \qquad l = 1, 2, \ldots, \frac{T_e - (n-1)T_0}{T_0}$$

For each pair (W, T_1), calculate

$$Z = \Lambda_1(W_0, T_1) - BP(W_0)W_0$$

and corresponding completion time T, where T is found from:

$$T = T^{(n)}$$
$$T^{(k)} = J^{(k-1)} + T_k(j^{(k-1)}T^{(k-1)}) \qquad (k = 2, 3, \ldots, n)$$
$$J^{(k)} = Q_k(J^{(k-1)}, T^{(k)})$$
$$T^{(1)} = t_1$$
$$J^{(1)} = Q_1(W_0, T_1)$$

The largest Z, called Z^*, and its corresponding (W_0, T_1) pair are retained. This Z^* is $Z^*(n, W_F)$. The optimal initial weight is W_0^*, optimal first period length T_1^*, and optimal completion time T^*. The complete solution is obtained from the tabulation of R_k, $X_k, T_k,$ and Q_k functions as displayed in Fig. 10.6.3.

The solution method of the original problem is extremely flexible. Additional constraints can be readily handled. Some of these considerations are discussed in [30]. A numerical example is also given in some detail in [30] with all the tabulations of the functions shown clearly.

Period	Length	Ration index	Ration quantity	Next weight	Next time
1	T_1^*	$R_1(W_0^*, T_1^*)$	$X_1(W_0^*, T_1^*)$	$J^{(1)} = Q_1(W_0^*, T_1^*)$	$I^{(1)} = T_1^*$
2	$T_2(J^{(1)}, I^{(1)})$	$R_2(J^{(1)}, I^{(1)})$	$X_2(J^{(1)}, I^{(1)})$	$J^{(2)} = Q_2(J^{(1)}, I^{(1)})$	$I^{(2)} = I^{(1)} + T_2(J^{(1)}, I^{(1)})$
$\cdots$	$\cdots$	$\cdots$	$\cdots$	$\cdots$	$\cdots$
k	$T_k(J^{(k-1)}, I^{(k-1)})$	$R_k(J^{(k-1)}, I^{(k-1)})$	$X_k(J^{(k-1)}, I^{(k-1)})$	$J^{(k)} = Q_k(J^{(k-1)}, I^{(k-1)})$	$I^{(k)} = I^{(k-1)} + T_k(J^{(k-1)}, I^{(k-1)})$
$\cdots$	$\cdots$	$\cdots$	$\cdots$	$\cdots$	$\cdots$
n	$T_n(J^{(n-1)}, I^{(n-1)})$	$R_n(J^{(n-1)}, I^{(n-1)})$	$X_n(J^{(n-1)})$	W_F	T^*

Fig. 10.6.3. Solution tabulation.

10.7. Optimal Investment in Human Capital

The general problem we address is the problem of optimal decision making by an individual who may or may not invest in education during his life. An individual who considers investment in education will want to consider the costs and benefits of such an investment. The alternatives available to him are to begin or continue his education or to enter the labor market at any given time. Costs and benefits include increased earnings as a result of education, alternative earnings without education, cost of education, lost earnings, probability of success at each stage, etc.

To formulate a model of this process we define an index k, $k = 0, 1, \ldots, n$, which will index the stages of education and entry into the labor market.

$k = 0$ entry into labor market

$k = 1$ public school

$k = 2, 3, \ldots, n$ higher education stages

We let S_k, $k = 1, 2, \ldots, n$ be a set of indices such that if an individual completes educational stage k he may continue to educational stage l only if $l \in S_k$. Thus, for example, the stage of graduate education is not in the feasible set of the public school stage. When an individual completes stage k successfully, he may enter the labor market or proceed to any school stage to which he is eligible, i.e., any of the schooling stages in S_k.

The benefit of continuing from stage k to l will be designated V_k, and is defined only for $l \in S_k$. V_k is defined as

V_k = net discounted stream of income (n.d.i.) following completion of stage k and movement to l, assuming *optimal* decisions for all stages *after l*.

V_{k0} is the net discounted income following stage k and entry into the labor market. V_k^* is the n.d.i. to an individual who chooses optimally at all stages, including the kth stage. C_k is the discounted cost of studies in stage k, and consists of out-of-pocket expenses discounted to the end of the studies. A summary of the notation and additional definitions of relevant quantities is as follows:

k = index of stages of education and entry into labor market.
S_k = set of feasible stages after k.
V_{kl} = n.d.i. following stage k assuming optimal decisions after l.
V_{k0} = n.d.i. following stage k and entry into labor market.
V_k^* = n.d.i. assuming optimal decisions at k and for all subsequent stages.
V_{k0}^- = n.d.i. for a drop-out at stage k.
C_k = discounted costs of stage k for someone who completes stage k.
C_k^- = discounted costs of stage k for a drop-out.
p_{kl} = probability of dropping out at stage l.
q_{kl} = probability of not being accepted into stage l.
r = discount rate.
t_k = length of stage k in years.
τ_k = length of stage k in years for a drop-out.

Figure 10.7.1 is a schematic representation of the possibilities at each stage.

V_{kl} is the value of entering stage l from k, assuming l is an intermediate stage, and has three possible income and cost components: that part accruing to an individual who is turned back at entry, that part accruing to a drop-out,[†] and finally the income stream and costs of an individual who completes stage l. The latter part consists of the costs of stage l and the benefits from an optimal choice *following l*. These three cost components

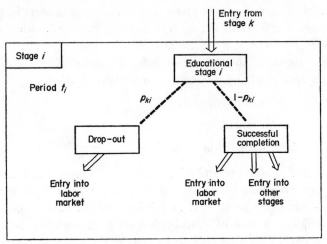

FIG. 10.7.1. Options available at stage i.

appear in the right-hand side of equation (10.7.1) which is the basic equation for expressing the income relationships at any stage. We then have

$$V_{kl} = q_{kl}V_{k0} + (1-q_{kl})p_{kl}\frac{1}{(1+r)^{\tau_i}}(V_{l0}^- - c_l^-)$$

$$+ (1-q_{kl})(1-p_{kl})\frac{1}{(1+r)^{t_i}} \; V_l^* - c_l) \qquad (10.7.1)$$

Equation (10.7.1) holds for

$$k, l \in \{i, j \,|\, S_i \neq \phi, \quad j \in S_i, S_j = \phi\}$$

When stage l is the final educational stage, $V^* = V_{l0}$ and

$$V_{kl} = q_{kl}V_{k0} + (1-q_{kl})p_{kl}\frac{1}{(1+r)^{\tau_i}}(V_{l0}^- - c_l^-)$$

$$+ (1-q_{kl})p_{kl}\frac{1}{(1+r)^{t_i}}(V_{l0} - c_l) \qquad (10.7.2)$$

Equation (10.7.2) holds for

$$k, l \in \{i, j \,|\, S_i \neq \phi, \; i \in S_i, S_j = \phi\}$$

[†] We assume that drop-outs, as well as those turned back at entry, go directly to the labor market instead of re-entering the educational stream at some other point. This assumption could be relaxed.

For all k,

$$V_{k*} = \max_l V_{kl}, \quad l \in S_k \quad \text{or} \quad l = 0 \tag{10.7.3}$$

We can simplify (10.7.1) and (10.7.2) by multiplying through and collecting constants to obtain

$$V_{kl} = a_{kl} + b_{kl} V_l^* \tag{10.7.4}$$

$$V_{kl} = a_{kl} \tag{10.7.5}$$

where

$$a_{kl} = q_{kl} V_{k0} + (1 - q_{kl}) p_{kl} \frac{1}{(1+r)^{\tau_l}} (V_{l0}^- - c_l^-)$$

$$- (1 - q_{kl})(1 - p_{kl}) \frac{1}{(1+r)^{t_l}} c_l + g \tag{10.7.6}$$

$$b_{kl} = \frac{(1 - q_{kl})(1 - p_{kl})}{(1+r)^{t_l}} \tag{10.7.7}$$

$$g = \begin{cases} 0, & S_l \neq \phi \\ (1 - q_{kl})(1 - p_{kl}) \dfrac{V_{l0}}{(1+r)^{t_l}}, & S_l = \phi \end{cases} \tag{10.7.8}$$

In [31] a detailed example of a multistage serial system, using data on the United States, is analyzed. Data on income by age and level of education and an assumed discount rate are used from US Census Bureau reports. Four educational stages—elementary school, high school, university, graduate school—are utilized in the calculation. In addition, several other possible applications of the methodology are suggested.

10.8. Optimal Crop Supply [32]

We discussed in Chapter 8 the structure of sequential decision processes. The governing property of such processes is that the decision maker must make two or more decisions at different points in time, and that the later decisions may be influenced not only by the previous decisions but also by some stochastic parameters whose values will actually have been observed before later decisions are made. We shall now examine an example of such a problem.

Consider a purchaser of agricultural products who first contracts for a certain amount of crop supply and then may make incremental additions or deletions (purchase or sales to others) at various points in time during the growing season. This may also include a final adjustment after the harvest in order to bring actual supply and desired supply in balance.

Purchases or sales made after the first contract usually have penalty costs associated with them and, generally, the penalties increase in magnitude with time. Given this general situation, we also assume that at each stage the decision maker has available to him a revised forecast of current crop supply which also includes the effects of purchases or sales made previously. We also assume that the process by which the data are generated is quasi-Markovian. The problem for the decision maker is to meet his crop supply requirement at minimum penalty cost, given the information available to him.

We define the following:

r = desired crop supply.

X_n = forecast of crop supply made at stage n, $n = 1, 2, \ldots, N$.

a_n = action taken by company at stage n to increase $(+)$ or decrease $(-)$ crop supply, $n = 1, 2, \ldots, N$.

a_N = $r - X_n$.

Z_n = ratio of $(n+1)$st forecast to nth forecast (adjusted by any action taken at the nth stage), $n = 1, 2, \ldots, N-1$.

$C_n(a_n)$ = penalty cost associated with action a_n taken at stage n, $n = 2, 3, \ldots, N$.

From the definition of Z_n, we have

$$Z_n = \frac{X_{n+1}}{X_n + a_n} \tag{10.8.1}$$

The objective is to minimize expected penalty costs (EPC) associated with obtaining the desired crop supply, i.e.,

$$\min_{a_n} EPC = \sum_{n=2}^{N} C_n(a_n) \tag{10.8.2}$$

If we assume that the hypothesis of independent conditional lognormal forecast changes has been substantiated,[†] then ratios of successive forecasts $\{Z_n\}$ are independent random variables, each conditionally lognormally distributed. We now formulate the dynamic programming solution method.

Define:

$f_n(X_n)$ = minimum expected penalty cost associated with observing forecast X_n at stage n, and behaving optimally from that point on.

We also note that

$$X_{n+1} = Z_n(X_n + a_n) \tag{10.8.3}$$

which is obtained from (10.8.1). We now invoke the principle of optimality, together with our definition of $f_n(X_n)$ and other assumptions, to obtain the recurrence relations:

$$f_n(X_n) = \min_{a_n} \left[C\,(a_n) + P_n f_{n+1}(X_n + a_n) \right.$$

$$\left. + (1 - P_n) \int_0^\infty f_{n+1}(Z_n(X_n + a_n))\, \phi_{LN}\,(Z_n \mid \mu_n, \sigma_n^2)\, dZ_n \right] \quad (n = 1, 2, \ldots, N-1) \tag{10.8.4}$$

and

$$f_N(X_n) = C_N(r - X_n)$$

---

† In [32] there is a lengthy examination of the empirical justification of such an assumption.

where P_n = probability that ratio of successive forecasts of $Z_n = 1$

and

$(1-P_n)$ = probability that the ratio is a lognormal variate with parameters μ_n, σ_n.

The parameters μ_n, σ_n, and P_n are estimated from historical data.

Equations (10.8.4) may be solved recursively, starting with (10.8.5), using values of the parameters of the lognormal density function ϕ_{LN} that have been estimated from historical data.

Using a grid of values of X_n at each stage, the optimal $a_n^*(X_n)$ which minimizes the expected penalty costs can be determined as a function of the state variable X_n. After carrying out the calculation from stage N to stage 1, the sequence of optimal decision rules, we obtain

$$\{a_1^*(X_1),\ a_2^*(X_2),\ \ldots,\ a_N^*(X_N)\}$$

as the optimal policy.

In [32] a numerical example is solved on a computer, for which $N = 5$ stages, $r = 10$ million lb,

$$C_n(a_n) = (.9)^{5-n}a_n^2 \quad (n = 2, 3, 4, 5)$$

Tables of μ_n, σ_n, p_n are given, as well as forecasts of crop supply which allow the estimation of the parameters.

10.9. A Style Goods Inventory Model [33]

The style goods (e.g., women's dresses) inventory problem is usually classified as a finite horizon, dynamic inventory problem with unknown demand. This problem has been formulated as a stochastic dynamic programming problem with two state variables, one for the on hand inventory plus that on order and one which reflects the current information on the demand for goods. We shall present here a model which requires only one state variable by making use of clustering of items with similar demand and similar costs.

We assume that a style goods inventory manager plans to introduce a new item to be carried in periods 1, 2, ..., n, which together are called a season. We assume that the cumulative demand s_{i+1} for the item in periods 1, 2, ..., i can be expressed as

$$s_{i+1} = r_i s_i, \quad s_1 = 1 \quad (i = 1, 2, \ldots, n) \tag{10.9.1}$$

and $r_1, r_2, \ldots, r_n$ are independent random variables with finite expectations and known distributions and that $r_1 > 0, r_2, \ldots, r_n \geqslant 1$. r_i is independent of s_i.

For each period i we have a unit cost c_i, a unit backorder cost p_i and a unit holding cost h_i (for the end of period i). We assume that

$$c_i + h_i > 0, \quad p_i + h_i \geqslant 0 \quad (i = 1, 2, \ldots, n) \tag{10.9.2}$$

We define

$$L(z) = \max(h_i z, -p_i z) \quad (i = 1, 2, \ldots, n) \tag{10.9.3}$$

$L_i(z)$ is called the holding and backorder cost function. $L_i(z)$ is a positively homogeneous function of degree 1, i.e.,

$$L_i(\lambda z) = \max(h_i\lambda z, -p_i\lambda z)$$
$$= \lambda \max(h_i z, -p_i z) = \lambda L_i(z)$$

for all $\lambda \geq 0$ and for all z.

At the beginning of period i we can observe the cumulative stock x which is purchased, as well as the cumulative demand $s_i = s$ incurred to that time. Then the cumulative stock purchased is increased to some level $y \geq x$. Therefore, the amount purchased in period i is $y-x$, and the stock on hand (or backorder) at the end of period i is $y-s_{i+1} = y-r_i s$.

We now define:

$g_i(x, s)$ = minimum expected cost in periods $i, i+1, \ldots, n$ when the cumulative stock ordered and demand incurred in periods $1, 2, \ldots, i-1$ are x and s, respectively.

Then, invoking the principle of optimality and the definition of $g_i(x, s)$ we obtain the recurrence relations

$$g_i(x, s) = \min_{y \geq x} [c_i(y-x)+EL_i(y-r_i s)+Eg_{i+1}(y, r_i s)]$$

$$(i = 1, 2, \ldots, n) \tag{10.9.4}$$

$$g_{n+1} \equiv 0 \tag{10.9.5}$$

where E is the expected value operator and will take the appropriate form for the given probability distribution.

It can be shown (see [33]) that there is a least $y = y_i^*(x, s)$. Hence the minimum in (10.9.4) can be achieved. It can also be shown that, since $L_i(z)$ is a positively homogeneous function, then $g_i(x, s)$ is also a positively homogeneous function. It is this result that enables the recurrence relation of (10.9.4) with two state variables to be reduced to one with one state variable.

In order to eliminate a state variable we can proceed as follows. The expected demand for the season, given the demand s_i up to the beginning of period i, is

$$E(s_{n+1}|s_i) = s_i \prod_{j=1}^{n} Er_j$$

Therefore

$$\frac{s_i}{E(s_{n+1}|s_i)} = \left(\prod_{j=1}^{n} Er_j\right)^{-1} \equiv t_i \quad (i = 1, 2, \ldots, n-1) \tag{10.9.6}$$

or from the independence of the r_i

$$t_i = [E(s_{n+1}|s_i)]^{-1} \tag{10.9.7}$$

where t_i is independent of s_i. Since $s_1 = 1$, t_1 is the reciprocal of the expected season demand. For $i > 1$, t_i is the fraction of expected season demand experienced by the beginning of period i.

Noting the above, we define

$$x' = xs^{-1}t_i$$

$$y' = ys^{-1}t_i$$

$$f_i(x') = g_i(x', t_i)$$ (10.9.8)

$$R_i = r_i(Er_i)^{-1}$$

We also note that $ER_i = 1$.

We now divide (10.9.4) by the conditional expected season demand st_i^{-1} and using the homogeneity of g_i and (10.9.8), we obtain

$$f_i(x_i') = \min_{y' \geq x'} [c_i(y'-x')+EL_i(y'-t_{i+1}R_i)+ER_if_{i+1}(y'R^{-1})] \quad (i = 1, 2, \ldots, n) \quad (10.9.9)$$

$$f_{n+1} = 0$$

An extensive numerical example is given in [33]. The values of t_i and the distribution of R_i are calculated and the results analyzed.

Sets, Convexity, and n-Dimensional Geometry

A.1. Sets and Set Notation

We shall confine ourselves in this section to *point sets*, i.e., a collection of objects or elements which consist of ordered lists of real numbers. For example, (x_1, x_2, x_3) is a "point" or element consisting of three numbers, and $(x_1, x_2, \ldots, x_n)$ is a "point" consisting of a list of n numbers. Each of the numbers in the list is sometimes called a *component* of the point.

We can speak of collections of such points as *sets*. For example, the set of all points with two components consists of all points (x_1, x_2) where each of the components x_1 and x_2 can have real numeric value. In this book, having confined ourselves to point sets, any point $(x_1, x_2, \ldots, x_n)$ will be a point in an n-dimensional Euclidean space E^n.

Very often it is necessary to impose conditions on sets of points. These are conditions or restrictions that some or all members of some set must satisfy. For example, we might wish to consider the set of all points in two-dimensional Euclidean space that lie on the line $x_1 + x_2 = 10$. We would then define or denote the set P as

$$P = \{(x_1, x_2) \mid x_1 + x_2 = 10\} \tag{A.1.1}$$

Equation (A.1.1) is read "P consists of the set of all points (x_1, x_2) such that $x_1 + x_2 = 10$". The vertical bar is read "such that". On the left of the bar we designate the general nature or form of the points; to the right of the bar we state whatever restrictions or conditions the points must satisfy in order to qualify for membership in the set P.

We designate any point $(x_1, x_2, \ldots, x_n)$ as $\mathbf{x}$. In order to indicate that $\mathbf{x}$ is a member of some set P, we write

$$\mathbf{x} \in P \tag{A.1.2}$$

(A.1.2) is read "$\mathbf{x}$ is a member of the set P". If $\mathbf{x}$ is not a member of P, we write $\mathbf{x} \notin P$.

The relationship given by (A.1.2) is between a set of points and the set P. It is also possible to have relationships between sets. One set might be part of another set. For example, the set P might be included in the set S. In this case P is said to be a subset of S. This relationship is denoted

$$P \subset S \tag{A.1.3}$$

and is read "P is a subset of S". It can also be written

$$S \supset P \qquad \text{(A.1.4)}$$

(A.1.3) and (A.1.4) are equivalent expressions.

We shall now define and discuss two important relationships concerning sets.

Intersection. The intersection of two sets S_1 and S_2 is the set of all points $\mathbf{x}$ such that $\mathbf{x}$ is a member of *both* S_1 and S_2. We can express this definition as follows. The intersection of two sets S_1 and S_2 defines a new set P, i.e.,

$$P = \{\mathbf{x} \,|\, \mathbf{x} \in S_1 \quad \text{and} \quad \mathbf{x} \in S_2\} \qquad \text{(A.1.5)}$$

The notation that is usually used to indicate the relationship described in (A.1.5)

$$P = S_1 \cap S_2 \qquad \text{(A.1.6)}$$

Equation (A.1.6) is read "P is the set given by the intersection of S_1 and S_2" or "P equals the intersection of S_1 and S_2".

It is simple to extend (A.1.6) to define the intersection of any finite number of sets. The intersection of n sets $S_1, S_2, \ldots, S_n$ is given by

$$P = S_1 \cap S_2 \cap \ldots \cap S_n = \bigcap_{i=1}^{n} S_i \qquad \text{(A.1.7)}$$

or equivalently

$$P = \{\mathbf{x} \,|\, \mathbf{x} \in S_1 \quad \text{and} \quad \mathbf{x} \in S_2 \quad \text{and} \quad \ldots \quad \text{and} \quad \mathbf{x} \in S_n\} \qquad \text{(A.1.8)}$$

A graphical representation of the intersection of two sets is shown in Fig. A.1.1.

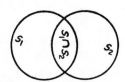

FIG. A.1.1. Intersection of two sets.

Union. The union of two sets S_1 and S_2 is the set of all points $\mathbf{x}$ such that $\mathbf{x}$ is a member of either S_1 or S_2. The union of two sets S_1 and S_2 defines a new set P, i.e.,

$$P = \{\mathbf{x} \,|\, \mathbf{x} \in S_1 \quad \text{or} \quad \mathbf{x} \in S_2\} \qquad \text{(A.1.9)}$$

or as it is usually written

$$P = S_1 \cup S_2 \qquad \text{(A.1.10)}$$

Equation (A.1.10) is read "P is the union of sets S_1 and S_2". The union of n sets $S_1, S_2, \ldots, S_n$ can be defined by

$$P = S_1 \cup S_2 \cup \ldots \cup S_n = \bigcup_{i=1}^{n} S_i \qquad \text{(A.1.11)}$$

or equivalently

$$P = \{x \,|\, x \in S_1 \quad \text{or} \quad x \in S_2 \quad \text{or} \quad \ldots \quad \text{or} \quad x \in S_n\} \qquad \text{(A.1.12)}$$

A graphical representation of the union of two sets is shown in Fig. A.1.2.

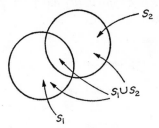

FIG. A.1.2. Union of two sets.

A.2. *n*-Dimensional Geometry and Sets

If we consider the set of all points (x_1, x_2) and providing a definition of distance is given between any such number pairs, this set is usually called a *two-dimensional Euclidean space* and we denote it by the symbol E^2. The distance between any two points in two-dimensional Euclidean space is well known to the reader. If we have two points $x_1 = (a_1, b_1)$ and $x_2 = (a_2, b_2)$, then the distance d is given by

$$d = [(a_2-a_1)^2+(b_2-b_1)^2]^{1/2} \qquad \text{(A.2.1)}$$

Similarly, three component points define a three-dimensional Euclidean space E^3 and distance is defined by

$$d = [(a_2-a_1)^2+(b_2-b_1)^2+(c_2-c_1)^2]^{1/2} \qquad \text{(A.2.2)}$$

Points such as (a_1, b_1) or (a_1, b_1, c_1) can be regarded as *vectors* (a matrix with a single column or a matrix with a single row) for which all the usual rules of matrix algebra apply. In terms of vector notation (A.2.1) or (A.2.2) can be written

$$d = [(\mathbf{x}_2-\mathbf{x}_1)(\mathbf{x}_2-\mathbf{x}_1)]^{1/2} \qquad \text{(A.2.3)}$$

which is represented in terms of the scalar product between two vectors.

The extension of the above from two- and three-dimensional spaces to an n-dimensional space is straightforward and is just precisely what one would expect from (A.2.3). We define the set of all n-component points or vectors as an n-dimensional space E^n. Thus, a point in E^n is an n-component vector or point with n components. Hence, the extension of the definition of distance to points in E^n is

$$d = [(\mathbf{x}-\mathbf{y})(\mathbf{x}-\mathbf{y})]^{1/2} = \left[\sum_{j=1}^{n} (\mathbf{x}_j - \mathbf{y}_j)^2 \right]^{1/2} \qquad \text{(A.2.4)}$$

where $\mathbf{x} = (x_1, x_2, \ldots, x_n)$ and $\mathbf{y} = (y_1, y_2, \ldots, y_n)$.

The generalization of distance between two points in two-dimensional space to "distance" between two points in n-dimensional space suggests that geometric figures of various kinds in two-dimensional space can be similarly generalized. For example, the equation of a line in E^2 is

$$a_1x_1+a_2x_2 = b \qquad\qquad\text{(A.2.5)}$$

where $\mathbf{x} = (x_1, x_2)$ is any point in E^2 and a_1, a_2 and b are scalar constants. If $\mathbf{a} = (a_1, a_2)$ then (A.2.5) can also be written as

$$\mathbf{ax} = b \qquad\qquad\text{(A.2.6)}$$

Similarly, a plane in E^3 can be represented as

$$a_1x_1+a_2x_2+a_3x_3 = b \qquad\qquad\text{(A.2.7)}$$

or

$$\mathbf{ax} = b$$

where $\mathbf{a} = (a_1, a_2, a_3)$ and $\mathbf{x} = (x_1, x_2, x_3)$. The generalization is to a *hyperplane* which is given by

$$a_1x_1+a_2x_2+ \ldots +a_nx_n = b \qquad\qquad\text{(A.2.8)}$$

where $\mathbf{a} = (a_1, a_2, \ldots, a_n)$ and $\mathbf{x} = (x_1, x_2, \ldots, x_n)$. It can be seen that when $n = 2$ or 3 in (A.2.8), a hyperplane becomes a line or a plane. A hyperplane of any kind is simply a *set of points*. This is seen if we define a hyperplane as a set H as follows:

$$H = \{\mathbf{x} = (x_1, x_2, \ldots, x_n)\,|\,\mathbf{ax} = b\} \qquad\qquad\text{(A.2.9)}$$

Hence a hyperplane is a set of points in E^n that satisfy (A.2.8).

A line in E^n is determined by any two points $\mathbf{x}_1$ and $\mathbf{x}_2$ in E^n. A line passing through these points is simply a set L which is given by

$$L = \{\mathbf{x}\,|\,\mathbf{x} = \lambda\mathbf{x}_1+(1-\lambda)\mathbf{x}_2\} \qquad\qquad\text{(A.2.10)}$$

for any scalar λ. If we wish to define a line segment between $\mathbf{x}_1$ and $\mathbf{x}_2$, we would use the following:

$$L_1 = \{\mathbf{x}\,|\,\mathbf{x} = \lambda\mathbf{x}_1+(1-\lambda)\mathbf{x}_2, \quad 0 \leqslant \lambda \leqslant 1\} \qquad\qquad\text{(A.2.11)}$$

since when $\lambda = 1$, $\mathbf{x} = \mathbf{x}_1$ and when $\lambda = 0$, $\mathbf{x} = \mathbf{x}_2$.

The n-dimensional extension of circles in E^2 or spheres in E^3 is called a *hypersphere*. Let us now consider its representation. In E^2 we can represent a circle whose center is at a point $\mathbf{a} = (a_1, a_2)$ and whose radius is r by

$$(x_1-a_1)^2+(x_2-a_2)^2 = r^2 \qquad\qquad\text{(A.2.12)}$$

Representations equivalent to (A.2.12) are

$$[(\mathbf{x}-\mathbf{a})\,(\mathbf{x}-\mathbf{a})]^{1/2} = r \qquad\qquad\text{(A.2.13)}$$

or

$$|\mathbf{x}-\mathbf{a}| = r \qquad\qquad\text{(A.2.14)}$$

Again, it should be realized that a circle is simply a set of points S_c which is defined by

$$S_c = \{\mathbf{x}\,|\,|\mathbf{x}-\mathbf{a}| = r\} \qquad\qquad\text{(A.2.15)}$$

Sometimes it is necessary to define the interior of a circle. This is given by

$$I_c = \{\mathbf{x} \mid |\mathbf{x}-\mathbf{a}| < r\} \tag{A.2.16}$$

Equations similar to (A.2.12) through (A.2.16) can be written for a sphere in E^3, the only difference being that $\mathbf{x} = (x_1, x_2, x_3)$ and $\mathbf{a} = (a_1, a_2, a_3)$.

The natural extension of the concept of a circle and sphere for points $\mathbf{x} \in E^n$, where $\mathbf{x} = (x_1, x_2, \ldots, x_n)$ is a set of points

$$H = \{\mathbf{x} \mid |\mathbf{x}-\mathbf{a}| = r\} \tag{A.2.17}$$

where $\mathbf{x} \in E^n$ and $\mathbf{a} = (a_1, a_2, \ldots, a_n)$. Equivalently, the equation of a hypersphere is again

$$|\mathbf{x}-\mathbf{a}| = r \tag{A.2.18}$$

or

$$\sum_{i=1}^{n} (x_i - a_i)^2 = r^2 \tag{A.2.19}$$

Similarly, the interior of a hypersphere is a set of points I_H

$$I_H = \{\mathbf{x} \mid |\mathbf{x}-\mathbf{a}| < r\} \tag{A.2.20}$$

The interior of a hypersphere with center at $\mathbf{a}$ *and radius* $\varepsilon > 0$ is also frequently called an ε-neighborhood of $\mathbf{a}$.

We will now discuss the notion of the "boundary" of a set of points. If we refer to Fig. A.2.1 we can see immediately that points such as $\mathbf{a}$, $\mathbf{b}$, or $\mathbf{c}$ are clearly boundary points of the set S. On the other hand, points such as $\mathbf{d}$, $\mathbf{e}$, or $\mathbf{f}$ are equally clearly

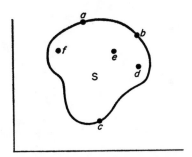

FIG. A.2.1. Boundary and interior points of S.

interior points of S. However, we need to make this notion somewhat more precise. If we consider a point such as $\mathbf{d}$ and we draw a circle around it, then if we make the radius of the circle sufficiently small, all points lying in the interior of this circle will be points in the set S. However, if we choose a point such as $\mathbf{b}$ and draw a circle around it, no matter how small we make this circle, some of the points in the interior of the circle will be outside the set S. With this discussion as background we make the following definitions.

Interior point. A point $\mathbf{x}$ is an interior point of a set S if there exists an ε-neighborhood of $\mathbf{x}$ which contains only points of S.

Boundary point. A point $\mathbf{x}$ is a boundary point of a set S if every ε-neighborhood of $\mathbf{x}$, no matter how small ε is, contains some points which are in S and some points which are not in S.

Two more definitions will also be useful.

Open set. A set S is an open set if it contains only interior points.

Closed set. A set S is a closed set if it contains all of its boundary points.

It should be noted that sets that contain some but not all of their boundary points are neither open nor closed.

A.3. Convex Sets

A set X_c is defined as a convex set if for any two points in X_c, the line segment joining the two points is also in the set. More precisely, for every pair of points $\mathbf{x}_1, \mathbf{x}_2 \in X_c$ the set S_L will be a subset of X_c where S_L is defined as

$$S_L = \{x \mid x = \lambda x_1 + (1-\lambda)x_2, \quad 0 \leqslant \lambda \leqslant 1\} \tag{A.3.1}$$

The expression $\lambda x_1 + (1-\lambda)x_2$, $0 \leqslant \lambda \leqslant 1$ is called a *convex combination* of the points $\mathbf{x}_1$ and $\mathbf{x}_2$. For any fixed value of λ, a convex combination of $\mathbf{x}_1$ and $\mathbf{x}_2$ gives a point on the line segment S_L defined by (A.3.1). A set consisting of a single point is a special case

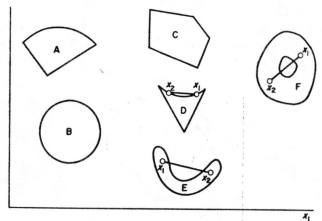

FIG. A.3.1. Some examples of convex and nonconvex sets.

($\lambda = 0$, $\mathbf{x} = \mathbf{x}_2$) and is therefore also convex by definition. By convention, an empty set (a "set" containing no points) can also be said to be convex.

Intuitively, a convex set is one that has no "indentations" or "holes" if one thinks of a set of points geometrically. Figure A.3.1 shows some examples of sets that are convex and not convex. In the geometric figures designated A, B, and C, we see that a line segment connecting any two points in that figure or set of points will be wholly within the figure. Hence, these represent convex sets of points. However, for the figures designated D, E, and F, it can readily be seen that the line segments connecting some pairs of points will lie partly or wholly outside the set. Hence, these represent sets that are not convex.

An important result concerning convex sets is the following, which we state without proof (see [1], chapter 3 for a proof).

THEOREM A.3.1. *The intersection of a finite number of convex sets is a convex set.*

Figure A.3.2 gives a simple illustration of the intersection of two convex sets.

A convex set like any other set has both interior and boundary points. However, some boundary points have an unusual characteristic that merits special attention. The boundary points of a convex set that often occur in "corners" (although this is not strictly accurate) are called *extreme points*. We now define these points.

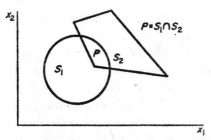

FIG. A.3.2. Intersection of convex sets.

EXTREME POINT. *A point* $\mathbf{x}$ *is an extreme point of a convex set if there do not exist different points* $\mathbf{x}_1$ *and* $\mathbf{x}_2$ *in the set such that for some* λ, $0 < \lambda < 1$, $\mathbf{x} = \lambda\mathbf{x}_1 + (1-\lambda)\mathbf{x}_2$.

What the foregoing definition means geometrically is that an extreme point cannot lie on a line segment joining any other two points in the set. In other language, an extreme point cannot be expressed as a convex combination of some two distinct points in the set.

In Fig. A.3.3 we show two convex sets. The set S_1 has four extreme points which are designated $\mathbf{x}_1$, $\mathbf{x}_2$, $\mathbf{x}_3$, $\mathbf{x}_4$. The set S_2 has an infinite number of extreme points. In addition to the points $\mathbf{a}$, $\mathbf{b}$, and $\mathbf{c}$, the circular arc of the lower boundary contains an infinite number of points, each of which is an extreme point.

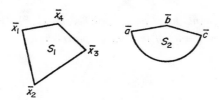

FIG. A.3.3. Convex sets and extreme points.

From the definition of an extreme point and the examples, two facts should be clear. The first is that while all extreme points are boundary points not all boundary points are extreme points. The second is that no interior point can be an extreme point.

In (A.3.1) we defined the convex combination of two points. We can generalize this in a natural way to the convex combination of any number of points as follows.

A *convex combination* of a finite set of points $x_1, x_2, \ldots, x_p$ is defined as a point

$$x = \sum_{i=1}^{p} a_i x_i \qquad \text{NB } a_i \in R \tag{A.3.2}$$

where $a_i \geqslant 0, i = 1, 2, \ldots, p$ and

$$\sum_{i=1}^{p} a_i = 1 \tag{A.3.3}$$

This definition enables us to state another important result.

THEOREM A.3.2. *The set S_c of all convex combinations of a finite number of points $x_1, x_2, \ldots, x_p$ is a convex set.*

For example, in Fig. A.3.3, the set S_1 can be regarded as the set of all convex combinations of the four points x_1, x_2, x_3, x_4.

It can be seen that in E^2 the set of all convex combinations of a finite set of points is a polygon (or polyhedron). In E^3 it is also a polyhedron. Let us generalize this notion.

For any given set S which does not happen to be convex, we may wish to find a convex set C (or the smallest convex set) which contains S. It is obvious that there are many convex sets which will contain S. This leads us to the concept of the "smallest" convex set C which contains S and the following definition:

CONVEX HULL. *The intersection of all convex sets which contain a given set S as a subset is called the* convex hull *of S.*

From the above definition the following result can be proven (see [1], chapter 3).

THEOREM A.3.3. *The convex hull of a finite set of points is the set of all convex combinations of those points.*

In E^2 the convex hull of a set of points $x_1, x_2, \ldots, x_p$ is a polyhedron. Similarly, in E^n we shall call the convex hull of a finite set of points the *convex polyhedron* formed from these points. Finally, one last important result should be stated.

THEOREM A.3.4. *Any point in a convex polyhedron can be represented as a convex combination of the extreme points of the convex polyhedron.*

References

[1] L. COOPER and D. I. STEINBERG, *Introduction to Methods of Optimization*, W. B. Saunders, Philadelphia, 1970.

[2] G. P. MCCORMICK, *Converting General Nonlinear Programming Problems to Separable Nonlinear Programming Problems*, George Washington University, Serial T-267, June 1972.

[3] R. E. BELLMAN, *Dynamic Programming*, Princeton University Press, Princeton, 1957.

[4] R. E. BELLMAN and S. E. DREYFUS, *Applied Dynamic Programming*, Princeton University Press, Princeton, 1962.

[5] R. E. BELLMAN, *Adaptive Control Processes: A Guided Tour*, Princeton University Press, Princeton, 1961.

[6] R. E. BELLMAN, *Introduction to the Mathematical Theory of Control Processes*, Academic Press, New York, 1967.

[7] R. A. HOWARD, *Dynamic Programming and Markov Processes*, Wiley, New York, 1960.

[8] L. G. MITTEN, Composition principles for synthesis of optimal multi-stage processes, *Operations Research* **12**, 610–619 (1964).

[9] E. V. DENARDO and L. G. MITTEN, *Elements of Sequential Decision Processes*, Report RM-5057-PR, The Rand Corporation, Santa Monica, 1966.

[10] R. M. KARP and M. HELD, Finite state processes and dynamic programming, *SIAM Journal on Applied Mathematics* **15**, 693–718 (1967).

[11] S. E. ELMAGHRABY, The concept of "States" in discrete dynamic programming, *J. of Math. Analysis and Applications* **29**, 523–557 (1970).

[12] S. E. DREYFUS, *Dynamic Programming and the Calculus of Variations*, Academic Press, New York, 1965.

[13] E. V. DENARDO and L. G. MITTEN, Elements of sequential decision processes, *J. of Industrial Eng.* **18**, 106–112 (1967).

[14] D. J. WHITE, *Dynamic Programming*, Holden-Day, San Francisco, 1969.

[15] G. L. NEMHAUSER, *Introduction to Dynamic Programming*, Wiley, New York, 1966.

[16] P. BONZON, Necessary and sufficient conditions for dynamic programming of combinatorial type, *J. Ass. for Computing Machinery* **17**, 675–682 (1970).

[17] J. RIORDAN, *An Introduction to Combinatorial Analysis*, Wiley, New York, 1958.

[18] R. BELLMAN, Combinatorial processes and dynamic programming, in *Proceedings of Symposia in Applied Mathematics*, Vol. X, American Mathematical Society, Providence, RI, 1960.

[19] A. H. STROUD and D. SECREST, *Gaussian Quadrature Formulas*, Prentice-Hall, Englewood Cliffs, New Jersey, 1966.

[20] R. BELLMAN, R. KALABA, and B. KOTKIN, Polynomial approximation – a new computational technique in dynamic programming: allocation processes, *Math. Tables and Other Aids to Computation* **16**, 155–161 (1962).

[21] L. COOPER and M. W. COOPER, Nonlinear integer programming, *Comp. and Maths. with Appls.* **1**, 215–222 (1975).

[22] M. W. COOPER, *An Improved Algorithm for Nonlinear Integer Programming*, Report IEOR 77005, Dept. of Industrial Engineering and Operations Research, Southern Methodist University, February 1977.

[23] G. HADLEY and T. M. WHITIN, *Analysis of Inventory Systems*, Prentice-Hall, Englewood Cliffs, New Jersey, 1963.

[24] D. R. SMITH, *Variational Methods in Optimization*, Prentice-Hall, Englewood Cliffs, New Jersey, 1974.

[25] H. M. WEINGARTNER, Municipal bond schedules with limitations on the number of coupons, *Management Science* **19**, 369–378 (1972).

[26] E. R. PETERSEN, A dynamic programming model for the expansion of electric power systems, *Management Science* **20**, 656–664 (1973).

[27] M. CHYUTIN and D. Z. MITTWOCH, *Optimization Method for the Design of a Hospital Ward*, Operations Research, Statistics and Economics, Mimeograph Series No. 196, Technion, Haifa, Israel, May 1977.

[28] M. CHYUTIN, The utilization of optimization techniques in the evaluation of architectural systems, PhD dissertation, Technion, Haifa, Israel, 1975.

[29] J. M. COZZOLINO, Optimal scheduling for investment of excess cash, *Decision Sciences* **2**, 265–283 (1971).

[30] C. F. MEYER and R. J. NEWETT, Dynamic programming for feedlot optimization, *Management Science* **16**, B-410–B-426 (1970).

[31] Y. COMAY, A. MELNIK, and M. A. POLLATSCHEK, *The Optimal Path of Investment in Human Capital*, Research Report, Technion, Haifa, Israel, 1971.

[32] W. H. HAUSMAN, Sequential decision problems: a model to exploit existing forecasters, *Management Science* **16**, B-93–B-111 (1969).

[33] P. H. HARTUNG, A simple style goods inventory model, *Management Science* **19**, 1452–1458 (1973).

Index